17.45   12/80

Beginning Algebra
Third Edition

Margaret L. Lial/Charles D. Miller

American River College   Sacramento, California

Beginning Algebra
Third Edition

Scott, Foresman and Company   Glenview, Illinois

Dallas, Tex.   Oakland, N.J.   Palo Alto, Cal.   Tucker, Ga.   London

Library of Congress Cataloging in Publication Data

Lial, Margaret L
    Beginning algebra.

    Includes index.
    1. Algebra.   I. Miller, Charles David, 1942–
II. Title.
QA152.2.L5   1980   512.9   79–26887
ISBN 0-673-15330-4

Cover Photo of Railroad Cars
© 1976 Dr. Georg Gerster/Photo Researchers, Inc.

2 3 4 5 6 7 8-KPF-86 85 84 83 82 81 80

Preface

The Third Edition of Beginning Algebra offers an accessible first course in algebra. We assume that many of the students using this book have never taken a course in algebra, while others may have taken such a course but are in need of a review. In either case the student's only prerequisite is some knowledge of arithmetic.

Feedback from instructors and students, and our own experience in teaching from the book, led us to make the following changes in the Third Edition:

- A review of the basic operations of arithmetic, with a special emphasis on fractions, is included in the appendix.
- Exponents are introduced in Chapter 1, so that the order of operations can be discussed completely at this time.
- Linear equations and inequalities are presented in a more easily taught sequence in Chapter 2.
- Prime factorization is covered in greater detail, and a table of prime factors is provided on page 318.
- Least common denominators are treated in a new section in Chapter 5, to prepare students to handle addition and subtraction of algebraic fractions.
- Word problems are discussed in greater detail, and new, more realistic, word problems have been added throughout the book.

- New examples have been included, and additional steps elaborate the solutions for existing examples.
- A new format has been adopted: examples are now easier to find, and summaries and rules are set off with colored boxes.
- Learning objectives have been included for each section.

Our program of supplements continues to be one of the most extensive of its kind available. With steadily increasing class sizes such a program is an important aid for today's instructor. The package of supplements includes the following:

- A **Study Guide,** in a fill-in-the-blank, semi-programmed format, reviews the material covered in the text. Answers at the side of the page provide immediate reinforcement. Chapter Summaries and Review Exercises for each chapter are also included in the Guide.
- The **Instructor's Manual** features answers to even numbered exercises, four forms of a test for each chapter, two sample final examinations, and a solutions manual for many of the exercises in the book. These solutions may be made available for student use as desired.
- **Audio Tapes** are available without cost to adopters of the book. These tapes are made by classroom teachers, and not by professional announcers, so that students find them much more "believable."

Many people helped us prepare this edition. We received much valuable help from Carol J. Achs, Mesa Community College; Charles D. Bedal, Maricopa Technical College; Dale E. Boye, Schoolcraft College; Elizabeth Dougherty, Louisiana State University; Tina Levy, Diablo Valley College; Florence Lincoln, Phoenix College; Bruce Wrenn, De Anza College. At American River College, Vern Heeren, Michael Karelius, Edward Harper, and Virginia-Jane Gleadall provided much good advice. It is a pleasure to acknowledge the aid of Dean Michael Collins. At Scott, Foresman, mathematics editor Pamela Carlson provided firm guidance. Karen Dean did a fine job in guiding the book through the production process. Additional help in planning the revision came from Hermann Lacher, John Gibbs, John Miller, Arnold Parker, Steve Jones, Ben Whitney, Sharon Noble, Greg Odjakjian, Peter Quass, Earl Karn, Jim Couhig, and Carl Tyson.

Margaret L. Lial
Charles D. Miller

To The Student

Studying algebra is different from studying history, English, or science. Here are some suggestions on how to get the most out of your algebra class and textbook.

1 Before going to class, look over the new section that the instructor will cover. Read the introductory paragraphs to see how the new ideas fit in with previous ones. Go through the section to see if any new formulas or rules are given.

2 Work through the examples in the text. First read the statement of the example and make sure you completely understand what the example asks. Write out the solution yourself, supplying any missing steps. When finished, check your answer to make sure it is correct.

3 Try a few exercises of each type. Check your answers with those in the back of the book to make sure you're on the right track.

4 There may be a few items that give you trouble. Go to class, and listen to the instructor's presentation. You will find that many of your trouble spots are cleared up during class discussion. Don't be afraid to ask questions. You are in class to learn, so go ahead and ask about anything that troubles you.

5   If not all your questions are cleared up in class, ask the instructor for help during office hours. If your school offers a mathematics lab or tutorial services, take advantage of them.

6   After class, work the assigned homework exercises.

7   After you finish the homework, look over the next section of new material.

8   At the end of each chapter, check your understanding of the topics by taking the Chapter Test.

9   If you would like some supplementary exercises, along with a Chapter Summary and Chapter Review Exercises, get a copy of the Study Guide for Beginning Algebra. Your bookstore should have copies. If not, they can order one for you.

10 When it comes time for the final exam, make up your own sample final, as follows. Go through the sections you studied, and write down the statement of some typical worked-out examples. Then work through the ones you have written down. You can then refer to the book to check your answers and to see how to work any items that may have given you trouble.

11 At this point you should be ready to take the next mathematics course you need.

Contents

3   Polynomials   93

4   Factoring   132

Tables 318

Appendices 320

Answers to Selected Problems   339

Diagnostic Pretest

Each problem in the following diagnostic pretest is worked out in this book, on the given page.

18. Solve the quadratic equation: $x^2 - 5x = -6$

19. The product of two consecutive odd integers is 1 less than 5 times their sum. Find the integers.

20. Find the product: $\dfrac{x^2 + 3x}{x^2 - 3x - 4} \cdot \dfrac{x^2 - 5x + 4}{x^2 + 2x - 3}$

21. Add the rational expressions: $\dfrac{x}{x^2 - 1} + \dfrac{x}{x + 1}$

22. Solve: $\dfrac{2}{x^2 - x} = \dfrac{1}{x^2 - 1}$

23. Graph: $4x - 5y = 20$

24. Graph: $x = 3$

25. Find the slope of the line that goes through the points $(-4, 7)$ and $(1, -2)$.

26. Graph: $2x - 5y \geq 10$

27. Let $P(x) = 5x^2 - 4x + 3$. Find: (a) $P(0)$

  (b) $P(-2)$

28. Solve the system: $2x + 3y = -15$
  $5x + 2y = 1$

29. Solve the system: $3x - y = 4$
  $-9x + 3y = -12$

30. Find each of the following: (a) $-\sqrt{1024}$
  (b) $\sqrt{256}$
  (c) $-\sqrt{900}$

31. Simplify: $\sqrt{72}$

32. Find the product: $\sqrt{9} \cdot \sqrt{75}$

33. Simplify: $2\sqrt{12} + 3\sqrt{75}$

34. Rationalize the denominator: $\sqrt{\dfrac{27}{5}}$

35. Solve: $3\sqrt{x} = \sqrt{x + 8}$

36. Find the solutions of the quadratic equation:
  $x^2 = 2x + 1$

37. Solve the equation: $\dfrac{1}{10}t^2 = \dfrac{2}{5} - \dfrac{1}{2}t$

38. Graph the parabola: $y = (x - 2)^2$

1

Number Systems

1.1 Symbols

- **Be able to find products and quotients.**
- **Know the meaning of $=$, $\neq$, $<$, $>$, $\leq$, and $\geq$.**
- **Translate word phrases to symbols.**

In many ways, algebra is a sort of advanced arithmetic. Algebra involves a lot of adding, subtracting, multiplying, and dividing, but these are done with *letters,* such as x and y, which represent numbers, and not with numbers themselves.

These basic **operations** (addition, subtraction, multiplication, and division) are written with symbols you probably have seen:

$+$ *(addition)* $\times$ *(multiplication)*

$-$ *(subtraction)* $\div$ *(division)*

Multiplication is used so often that there are special symbols for it: 8×4 is also written with a dot, as $8 \cdot 4$; or with parentheses, such as $8(4)$, $(8)4$, or $(8)(4)$. All of these give an answer of 32:

$$8 \times 4 = 32, \qquad 8 \cdot 4 = 32, \qquad 8(4) = 32, \qquad (8)4 = 32, \qquad (8)(4) = 32.$$

The answer to a multiplication problem is called the **product.** For example, the product of 9 and 7 is 63:

$$9 \cdot 7 = 63.$$

EXAMPLE 1   Find the following products.

(a) $3 \cdot 5 = 15$

(b) $5(15) = 75$

(c) $(82)(91) = 7462$

In arithmetic, division is often indicated by the symbol $\div$. In algebra, a fraction bar is more common. Instead of writing $20 \div 4$ to show "20 divided by 4," use a fraction bar instead:

$$\frac{20}{4} = 5.$$

The answer to a division problem is called a **quotient.**
The quotient of "20 divided by 4" is 5.

EXAMPLE 2   Find quotients for the following problems.

(a) $\frac{8}{2} = 4$

(b) $\frac{15}{3} = 5$

(c) $\frac{280}{10} = 28$

Another common symbol is the one for equality, $=$, which tells us that two numbers are equal. This symbol with a slash through it, $\neq$, means "does *not* equal." For example,

$$7 \neq 8$$

says that 7 is not equal to 8.

If two numbers are not equal, then one of the numbers must be smaller than the other. The symbol $<$ represents "is less than," so that "7 is less than 8" is written

$$7 < 8.$$

Also, "6 is less than 9" is written

$$6 < 9.$$

The symbol $>$ means "is greater than." In saying "8 is greater than 2," we write

$$8 > 2.$$

The statement "17 is greater than 11" is written

$$17 > 11.$$

To keep the symbols $<$ and $>$ straight, remember that the symbol always points to the smaller number. To write "8 is less than 15," point the symbol towards the 8:

$$8 < 15.$$

EXAMPLE 3   Write each word statement in symbols.

(a) Twelve equals ten plus two.

$$12 = 10 + 2$$

(b) Nine is less than ten.

$$9 < 10$$

(c) Fifteen is not equal to eighteen.

$$15 \neq 18$$

(d) Seven is greater than four.

$$7 > 4$$

Two other symbols, $\leq$ and $\geq$, also represent the idea of inequality. The symbol $\leq$ means "is less than or equal to," so that

$$5 \leq 9$$

means "5 is less than or equal to 9." This statement is true, since $5 < 9$ is true. If either the $<$ part, or the $=$ part is true, then the inequality symbol $\leq$ may be used.

The symbol $\geq$ means "is greater than or equal to." Again,

$$9 \geq 5$$

is true because $9 > 5$ is true. Also, $8 \leq 8$ or $8 \geq 8$ is true since $8 = 8$ is true. But it is not true that $13 \leq 9$ because neither $13 < 9$ nor $13 = 9$ is true.

EXAMPLE 4   Write *true* or *false* for each statement.

(a) $15 \leq 20$
   Since $15 < 20$, the statement $15 \leq 20$ is *true*.

(b) $25 \geq 30$
   Since both parts of this statement, $25 > 30$ and $25 = 30$, are false, $25 \geq 30$ is *false*.

(c) $12 \geq 12$

Since $12 = 12$, this statement is *true*.

Any statement with $<$ can be converted to one with $>$, and any statement with $>$ can be converted to one with $<$. We do this by reversing the order of the numbers and the direction of the symbol. For example, the statement $6 < 10$ can be written with $>$ by writing

$$10 > 6.$$

Similarly, any statement containing $\leq$ can be changed to one with $\geq$, and any statement with $\geq$ can be changed to one with $\leq$. For example, the statement $4 \leq 10$ can be changed to

$$10 \geq 4.$$

EXAMPLE 5   The following list shows the same statement written in two ways.

(a) $9 < 16$ $16 > 9$

(b) $5 > 2$ $2 < 5$

(c) $3 \leq 8$ $8 \geq 3$

(d) $12 \geq 5$ $5 \leq 12$

Here is a summary of the symbols discussed in this section:

$=$	*is equal to*
$\neq$	*is not equal to*
$<$	*is less than*
$>$	*is greater than*
$\leq$	*is less than or equal to*
$\geq$	*is greater than or equal to*

EXERCISES 1.1   *Work the following problems. See Examples 1 and 2. If you need a review of fractions, see Appendix A at the back of the book.*

1. $6(9)$ **2.** $5(8)$ **3.** $12(76)$ **4.** $8(51)$

5. $(32)(17)$ **6.** $(55)(43)$ **7.** $(9)11$ **8.** $(15)7$

9. $42 \cdot 3$ **10.** $6 \cdot 19$ **11.** $23 \cdot 12$ **12.** $32 \cdot 56$

13. $\frac{5}{8} \cdot 16$ **14.** $\frac{2}{3} \cdot 24$ **15.** $\frac{3}{7} \cdot \frac{2}{9}$ **16.** $\frac{4}{5} \cdot \frac{3}{8}$

17. $\frac{30}{5}$ **18.** $\frac{25}{5}$ **19.** $\frac{100}{2}$ **20.** $\frac{36}{18}$

Which of the symbols $<$, $>$, $\le$, or $\ge$ make the following statements true? Give all possible correct answers.

21. $6 \le 9$ **22.** $18 \_ 12$ **23.** $51 \_ 50$ **24.** $0 \le 12$

25. $5 \_ 5$ **26.** $10 \_ 10$ **27.** $48 \_ 0$ **28.** $100 \_ 1000$

29. $16 \_ 10$ **30.** $5 \_ 3$ **31.** $\frac{1}{4} \_ 1$ **32.** $\frac{2}{3} \_ 0$

Write the following word statements in symbols. See Example 3.

33. Seven equals five plus two.

34. Nine is greater than the product of four and two.

35. Three is less than the quotient of fifty and five.

36. Five equals ten minus five.

37. Twelve is not equal to five.

38. Fifteen does not equal sixteen.

39. Zero is greater than or equal to zero.

40. Six is less than or equal to six.

Answer true or false for each statement. See Example 4.

41. $8 + 2 = 10$ **42.** $8 \ne 9 - 1$

43. $12 \ge 10$ **44.** $45 < 45$

45. $0 < 15$ **46.** $16 \ge 10$

47. $9 + 12 = 21$ **48.** $9 < 12$

49. $25 \ge 19$ **50.** $18 < 5$

51. $9 < 0$ **52.** $15 \le 32$

53. $6 \ne 5 + 1$ **54.** $15 < 21$

55. $11 < 11$ **56.** $29 \ge 30$

57. $8 \le 0$ **58.** $26 \ge 50$

Rewrite the following statements so the inequality symbol points in the opposite direction. See Example 5.

59. $6 < 14$ **60.** $8 \le 9$ **61.** $15 \ge 3$ **62.** $29 > 4$

63. $9 > 8$ **64.** $12 < 17$ **65.** $0 \le 6$ **66.** $7 \le 12$

67. $18 \ge 15$ **68.** $25 \ge 1$

1.2 Exponents; Order of Operations

- **Define** *exponent.*
- **Use the order of operations.**

It is common in algebra to have a multiplication problem in which the same number appears several times. For example,

$$3 \cdot 3 \cdot 3 \cdot 3 = 81.$$

To save time, the repeated numbers are written with an *exponent*. In $3 \cdot 3 \cdot 3 \cdot 3$, the number 3 appears four times, and can be written as 3^4.

$$3 \cdot 3 \cdot 3 \cdot 3 = 3^4.$$

The number 4 is the **exponent** and 3 is the **base.** An exponent, then, tells how many times the base is used in the multiplication problem.

EXAMPLE 1 Find the values of the following.

(a) $5^2 = 5 \cdot 5$

$\quad\quad = 25$

Read 5^2 as "5 squared."

(b) $6^3 = 6 \cdot 6 \cdot 6$

$\quad\quad = 216$

Read 6^3 as "6 cubed."

(c) $2^5 = 2 \cdot 2 \cdot 2 \cdot 2 \cdot 2$

$\quad\quad = 32$

Read 2^5 as "2 to the fifth power."

(d) $7^4 = 7 \cdot 7 \cdot 7 \cdot 7$

$\quad\quad = 2401$

Read 7^4 as "7 to the fourth power."

(e) $1^6 = 1 \cdot 1 \cdot 1 \cdot 1 \cdot 1 \cdot 1$

$\quad\quad = 1$

Read 1^6 as "1 to the sixth power."

Many of the problems that we will work involve more than one symbol of arithmetic. For example,

$$5 + 2 \cdot 3.$$

It appears that we can first multiply 2 and 3, or we can first add 5 and 2. If we first multiply 2 and 3, and then add 5, the result is

$$5 + 2 \cdot 3 = 5 + 6$$

$$= 11.$$

If we first add 5 and 2, and then multiply by 3, the answer is

$$5 + 2 \cdot 3 = 7 \cdot 3$$
$$= 21.$$

To make sure that each expression of this type has only one answer, the following **order of operations** has been agreed upon:

Order of Operations

If no parentheses are present:

1. Find the value of any numbers with exponents first.

2. Do any multiplications or divisions in the order in which they occur, working from left to right.

3. Do any additions or subtractions in the order in which they occur, working from left to right.

4. If the expression has a fraction bar, do all work above and below the bar separately, and then simplify if possible.

If parentheses are present:

Use the rules above within each set of parentheses, starting with the innermost and working outward.

EXAMPLE 2   Find the value of $5 + 2 \cdot 3$.

Using the order of operations given above, first multiply 2 and 3, and then add 5.

$$5 + 2 \cdot 3 = 5 + 6$$
$$= 11$$

Therefore, $5 + 2 \cdot 3 = 11$. By following the order of operations given above, this is the only possible answer for this problem.

EXAMPLE 3   Use the order of operations to find the values of the following.

(a) $6 \cdot 8 + 5 \cdot 2$

Do any multiplications, working from left to right, and then add.

$$6 \cdot 8 + 5 \cdot 2 = 48 + 10 \qquad \text{Multiply}$$
$$= 58 \qquad\qquad \text{Add}$$

(b) $9(6 + 11)$

This expression can be simplified by first working inside the parentheses.

$$9(6 + 11) = 9(17) \qquad \text{Work inside parentheses}$$
$$= 153 \qquad \text{Multiply}$$

(c) $2(5 + 6) + 7 \cdot 3 = 2(11) + 7 \cdot 3 \qquad \text{Work inside parentheses}$
$$= 22 + 21 \qquad \text{Multiply}$$
$$= 43 \qquad \text{Add}$$

(d) $\dfrac{4(5 + 3) + 3}{2(3) - 1}$

Simplify the top and bottom of the fraction separately.

$$\frac{4(5 + 3) + 3}{2(3) - 1} = \frac{4(8) + 3}{2(3) - 1} \qquad \text{Work inside parentheses}$$

$$= \frac{32 + 3}{6 - 1} \qquad \text{Multiply}$$

$$= \frac{35}{5} \qquad \text{Add or subtract}$$

$$= 7 \qquad \text{Divide}$$

(e) $9 + 2^3 - 5$

Work out 2^3 first.

$$9 + 2^3 - 5 = 9 + 8 - 5 \qquad \text{Evaluate the exponent}$$
$$= 12 \qquad \text{Add or subtract}$$

An expression with double parentheses, such as $2(8 + 3(6 + 5))$, can be confusing. To eliminate this, square brackets, [ ], can be used instead of one of the pairs of parentheses.

EXAMPLE 4 Simplify $2[8 + 3(6 + 5)]$.
Work first with the innermost parentheses, until a single number is found for the terms inside the brackets.

$$2[8 + 3(6 + 5)] = 2[8 + 3(11)]$$
$$= 2[8 + 33]$$
$$= 2[41]$$
$$= 82$$

EXERCISES 1.2 *Find the values of the following. See Example 1.*

1. 6^2 2. 9^2 3. 8^2 4. 10^2

5. 17^2 6. 22^2 7. 5^3 8. 7^3

9. 6^4 10. 3^4 11. 2^5 12. 4^5

13. 3^6 **14.** 2^6 **15.** $\left(\frac{1}{2}\right)^2$ **16.** $\left(\frac{3}{4}\right)^2$

17. $\left(\frac{2}{5}\right)^3$ **18.** $\left(\frac{3}{7}\right)^3$

Work the following problems. Then decide whether the given statement is true or false. See Examples 2, 3, and 4.

19. $3 \cdot 4 + 7 < 10$

20. $8 \cdot 2 - 5 > 12$

21. $9 \cdot 3 - 11 \leq 16$

22. $6 \cdot 5 - 12 \leq 18$

23. $3 \cdot 8 - 4 \cdot 6 \leq 0$

24. $2 \cdot 20 - 8 \cdot 5 \geq 0$

25. $5 \cdot 11 + 2 \cdot 3 \leq 60$

26. $9 \cdot 3 + 4 \cdot 5 \geq 48$

27. $9 \cdot 2 - 6 \cdot 3 \geq 2$

28. $8 \cdot 3 - 4 \cdot 6 < 1$

29. $12 \cdot 3 - 6 \cdot 6 \leq 0$

30. $13 \cdot 2 - 15 \cdot 1 \geq 10$

31. $6 \cdot 5 + 3 \cdot 10 \leq 0$

32. $5 \cdot 8 + 10 \cdot 4 \geq 0$

33. $4[2 + 3(4)] \geq 50$

34. $3[5(2) - 3] < 20$

35. $5[8 + (2 + 3)] > 60$

36. $9[(14 + 5) - 10] > 80$

37. $2[2 + 3(2 + 5)] \leq 45$

38. $3[4 + 3(4 + 1)] \leq 55$

39. $\dfrac{5(4 - 1) + 3}{2 \cdot 4 + 1} \geq 3$

40. $\dfrac{7(3 + 1) - 2}{5 \cdot 2 + 3} \leq 2$

41. $\dfrac{2(5 + 3) + 2 \cdot 2}{2(4 - 1)} > 4$

42. $\dfrac{9(7 - 1) - 8 \cdot 2}{4(6 - 1)} > 2$

43. $\dfrac{2(5 + 1) - 3(1 + 1)}{5(8 - 6) - 4 \cdot 2} \leq 3$

44. $\dfrac{3(8 - 3) + 2(4 - 1)}{9(6 - 2) - 11(5 - 2)} \geq 7$

45. $63 \leq 8^2 + 2$

46. $9 \leq 4^2 - 8$

47. $5^2 + 2^2 \geq 30$

48. $6^2 - 3^2 > 25$

49. $36 < 3^3 + 3^2$

50. $15 > 2^4 - 2^3$

Insert parentheses in each expression so that the resulting statement is true. Some problems require no parentheses.

EXAMPLE   The statement $9 - 3 - 2 = 8$ will be true if parentheses are inserted around $3 - 2$. Thus,

$$9 - (3 - 2) = 8.$$

It is not true that $(9 - 3) - 2 = 8$, because $6 - 2 \neq 8$.

51. $10 - 7 - 3 = 6$

52. $16 - 4 - 3 = 15$

53. $3 \cdot 5 + 7 = 22$

54. $3 \cdot 5 + 7 = 36$

55. $3 \cdot 5 - 4 = 3$

56. $3 \cdot 5 - 4 = 11$

57. $3 \cdot 5 + 2 \cdot 4 = 23$

58. $3 \cdot 5 + 2 \cdot 4 = 84$

59. $3 \cdot 5 + 2 \cdot 4 = 68$

60. $3 \cdot 5 - 2 \cdot 4 = 36$

61. $3 \cdot 5 - 2 \cdot 4 = 7$

62. $7 \cdot 8 - 4 \cdot 3 = 84$

63. $100 \div 20 \div 5 = 1$

64. $360 \div 18 \div 4 = 5$

65. $100 \div 20 \div 5 = 25$

66. $4096 \div 256 \div 4 = 4$

67. $2^2 + 4 \cdot 2 = 16$

68. $6 + 5 \cdot 3^2 = 99$

69. $3^3 - 2 \cdot 4 = 100$

70. $8 - 2^2 \cdot 2 = 16$

1.3   Variables and Equations

- Define *variable*.
- Find the value of algebraic expressions for given values of the variable.
- Convert word phrases to algebraic expressions.
- Identify solutions of equations.

A **variable** is a letter, such as x, y, or z, that represents an unknown number. An **algebraic expression** is a collection of numbers, variables, symbols for operations, and symbols for grouping. For example,

$$x + 5, \qquad 2m - 9, \qquad \text{and} \qquad 8p^2 + 6p + 2$$

are all algebraic expressions. In the algebraic expression $2m - 9$, the expression $2m$ indicates the product of 2 and m, just as $8p^2$ shows the product of 8 and p^2.

An algebraic expression takes on different numerical values as the variables take on different values.

EXAMPLE 1   Find the values of the following algebraic expressions when $m = 5$ and when $m = 9$.

(a) $8m$

First, replace m with 5, to get

$$8m = 8 \cdot 5$$
$$= 40.$$

If $m = 9$, we have

$$8m = 8 \cdot 9$$
$$= 72.$$

(b) $3m^2$

For $m = 5$, $\qquad 3m^2 = 3 \cdot 5^2$
$$= 3 \cdot 25$$
$$= 75.$$

$$\text{For } m = 9, \quad 3\,m^2 = 3 \cdot 9^2$$
$$= 3 \cdot 81$$
$$= 243$$

EXAMPLE 2 Find the values of the following when $x = 5$ and $y = 3$.

(a) $2x + 5y$

Replace x with 5 and y with 3. Do the multiplications first and then add.

$$2x + 5y = 2 \cdot 5 + 5 \cdot 3 \qquad \text{Let } x = 5 \text{ and } y = 3$$
$$= 10 + 15 \qquad \text{Multiply}$$
$$= 25 \qquad \text{Add}$$

(b) $\dfrac{9x - 8y}{2x - y}$

$$\frac{9x - 8y}{2x - y} = \frac{9 \cdot 5 - 8 \cdot 3}{2 \cdot 5 - 3} \qquad \text{Let } x = 5 \text{ and } y = 3$$
$$= \frac{45 - 24}{10 - 3} \qquad \text{Multiply}$$
$$= \frac{21}{7} \qquad \text{Subtract}$$
$$= 3 \qquad \text{Divide}$$

(c) $x^2 - 2y^2 = 5^2 - 2 \cdot 3^2 \qquad \text{Let } x = 5 \text{ and } y = 3$

$$= 25 - 2 \cdot 9 \qquad \text{Evaluate the exponents}$$
$$= 25 - 18 \qquad \text{Multiply}$$
$$= 7 \qquad \text{Subtract}$$

Variables are used in changing word phrases into algebraic expressions. The next example shows how to do this.

EXAMPLE 3 Change the following word phrases to algebraic expressions. Use x as the variable.

(a) the sum of a number and 9

"Sum" is the answer to an addition problem. This phrase translates as

$$x + 9 \qquad \text{or} \qquad 9 + x.$$

(b) 7 minus a number

"Minus" indicates subtraction, so the answer is

$$7 - x.$$

($x - 7$ would *not* be correct)

(c) the product of 11 and a number

$$11 \cdot x \qquad \text{or} \qquad 11x$$

(d) 5 divided by a number

$$\frac{5}{x}$$

(e) the product of 2, and the sum of a number and 8

$$2(x + 8)$$

An **equation** is a statement that says two mathematical expressions are equal. Examples of equations include

$$x + 4 = 11, \qquad 2y = 16, \qquad \text{and} \qquad 4p + 1 = 25 - p.$$

To solve an equation, find all the values of the variable that make the equation true. The values of the variable that make the equation true are called the **solutions** of the equation.

EXAMPLE 4   Decide whether the given number is a solution of the equation.
(a) $5p + 1 = 36$;   7
Replace p with 7.

$$5p + 1 = 36$$
$$5 \cdot 7 + 1 = 36 \qquad \text{Let } p = 7$$
$$35 + 1 = 36$$
$$36 = 36 \qquad\qquad \text{True}$$

The number 7 is a solution of the equation.

(b) $9m - 6 = 32$;   4

$$9m - 6 = 32$$
$$9 \cdot 4 - 6 = 32 \qquad \text{Let } m = 4$$
$$36 - 6 = 32$$
$$30 = 32 \qquad \text{False}$$

The number 4 is not a solution of the equation.

EXERCISES 1.3   *Find the numerical values of the following when (a) $x = 3$ and (b) $x = 15$. See Examples 1 and 2.*

1. $x + 9$ **2.** $x - 1$ **3.** $5x$ **4.** $7x$

5. $2x + 8$ **6.** $9x - 5$ **7.** $\dfrac{x + 1}{3}$ **8.** $\dfrac{x - 2}{5}$

9. $\dfrac{3x - 5}{2x}$ **10.** $\dfrac{8x + 7}{3x}$ **11.** $\dfrac{x + 2}{x - 1}$ **12.** $\dfrac{2x - 3}{2x + 1}$

13. $3x^2 + x$ **14.** $2x + x^2$

Find the numerical values of the following when x = *4 and* y = *2. See Example 2.*

15. $x + y$

16. $x - y$

17. $8x + 3y + 5$

18. $4x + 2y + 7$

19. $3(x + 2y)$

20. $2(2x - y)$

21. $x + \dfrac{4}{y}$

22. $y + \dfrac{8}{x}$

23. $\dfrac{y}{3} + \dfrac{5}{y}$

24. $\dfrac{x}{5} + \dfrac{y}{4}$

25. $5(4x - 7y)$

26. $8(5x - 9y)$

27. $\dfrac{2x + 3y}{x + y + 1}$

28. $\dfrac{5x - 3y + 1}{2x}$

29. $\dfrac{2x + 4y - 6}{5y + 2}$

30. $\dfrac{4x + 3y - 1}{x}$

31. $x^2 + y^2$

32. $x^2 - y^2$

33. $2y^2 + 5x$

34. $6x^2 - 4y$

35. $\dfrac{x^2 - y^2}{x - y}$

36. $\dfrac{9x^2 - 4y^2}{3x^2 + 2y}$

Change the word phrases to algebraic expressions. Use x *to represent the variable. See Example 3.*

37. 8 times a number

38. 15 times a number

39. twice (2 times) a number

40. five times a number

41. 6 added to a number

42. 4 added to a number

43. a number subtracted from 8

44. 9 subtracted from a number

45. 8 added to three times a number

46. 6 subtracted from 5 times a number

47. twice a number, subtracted from 15

48. 8 times a number, added to 52

Decide whether the given number is a solution of the equation. See Example 4.

49. $x + 6 = 15;$ 9

50. $p - 5 = 12;$ 17

51. $3r + 5 = 8;$ 2

52. $5m + 2 = 7;$ 2

53. $6a + 2(a + 3) = 14;$ 1

54. $2y + 3(y - 2) = 14;$ 4

55. $2x + 3x + 8 = 38;$ 6   56. $6p + 4p - 9 = 11;$ 2

57. $2 + 3y + 4y = 20;$ 3   58. $6 + 8r - 3r = 11;$ 5

59. $2x^2 + 1 = 19;$ 3   60. $3r^2 - 2 = 46;$ 4

61. $\dfrac{x + 6}{x - 2} = 9;$ 3   62. $\dfrac{z + 4}{z - 2} = 2;$ 8

Change the word statements to equations. Use x *as the variable. Find the solutions from the list 0, 2, 4, 6, 8, 10. See Examples 3 and 4.*

EXAMPLE   The sum of a number and 4 is six.
First write the sentence in symbols, as $x + 4 = 6$. ("Is" translates as =.) Then find the solution from the list; the solution is 2.

63. The sum of a number and 8 is 12.

64. A number minus 3 equals 7.

65. The sum of a number and 2 is 10.

66. The sum of twice a number and 6 is 18.

67. 5 more than twice a number is 13.

68. The product of a number and 3 is 24.

69. Three times a number is equal to two more than twice the number.

70. Twelve divided by a number equals three times that number.

71. Twenty divided by five times a number is 2.

72. The sum of a number and 1, divided by 3, is 3.

1.4 Real Numbers and the Number Line

- **Graph number lines.**
- **Identify whole numbers, integers, rational numbers, irrational numbers, and real numbers.**
- **Find additive inverses.**
- **Tell which real number is smaller.**
- **Find absolute values.**

When studying numbers in algebra, it is often helpful to draw graphs showing the numbers. This is done with a **number line,** such as the one in Figure 1.1.

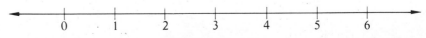

Figure 1.1

To set up a number line, locate any point on the line and call it 0. Choose any point to the right of 0 and call it 1. The distance between 0 and 1 gives a unit of measure used to locate other points, as shown in Figure 1.1. The set of points labeled in Figure 1.1 correspond to the set of **whole numbers:**

Whole Numbers   {0, 1, 2, 3, 4, 5, · · ·}

The three dots show that the list of numbers continues in the same way indefinitely.

All the whole numbers starting with 1 are to the right of 0 on the number line. But we may also place numbers to the left of 0. These numbers, written −1, −2, −3, and so on, are shown in Figure 1.2.

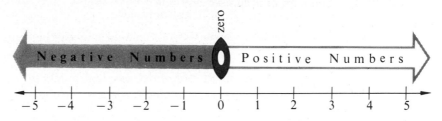

Figure 1.2

The numbers to the *left* of 0 on the number line are **negative numbers.** Numbers to the *right* of 0 are **positive numbers.** The number 0 itself is neither positive nor negative.

There are many practical applications of negative numbers. For example, the altitude of Badwater in Death Valley is −282 feet (282 feet below sea level, which is taken to be 0). A temperature on a cold January day can be written as −10°, or 10 degrees below zero. A business that spends more than it takes in has a negative "profit."

The set of numbers, including positive and negative numbers, shown in Figure 1.2 is called the set of **integers:**

Integers   {· · · , −3, −2, −1, 0, 1, 2, 3, · · ·}

Not all numbers are integers. For example, $\frac{1}{2}$ is not; it is a number halfway between 0 and 1. Also $3\frac{1}{4}$ is not an integer. Several such numbers are shown in Figure 1.3.

Figure 1.3

All the numbers in Figure 1.3 can be written as quotients of integers. These numbers are called **rational numbers:**

Rational Numbers   {quotient of two integers, with
                          denominator not 0}

Since any integer can be written as the quotient of itself and 1, all integers are rational numbers.

Although a great many numbers are rational, not all are. For example, a floor tile one foot on a side has a diagonal whose length is the square root of 2 (written $\sqrt{2}$). This number is not rational, it is **irrational.**

Irrational Numbers   {numbers represented by points on the number line which are not rational}

Examples of irrational numbers include $\sqrt{3}$, $\sqrt{7}$, $-\sqrt{10}$, and π, which is the ratio of the distance around a circle to the distance across it.

Finally, the set of *all* numbers that can be represented by a point on the number line is the set of **real numbers.**

Real Numbers   {all numbers that can be represented on the number line}

All the numbers mentioned above are real numbers. The relationships between the various sets of numbers is shown in Figure 1.4.

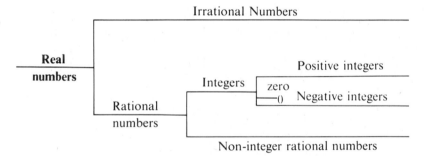

Figure 1.4

One property of the real numbers tells us that, if we select any real number x (except 0), we can find exactly one number on the number line the same distance from 0 as x, but on the opposite side of 0.

For example, Figure 1.5 shows that the numbers 3 and -3 are each the same distance from 0 but are on opposite sides of 0. The numbers 3 and -3 are called **additive inverses,** or **negatives,** of each other.

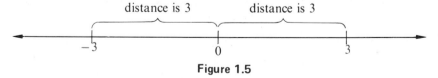

Figure 1.5

In general, the additive inverse of a number x is that number which is the same distance from 0 on the number line as x, but on the opposite side of 0.

The additive inverse of the number 0 is 0 itself. This makes 0 the only real number that is its own additive inverse. Other additive inverses occur in pairs. For example, 4 and -4, 3 and -3, and 5 and -5 are additive inverses of each other. Several pairs of additive inverses are shown in Figure 1.6.

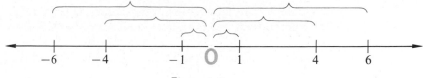

Figure 1.6

The additive inverse of a number can be indicated by writing the symbol − in front of the number. With this symbol, the additive inverse of 7 is written −7. The additive inverse of −3 can be written −(−3). We know that 3 is an additive inverse of −3. Since a number can have only one additive inverse, the symbols 3 and −(−3) must represent the same number, which means that

$$-(-3) = 3.$$

In general, for any real number x,

$$-(-x) = x.$$

EXAMPLE 1 Find the additive inverse of each number.

Number	Additive inverse
−3	3
−4	−(−4), or 4
0	−0, or 0
−2	−(−2), or 2
5	−5
19	−19

As Example 1 shows,

> to find the additive inverse of a number, change the sign of the number.

If you are given any two whole numbers, you probably can tell which number is smaller. But what happens when we look at negative numbers, such as those in the set of integers? Positive numbers increase as the corresponding points on the number line go to the right. For example, $8 < 12$, and 8 is to the left of 12 on the number line. We can extend this idea to all real numbers.

The smaller of any two different real numbers is the one farther to the left on the number line.

Then any negative number is smaller than 0, and any negative number is smaller than any positive number. Also, 0 is smaller than any positive number.

EXAMPLE 2 Is it true that $-3 < -1$?

To decide whether the statement $-3 < -1$ is true, locate both numbers,

−3 and −1, on a number line, as in Figure 1.7. Since −3 is to the left of −1 on the number line, −3 is smaller than −1. The statement −3 < −1 is *true*.

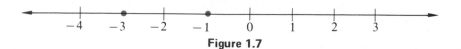

Figure 1.7

As we said earlier, additive inverses are numbers that are the same distance from 0 on the number line. To express this, we say that additive inverses have the same absolute value. The **absolute value** of a number is defined as the distance between 0 and the number on the number line.

The symbol for the absolute value of the number x is $|x|$, read "the absolute value of x." For example, the distance between 2 and 0 on the number line is 2 units, so that

$$|2| = 2.$$

Also, the distance between −2 and 0 on the number line is 2 units, so that

$$|-2| = 2.$$

Since distance is a physical measurement, which is never negative, the absolute value of a number can never be negative. For example, $|12| = 12$ and $|-12| = 12$, since both 12 and −12 lie at a distance of 12 units from 0 on the number line. Since 0 is a distance 0 units from 0, we have $|0| = 0$.

We formally define absolute value as follows:

$$|x| = x \text{ if } x \geq 0, \qquad |x| = -x \text{ if } x < 0.$$

The second part of this definition is a little tricky. Since x is a variable, it can be either positive or negative. So in the second part of the definition, we say that $|x| = -x$ if $x < 0$. If $x < 0$ then x is already negative by definition, so that $-x$ will be *positive*.

The absolute value of a number is never negative.

EXAMPLE 3 Simplify by removing absolute value symbols.

(a) $|5| = 5$

(b) $|-5| = 5$

(c) $-|5| = -(5) = -5$

(d) $-|-14| = -(14) = -14$

(e) $-|-8| = -(8) = -8$

EXERCISES 1.4 *Find the additive inverse of each number. For the exercises with absolute value, simplify first before deciding on the additive inverse. See Examples 1 and 3.*

1. 8   **2.** 12   **3.** −9   **4.** −11

5. -2 **6.** -3 **7.** $|15|$ **8.** $|5|$

9. $|8|$ **10.** $|0|$

Select the smaller of the two given numbers. See Examples 2 and 3.

11. $-5, 5$ **12.** $9, -3$

13. $-12, -4$ **14.** $-9, -14$

15. $-8, -1$ **16.** $-15, -16$

17. $3, |-4|$ **18.** $5, |-2|$

19. $|-3|, |-4|$ **20.** $|-8|, |-9|$

21. $-|-6|, -|-4|$ **22.** $-|-2|, -|-3|$

Write true *or* false *for each of the following. See Examples 2 and 3.*

23. $-2 < -1$ **24.** $-8 < -4$

25. $-3 \geq -7$ **26.** $-9 \geq -12$

27. $-15 \leq -20$ **28.** $-21 \leq -27$

29. $-8 \leq -(-4)$ **30.** $-9 \leq -(-6)$

31. $0 \leq -(-4)$ **32.** $0 \geq -(-6)$

33. $-9 \leq -(-6)$ **34.** $8 \leq -(-4)$

35. $6 > -(-2)$ **36.** $-8 > -(-2)$

37. $-4 < -(-5)$ **38.** $-6 \leq -0$

39. $|-6| < |-9|$ **40.** $|-12| < |-20|$

41. $-|8| > |-9|$ **42.** $-|12| > |-15|$

43. $-|-5| \geq -|-9|$ **44.** $-|-12| \leq -|-15|$

Graph each group of numbers on a number line.

45. $0, 3, -5, -6$ **46.** $2, 6, -2, -1$

47. $-2, -6, |-4|, 3, -|4|$ **48.** $-5, -3, -|-2|, -0, |-4|$

49. $\frac{1}{4}, 2\frac{1}{2}, -3\frac{4}{5}, -4, -1\frac{5}{8}$ **50.** $5\frac{1}{4}, 4\frac{5}{9}, -2\frac{1}{3}, 0, -3\frac{2}{5}$

51. $|3|, -|3|, -|-4|, -|-2|$ **52.** $|6|, -|6|, -|-8|, -|-3|$

1.5   Addition of Real Numbers

- **Add real numbers on a number line.**
- **Add mentally.**
- **Use the order of operations with real numbers.**

We can use the number line to illustrate the addition of real numbers, as shown by the following examples.

EXAMPLE 1   Use the number line to find the sum 2 + 3.

To add the positive numbers 2 and 3 on the number line, start at 0 and draw an arrow two units to the *right* as shown in Figure 1.8. This arrow represents the number 2 in the sum 2 + 3. Then, from the right end of this arrow draw another arrow 3 units to the right. The number below the end of this second arrow is 5, so 2 + 3 = 5.

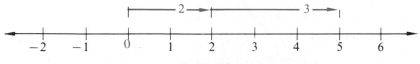

Figure 1.8

EXAMPLE 2   Use the number line to find the sum −2 + (−4). (We placed parentheses around the −4 to avoid the confusing use of + and − next to each other.)

To add the negative numbers −2 and −4 on the number line, again start at 0 and draw an arrow two units to the *left,* as shown in Figure 1.9. We draw the arrow to the left to represent the addition of a *negative* number. From the left end of this first arrow, draw a second arrow four units to the left. The number below the end of this second arrow is −6, so −2 + (−4) = −6.

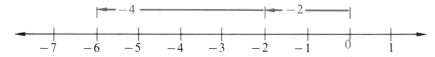

Figure 1.9

Refer back to Example 2. Notice that the sum of the two negative numbers −2 and −4 is a negative number whose distance from 0 is the sum of the distance of −2 from 0 and the distance of −4 from 0. That is, *the sum of two negative numbers is the negative of the sum of their absolute values.*

$$-2 + (-4) = -(|-2| + |-4|) = -6$$

To add two numbers having the same signs, add the absolute values of the numbers. The result has the same sign as the numbers being added.

EXAMPLE 3   Find the sums.

(a) −2 + (−9) = −11

(b) −8 + (−12) = −20

(c) −15 + (−3) = −18

To find the sum of a positive number and a negative number, we again use the number line.

EXAMPLE 4   Use the number line to find the sum −2 + 5.

To find the sum −2 + 5 on the number line, start at 0 and draw an arrow two units to the left. From the left end of this arrow, draw a second arrow 5 units to the right, as shown in Figure 1.10. The number below the end of the second arrow is 3, so $-2 + 5 = 3$.

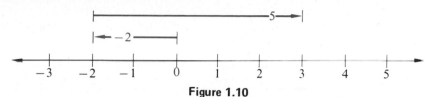

Figure 1.10

EXAMPLE 5 Use the number line to find the sum $4 + (-6)$.

To find the sum $4 + (-6)$ on the number line, start at 0 and draw arrows as shown in Figure 1.11. The number below the end of the second arrow is -2, so $4 + (-6) = -2$.

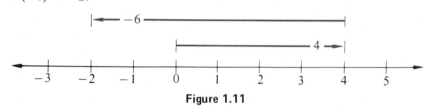

Figure 1.11

EXAMPLE 6 Check each answer, trying to work the addition mentally. If you get stuck, use a number line.

(a) $7 + (-4) = 3$

(b) $-8 + 12 = 4$

(c) $-11 + 15 = 4$

(d) $-\dfrac{1}{2} + \dfrac{1}{8} = -\dfrac{4}{8} + \dfrac{1}{8} = -\dfrac{3}{8}$ (Remember to obtain a common denominator first.)

(e) $\dfrac{5}{6} + \left(-\dfrac{4}{3}\right) = -\dfrac{1}{2}$

(f) $-4.6 + 8.1 = 3.5$

Addition of a positive number and a negative number can also be defined using absolute value.

To add a positive number and a negative number, find the absolute values of the numbers and subtract the smaller from the larger. The answer is given the sign of the number with the larger absolute value.

For example, to add -12 and 5, find their absolute values: $|-12| = 12$ and $|5| = 5$. Then subtract these absolute values: $12 - 5 = 7$. Since $|-12| > |5|$, the sum will be negative, so that the final answer is $-12 + 5 = -7$.

Sometimes a problem involves square brackets, [ ]. As mentioned earlier, brackets are treated just like parentheses. Do the calculations inside the brackets until a single number is obtained. Remember to use the order of operations given in Section 1.2 when adding more than two numbers.

EXAMPLE 7   Find the sums.

(a) $-3 + [4 + (-8)]$

First work inside the brackets. Follow the rules for the order of operations given in Section 1.2.

$$-3 + [4 + (-8)] = -3 + (-4)$$
$$= -7$$

(b) $8 + [(-2 + 6) + (-3)] = 8 + [4 + (-3)]$
$$= 8 + 1$$
$$= 9$$

EXERCISES 1.5   *Find the sums. See Examples 1–7.*

1. $5 + (-3)$

2. $11 + (-8)$

3. $6 + (-8)$

4. $3 + (-7)$

5. $-6 + (-2)$

6. $-8 + (-3)$

7. $-9 + (-2)$

8. $-15 + (-6)$

9. $-3 + (-9)$

10. $-11 + (-5)$

11. $12 + (-8)$

12. $10 + (-2)$

13. $4 + [13 + (-5)]$

14. $6 + [2 + (-13)]$

15. $8 + [-2 + (-1)]$

16. $12 + [-3 + (-4)]$

17. $-2 + [5 + (-1)]$

18. $-8 + [9 + (-2)]$

19. $-6 + [6 + (-9)]$

20. $-3 + [4 + (-8)]$

21. $[9 + (-2)] + 6$

22. $[8 + (-14)] + 10$

23. $[(-9) + (-14)] + 12$

24. $[(-8) + (-6)] + 10$

25. $-\dfrac{1}{6} + \dfrac{2}{3}$

26. $\dfrac{9}{10} + \left(-\dfrac{3}{5}\right)$

27. $\dfrac{5}{8} + \left(-\dfrac{17}{12}\right)$

28. $-\dfrac{6}{25} + \dfrac{19}{20}$

29. $2\dfrac{1}{2} + \left(-3\dfrac{1}{4}\right)$

30. $-4\dfrac{3}{8} + 6\dfrac{1}{2}$

31. $7.9 + (-8.4)$

32. $11.6 + (-15.4)$

33. $-6.1 + [3.2 + (-4.8)]$

34. $-9.4 + [-5.8 + (-1.4)]$

35. $[-3 + (-4)] + [5 + (-6)]$

36. $[-8 + (-3)] + [-7 + (-6)]$

37. $[-4 + (-3)] + [8 + (-1)]$

38. $[-5 + (-9)] + [16 + (-21)]$

39. $[-4 + (-6)] + [(-3) + (-8)] + [12 + (-11)]$

40. $[-2 + (-11)] + [12 + (-2)] + [18 + (-6)]$

Write true *or* false.

41. $-4 + 0 = -4$

42. $-6 + 5 = -1$

43. $-8 + 12 = 8 + (-12)$

44. $15 + (-8) = 8 + (-15)$

45. $-9 + 5 + 6 = -2$

46. $-6 + 3 = -3$

47. $-3 + 5 = 5 + (-3)$

48. $11 + (-6) = -6 + 11$

49. $|-8 + 3| = 8 + 3$

50. $|-4 + 2| = 4 + 2$

51. $|12 - 3| = 12 - 3$

52. $|-6 + 10| = 6 + 10$

53. $[4 + (-6)] + 6 = 4 + (-6 + 6)$

54. $[(-2) + (-3)] + (-6) = 12 + (-1)$

55. $-7 + [-5 + (-3)] = [(-7) + (-5)] + 3$

56. $6 + [-2 + (-5)] = [(-4) + (-2)] + 5$

57. $-5 + (-|-5|) = -10$

58. $|-3| + (-5) = -2$

Find all solutions for the following equations from the list $-3, -2, -1, 0, 1, 2, 3$.

59. $x + 2 = 0$

60. $x + 3 = 0$

61. $x + 1 = -2$

62. $x + 2 = -1$

63. $14 + x = 12$

64. $x + 8 = 7$

65. $x + (-4) = -6$

66. $x + (-2) = -5$

67. $-8 + x = -6$

68. $-2 + x = -1$

Solve the following word problems.

69. Joann has $15. She then spends $6. How much is left?

70. An airplane is at an altitude of 6000 feet. It then descends 4000 feet. What is its final altitude?

71. Chuck is standing 15 feet below sea level in Death Valley. He then goes down another 120 feet. Find his final altitude.

72. Donna has $11 and spends $19. What is her final balance? (Write the answer with a negative number.)

73. Nancy's blood pressure was 120, but then it changed by -30. Find her present blood pressure.

74. The temperature was $-14°$, but then it went down 12°. Find the present temperature.

75. The temperature at 4 A.M. was $-22°$, but it went up 35° by noon. What was the temperature at noon?

76. A man owes $94 to a credit card company. He makes a payment of $60. What amount does he still owe?

1.6 Subtraction

- • **Find a difference on the number line.**
- • **Use the definition of subtraction.**
- • **Work subtraction problems involving brackets.**

We already know how to subtract a positive number from a larger positive number (for example, $7 - 4$). The answer to such a subtraction problem is called the **difference.** The difference can be found by using a number line. Since addition of a positive number on the number line is shown by an arrow to the right, it is reasonable to represent subtraction of a positive number by an arrow going to the left.

EXAMPLE 1   Use the number line to find the difference $7 - 4$.

To find the difference of $7 - 4$ on the number line, begin at 0 and draw an arrow 7 units to the right. From the right end of this arrow, draw an arrow 4 units to the left, as shown in Figure 1.12. The number below the end of the second arrow is 3, so $7 - 4 = 3$.

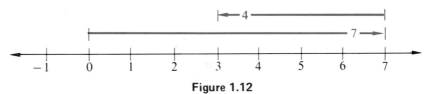

Figure 1.12

The procedure used in Example 1 above to find $7 - 4$ is exactly the same procedure that would be used to find $7 + (-4)$ so that

$$7 - 4 = 7 + (-4).$$

Based on this, it seems that subtraction of a positive number from a larger positive number is the same as adding the additive inverse of the smaller number to the larger. We extend this definition of subtraction to all real numbers.

For any two real numbers, x and y,

$$x - y = x + (-y).$$

In other words, to subtract y from x, add the additive inverse of y to x.

EXAMPLE 2   Find the differences using the formula $x - y = x + (-y)$.

(a) $12 - 3 = 12 + (-3)$
$= 9$

(b) $5 - 7 = 5 + (-7)$
$= -2$

(c) $8 - 15 = 8 + (-15)$
$= -7$

(d) $-3 - (-5) = -3 + (5)$
$= 2$

(e) $-6 - (-9) = -6 + (9)$
$= 3$

(f) $8 - (-5) = 8 + (5)$
$= 13$

We have now used the symbol $-$ for a variety of purposes. One use is to represent subtraction, as in $9 - 5$. The symbol $-$ is also used to represent negative numbers, such as $-10, -2, -3$, and so on. Finally, the symbol $-$ is used to represent the additive inverse of a number. More than one use may appear in the same problem, such as $-6 - (-9)$, where -9 is subtracted from -6. The meaning of the symbol depends on its position in the algebraic expression.

EXAMPLE 3 When working problems involving both parentheses and brackets, first do any operations inside the parentheses or brackets from the inside out.

(a) $-6 - [2 - (8 + 3)] = -6 - [2 - 11]$
$= -6 - (-9)$
$= -6 + (9)$
$= 3$

(b) $5 - [(-3 - 2) - (4 - 1)] = 5 - [(-3 + (-2)) - 3]$
$= 5 - [(-5) - 3]$
$= 5 - [(-5) + (-3)]$
$= 5 - (-8)$
$= 5 + 8$
$= 13$

EXERCISES 1.6 *Subtract. See Examples 1 and 2.*

1. $3 - 6$ **2.** $7 - 12$

3. $5 - 9$ **4.** $8 - 13$

5. $-6 - 2$ **6.** $-11 - 4$

7. $-9 - 5$ **8.** $-12 - 15$

9. $6 - (-3)$ **10.** $8 - (-5)$

11. $5 - (-12)$ **12.** $12 - (-2)$

13. $-6 - (-2)$

14. $-7 - (-5)$

15. $2 - (3 - 5)$

16. $5 - (6 - 13)$

17. $-2 - (5 - 8)$

18. $-3 - (4 - 11)$

19. $\frac{1}{2} - \left(-\frac{1}{4}\right)$

20. $\frac{1}{3} - \left(-\frac{4}{3}\right)$

21. $-\frac{3}{4} - \frac{5}{8}$

22. $-\frac{5}{6} - \frac{1}{2}$

23. $\frac{5}{8} - \left(-\frac{1}{2} - \frac{3}{4}\right)$

24. $\frac{9}{10} - \left(\frac{1}{8} - \frac{3}{10}\right)$

25. $3.4 - (-8.2)$

26. $5.7 - (-11.6)$

27. $-6.4 - 3.5$

28. $-4.4 - 8.6$

Perform the indicated operations. See Example 3.

29. $(4 - 6) + 12$

30. $(3 - 7) + 4$

31. $(8 - 1) - 12$

32. $(9 - 3) - 15$

33. $6 - (-8 + 3)$

34. $8 - (-9 + 5)$

35. $2 + (-4 - 8)$

36. $6 + (-9 - 2)$

37. $(-5 - 6) - (9 - 2)$

38. $(-4 - 8) - (6 - 1)$

39. $(-8 - 2) - (-9 - 3)$

40. $(-4 - 2) - (-8 - 1)$

41. $-9 - [(3 - 2) - (-4 - 2)]$

42. $-8 - [(-4 - 1) - (9 - 2)]$

43. $-3 + [(-5 - 8) - (-6 + 2)]$

44. $-4 + [(-12 + 1) - (-1 - 9)]$

Write each problem in symbols (no variables are needed). Then solve.

45. Subtract -6 from 12.

46. Subtract -8 from 15.

47. From -25, subtract -4.

48. What number is 6 less than -9?

49. The number -24 is how much greater than -27?

50. How much greater is 8 than -5?

Work the word problems.

51. The temperature dropped 10° below the previous temperature of $-5°$. Find the new temperature.

52. Bill owed his brother $10. He repaid $6 and later borrowed $7. What positive or negative number represents his present financial status?

53. The bottom of Death Valley is 282 feet below sea level. The top of Mt. Whitney, visible from Death Valley, has an altitude of 14,494 feet above sea level. Find the difference between these two elevations.

54. Harriet has $15, while Anna is $12 in debt. Find the difference in their financial positions.

1.7 Multiplication

- **Multiply a positive and a negative number.**
- **Multiply two negative numbers.**
- **Simplify numerical expressions with positive and negative numbers.**
- **Substitute numerical values for variables.**

We already know the rules for multiplying positive numbers. For example,

the product of two positive numbers is positive.

But what about multiplying other real numbers? Any rules we develop for multiplication of real numbers ought to be consistent with the rules for multiplication of positive numbers. For example, we would want the product of 0 and any real number (positive or negative) to be 0.

$$x \cdot 0 = 0$$

In order to define the product of a positive and a negative number so that the result is consistent with our definition of multiplying two positive numbers, we look at the following pattern.

$$3 \cdot 5 = 15$$
$$3 \cdot 4 = 12$$
$$3 \cdot 3 = 9$$
$$3 \cdot 2 = 6$$
$$3 \cdot 1 = 3$$
$$3 \cdot 0 = 0$$
$$3 \cdot (-1) = ?$$

What number should we assign to the product $3(-1)$ so that the pattern is maintained? The numbers on the left of the equals sign (in heavy type) decrease by 1 as we go down the list. Also, the products on the right decrease by 3 as we go down the list. To maintain this pattern, the number on the right in the bottom row must be 3 less than 0, which is -3. Therefore, we must have

$$3(-1) = -3.$$

The pattern continues with

$$3(-2) = -6$$
$$3(-3) = -9$$
$$3(-4) = -12,$$

and so on.

In general, if both x and y represent positive numbers, then

$$x(-y) = -(xy) \qquad \text{or}$$
$$(-x)y = -(xy).$$

In words,

the product of a postive number and a negative number is negative.

EXAMPLE 1　Find the products using the multiplication formula given above.

(a) $8(-5) = -(8 \cdot 5)$
$\qquad = -40$

(b) $5(-4) = -(5 \cdot 4)$
$\qquad = -20$

(c) $(-7)(2) = -(7 \cdot 2)$
$\qquad = -14$

(d) $(-9)(3) = -(9 \cdot 3)$
$\qquad = -27$

(e) $(-6)(4) = -24$

We know that the product of two positive numbers is positive, and we have seen that the product of a positive and a negative number is negative. What about the product of two negative numbers? Consider another pattern.

$$(-5)(4) = -20$$
$$(-5)(3) = -15$$
$$(-5)(2) = -10$$
$$(-5)(1) = -5$$
$$(-5)(0) = 0$$
$$(-5)(-1) = ?$$

The numbers on the left of the equals sign decrease by 1 as we go down the list. Also, the products on the right increase by 5 as we go down the list. To maintain this pattern, we will have to agree that $(-5)(-1)$ is 5 more than $(-5)(0)$. Therefore, we must have

$$(-5)(-1) = 5.$$

The pattern continues with

$$(-5)(-2) = 10$$
$$(-5)(-3) = 15$$
$$(-5)(-4) = 20$$
$$(-5)(-5) = 25$$

and so on.

In general, if x and y both represent positive numbers, then

$$(-x)(-y) = xy.$$

In words,

the product of two negative numbers is positive.

EXAMPLE 2   Find the products using the multiplication formula given above.

(a) $(-9)(-2) = 9 \cdot 2$
$= 18$

(b) $(-6)(-12) = 6 \cdot 12$
$= 72$

(c) $(-8)(-1) = 8 \cdot 1$
$= 8$

(d) $(-15)(-2) = 15 \cdot 2$
$= 30$

In summary,

the product of two numbers having the *same* signs is *positive,* and the product of two numbers having *different* signs is *negative.*

EXAMPLE 3   Simplify according to the multiplication definitions given in this chapter and the rules for the order of operations given earlier.

(a) $(-9)(2) - (-3)(2)$

To simplify, first find all the products working from left to right.

$$(-9)(2) - (-3)(2) = -18 - (-6)$$

Now perform the subtraction.

$$= -18 + 6$$
$$= -12$$

(b) $(-6)(-2) - (3)(-4) = 12 - (-12)$
$$= 12 + 12$$
$$= 24$$

(c) $-5(-2 - 3) = -5(-5) = 25$

EXAMPLE 4   Evaluate $(3x + 4y)(-2m)$, given $x = -1$, $y = -2$, and $m = -3$.
First substitute the given values. Then find the value of the expression.

$$(3x + 4y)(-2m) = [3(-1) + 4(-2)] [-2(-3)]$$
$$= [-3 + (-8)] [6]$$
$$= (-11)(6)$$
$$= -66$$

EXERCISES 1.7   *Find the products. See Examples 1 and 2.*

1. $(-3)(-4)$ 2. $(-3)(4)$

3. $3(-4)$ 4. $-2(-8)$

5. $(-1)(-5)$ **6.** $(-9)(-5)$

7. $(-4)(-11)$ **8.** $(-5)(7)$

9. $(-10)(-12)$ **10.** $9(-5)$

11. $(8)(-6)$ **12.** $(13)(-2)$

13. $(-6)(5)$ **14.** $(-9)(0)$

15. $(13)(-5)$ **16.** $(12)(5)$

17. $0(-11)$ **18.** $3(-15)$

19. $(15)(-11)$ **20.** $(-9)(-4)$

21. $-\dfrac{3}{8} \cdot -\dfrac{10}{9}$ **22.** $-\dfrac{5}{4} \cdot \dfrac{6}{15}$

23. $(-5.1)(.02)$ **24.** $(-3.7)(-2.1)$

Perform the indicated operations. See Example 3.

25. $6 - 4 \cdot 5$ **26.** $3 - 2 \cdot 9$

27. $-9 - (-2) \cdot 3$ **28.** $-11 - (-7) \cdot 4$

29. $9(6 - 10)$ **30.** $5(12 - 15)$

31. $-6(2 - 4)$ **32.** $-9(5 - 8)$

33. $(4 - 9)(2 - 3)$ **34.** $(6 - 11)(3 - 6)$

35. $(2 - 5)(3 - 7)$ **36.** $(5 - 12)(2 - 6)$

37. $(-4 - 3)(-2) + 4$ **38.** $(-5 - 2)(-3) + 6$

39. $5(-2) - 4$ **40.** $9(-6) - 8$

41. $3(-4) - (-2)$ **42.** $5(-2) - (-9)$

43. $(-8 - 2)(-4) - (-5)$ **44.** $(-9 - 1)(-2) - (-6)$

45. $|-4(-2)| + |-4|$ **46.** $|8(-5)| + |-2|$

47. $|2|(-4) + |6| \cdot |-4|$ **48.** $|-3|(-2) + |-8| \cdot |5|$

Evaluate each of the following expressions, given $x = -2$, $y = 3$, and $a = -4$. See Example 4.

49. $2x + 7y$ **50.** $3x + 5y$

51. $5x - 2y + 3a$ **52.** $6x - 5y + 4a$

53. $(2x + y)(3a)$ **54.** $(5x - 2y)(-2a)$

55. $(3x - 4y)(-5a)$ **56.** $(6x + 2y)(-3a)$

57. $(-5 + x)(-3 + y)(2 - a)$ **58.** $(6 - x)(5 + y)(3 + a)$

59. $-2y^2 + 3a$ **60.** $5x - 4a^2$

61. $3a^2 - x^2$ **62.** $4y^2 - 2x^2$

Find the solution for the following equations from the list $-3, -2, -1, 0, 1, 2, 3$.

63. $2x = -4$ **64.** $3k = -6$

65. $-4m = 0$

66. $-9y = 0$

67. $-8p = 16$

68. $-9r = 27$

69. $2x + 1 = -3$

70. $3w + 3 = -3$

71. $-4a + 2 = 10$

72. $-5t + 6 = 11$

1.8 Division

- **Find the multiplicative inverse or reciprocal of a number.**
- **Divide positive and negative numbers.**
- **Simplify numerical expressions.**

We have seen that a subtraction problem can be worked by adding the additive inverse of the second number to the first. Division problems are related to multiplication in a similar way. To subtract, we use the additive inverse; to divide, we use the multiplicative inverse. The multiplicative inverse of 8 is $\frac{1}{8}$, and of $\frac{5}{4}$ is $\frac{4}{5}$. Note that

$$8 \cdot \frac{1}{8} = \frac{8}{8} = 1 \qquad \text{and} \qquad \frac{5}{4} \cdot \frac{4}{5} = \frac{20}{20} = 1.$$

(Remember that any number except 0 divided by itself is 1.)

Pairs of numbers whose product is 1 are **multiplicative inverses** or **reciprocals** of each other.

EXAMPLE 1 Find the multiplicative inverse of each number.

Number	Multiplicative Inverse (Reciprocal)
4	$\frac{1}{4}$
-5	$\frac{1}{-5}$ or $-\frac{1}{5}$
$\frac{3}{4}$	$\frac{4}{3}$
$-\frac{5}{8}$	$-\frac{8}{5}$
0	None

Why is there no multiplicative inverse for the number 0? Suppose k is to be the multiplicative inverse of 0. Then $k \cdot 0$ should equal 1. But $k \cdot 0 = 0$ for any number k. So there is no value of k which is a solution of the equation $k \cdot 0 = 1$.

The number 0 has no multiplicative inverse.

By definition, the quotient of x divided by y is the product of x and the multiplicative inverse of y. That is, for any real numbers x and y,

$$\frac{x}{y} = x \cdot \frac{1}{y} \quad (y \neq 0).$$

In the definition above, we said that y, the number we divide by, cannot be 0. The reason is that 0 has no multiplicative inverse, so that $\frac{1}{0}$ is not a number. For this reason, division by 0 is meaningless and is never permitted. If a division problem turns out to involve division by 0, write "no such number."

Since division is defined in terms of multiplication, all the rules for multiplication of signed numbers also apply to division.

EXAMPLE 2   Find the quotients using the formula for division.

(a) $\dfrac{12}{3} = 12 \cdot \dfrac{1}{3}$

$\qquad = 4$

(b) $\dfrac{-10}{2} = -10 \cdot \dfrac{1}{2}$

$\qquad = -5$

(c) $\dfrac{8}{-4} = 8 \cdot \left(\dfrac{1}{-4}\right)$

$\qquad = -2$

(d) $\dfrac{-14}{-7} = -14 \left(\dfrac{1}{-7}\right)$

$\qquad = 2$

(e) $\dfrac{-100}{-20} = -100 \left(\dfrac{1}{-20}\right)$

$\qquad = 5$

(f) $\dfrac{-10}{0}$ no such number

In practice, when we divide with positive or negative numbers, we disregard all signs and divide as if both numbers were positive. The answer will be positive if both numbers have like signs, and negative if both numbers do not have like signs.

EXAMPLE 3   Find the quotients.

(a) $\dfrac{8}{-2} = -4$

(b) $\dfrac{-45}{-9} = 5$

(c) $-\dfrac{1}{8} \div -\dfrac{3}{4} = -\dfrac{1}{8} \cdot -\dfrac{4}{3} = \dfrac{1}{6}$

From the definitions of multiplication and division of real numbers,

$$\dfrac{-40}{8} = -40 \cdot \dfrac{1}{8}$$
$$= -5,$$

and

$$\dfrac{40}{-8} = 40 \left(\dfrac{1}{-8}\right)$$
$$= -5,$$

so that

$$\dfrac{-40}{8} = \dfrac{40}{-8}.$$

In general, if $y \neq 0$, then we can express the quotient of a positive and a negative number in three forms.

$$\dfrac{-x}{y} = \dfrac{x}{-y} = -\dfrac{x}{y}$$

The form $\dfrac{x}{-y}$ is seldom used.

In general, if $y \neq 0$,

$$\dfrac{-x}{-y} = \dfrac{x}{y}.$$

EXAMPLE 4   Simplify $\dfrac{5(-2) - (3)(4)}{2(1 - 6)}$.

Simplify the numerator and denominator separately. Then divide.

$$\dfrac{5(-2) - (3)(4)}{2(1 - 6)} = \dfrac{-10 - 12}{2(-5)}$$
$$= \dfrac{-22}{-10}$$
$$= \dfrac{11}{5}$$

EXERCISES 1.8   *Give the multiplicative inverse where one exists. See Example 1.*

1. 9

2. 8

3. -4

4. -10

5. $\dfrac{2}{3}$

6. $\dfrac{3}{4}$

7. $\dfrac{-9}{10}$

8. $\dfrac{-4}{5}$

9. 0

10. $\dfrac{0}{5}$

11. $\dfrac{-6}{17}$

12. $\dfrac{-15}{23}$

Find the quotients. See Examples 2 and 3.

13. $\dfrac{-10}{5}$ **14.** $\dfrac{-12}{3}$ **15.** $\dfrac{-15}{5}$ **16.** $\dfrac{-20}{2}$

17. $\dfrac{18}{-3}$ **18.** $\dfrac{24}{-6}$ **19.** $\dfrac{100}{-20}$ **20.** $\dfrac{250}{-25}$

21. $\dfrac{-12}{-6}$ **22.** $\dfrac{-25}{-5}$ **23.** $\dfrac{-150}{-10}$ **24.** $\dfrac{-280}{-20}$

25. $\dfrac{-180}{-5}$ **26.** $\dfrac{-350}{-7}$ **27.** $\dfrac{0}{-2}$ **28.** $\dfrac{0}{12}$

29. $-\dfrac{1}{2} \div -\dfrac{3}{4}$ **30.** $-\dfrac{5}{8} \div -\dfrac{3}{16}$

31. $(-4.2) \div (-2)$ **32.** $(-9.8) \div (-7)$

33. $\dfrac{4}{-.8}$ **34.** $\dfrac{-6}{.3}$

35. $\dfrac{12}{2-5}$ **36.** $\dfrac{15}{3-8}$

37. $\dfrac{50}{2-7}$ **38.** $\dfrac{30}{5-8}$

39. $\dfrac{-30}{2-8}$ **40.** $\dfrac{-50}{6-11}$

41. $\dfrac{-40}{8-(-2)}$ **42.** $\dfrac{-72}{6-(-2)}$

43. $\dfrac{-120}{-3-(-5)}$ **44.** $\dfrac{-200}{-6-(-4)}$

45. $\dfrac{-15-3}{3}$ **46.** $\dfrac{16-(-2)}{-6}$

47. $\dfrac{-30-(-8)}{-11}$ **48.** $\dfrac{-17-(-12)}{5}$

Simplify the numerator and denominator separately. Then find the quotient. See Example 4.

49. $\dfrac{-8(-2)}{3-(-1)}$ **50.** $\dfrac{-12(-3)}{-15-(-3)}$

51. $\dfrac{-15(2)}{-7-3}$ **52.** $\dfrac{-20(6)}{-5-1}$

53. $\dfrac{-2(6)+3}{2-(-1)}$ **54.** $\dfrac{3(-8)+4}{-6+1}$

55. $\dfrac{-5(2)+3(-2)}{-3-(-1)}$ **56.** $\dfrac{4(-1)+3(-2)}{-2-3}$

57. $\dfrac{2-4(2)}{4-1}$ **58.** $\dfrac{-4-3(-2)}{5-3}$

59. $\dfrac{-9(-2) - (-4)(-2)}{-2(3) - 2(2)}$ **60.** $\dfrac{5(-2) - 3(4)}{-2[3 - (-2)] - 1}$

61. $\dfrac{4(-2) - 5(-3)}{2[-1 + (-3)] - (-8)}$ **62.** $\dfrac{5(-3) - (-2)(-4)}{5[-4 + (-2)] + 3(10)}$

63. $\dfrac{4^2 - 5^2}{3(6 - 9 + 2)}$ **64.** $\dfrac{6^2 + 4^2}{5(2 + 13)}$

65. $\dfrac{3^2 + 5^2}{4^2 + 1^2}$ **66.** $\dfrac{10^2 - 5^2}{8^2 + 3^2 + 2}$

Find the solution of each equation from the list $-8, -6, -4, -2, 0, 2, 4,$
6, 8.

67. $\dfrac{x}{4} = -2$ **68.** $\dfrac{x}{2} = -1$

69. $\dfrac{n}{-2} = 3$ **70.** $\dfrac{t}{-2} = -2$

71. $\dfrac{q}{-3} = 0$ **72.** $\dfrac{p}{5} = 0$

73. $\dfrac{m}{-2} = -4$ **74.** $\dfrac{y}{-1} = 2$

75. $\dfrac{k}{4} = -1$ **76.** $\dfrac{z}{3} = -2$

*Write each of the following in symbols and find the solution. All solutions
come from the list of integers between* -10 *and* 10.

77. Six times a number is -42.

78. Four times a number is -32.

79. When a number is divided by 5, the result is -1.

80. When a number is divided by 2, the result is -3.

81. When a number is divided by 3, the result is -3.

82. When a number is divided by -4, the result is 2.

83. The quotient of a number and 2 is -4.

84. The quotient of a number and -5 is 2.

85. The quotient of 6 and one more than a number is 3.

86. When the square of a number is divided by 3, the result is 12.

1.9 Properties of Real Numbers

- **Identify the following properties:**
  closure, commutative, associative, identity, inverse, and distributive.

In this section, we list some of the properties of addition and multiplication of real numbers. In the following statements, x, y, and z are all real numbers.

Closure properties   The closure properties tell us that the sum of two real numbers is a real number and that the product of two real numbers is a real number.

$$x + y \text{ is a real number}$$

$$xy \text{ is a real number}$$

Although the closure property may seem obvious, it is not true for all operations or for all sets of numbers.

EXAMPLE 1   Does the set of positive numbers have a closure property for subtraction?

For the answer to be *yes*, we must be able to subtract any two positive numbers and get a positive answer. The numbers 4 and 6 are both positive. However, $4 - 6 = -2$, which is not positive. Because of this, subtraction with positive numbers does not have the closure property.

Commutative properties   The commutative properties tell us that two numbers can be added or multiplied in any order.

$$x + y = y + x$$

$$xy = yx$$

EXAMPLE 2   Use a commutative property to complete each statement.

(a) $-8 + 5 = 5 + \underline{\hspace{1cm}}$

By the commutative property for addition, the answer is -8, since $-8 + 5 = 5 + (-8)$.

(b) $(-2)(7) = \underline{\hspace{1cm}}(-2)$

By the commutative property for multiplication, the answer is 7, since $(-2)(7) = (7)(-2)$.

Associative properties   The associative properties tell us that when we are adding or multiplying three numbers, the first two may be grouped together or the last two may be grouped together without affecting the answer.

$$(x + y) + z = x + (y + z)$$

$$(xy)z = x(yz)$$

EXAMPLE 3   Use an associative property to complete each statement.

(a) $8 + (-1 + 4) = (8 + \underline{\hspace{1.5cm}}) + 4$

The answer is -1.

(b) $[2 + (-7)] + 6 = 2 + \underline{\hspace{1.5cm}}$

The answer is $(-7 + 6)$.

By the associative property of addition, the sum of three numbers will be the same however we "associate" the numbers in groups. For this reason, parentheses can be left out in many addition problems. For example, we can write

$$-1 + 2 + 3$$

instead of

$$(-1 + 2) + 3 \qquad \text{or} \qquad -1 + (2 + 3).$$

In the same way, parentheses can also be left out of many multiplication problems.

EXAMPLE 4   Decide whether each equation is an example of the commutative property, the associative property, or both.

(a) $(2 + 4) + 5 = 2 + (4 + 5)$

The order of the three numbers is the same on both sides of the equals sign. The only change is in the grouping of the numbers. Therefore, this is an example of the associative property.

(b) $6(3 \cdot 10) = 6(10 \cdot 3)$

Here, the same numbers, 3 and 10, are grouped. However, on the left the 3 appears first in $(3 \cdot 10)$. On the right the 10 appears first. Since the only change involves the order of the numbers, this is an example of the commutative property.

(c) $(8 + 1) + 7 = 8 + (7 + 1)$

In the statement both the order and the grouping are changed. On the left, the order of the three numbers is 8, 1, and 7. On the right, it is 8, 7, and 1. On the left, the 8 and 1 are grouped, while on the right, the 7 and 1 are grouped. Therefore, in this example, both the associative and the commutative properties are used.

Identity properties   The identity properties tell us that we can add 0 to any number and get the same number, and we can multiply 1 by any number and get the same number.

$$x + 0 = x \quad \text{and} \quad 0 + x = x$$
$$x \cdot 1 = x \quad \text{and} \quad 1 \cdot x = x$$

The number 0 leaves the identity, or value, of any real number unchanged by addition. For this reason, 0 is called the **identity element for addition.** In a similar way, multiplication by 1 leaves any real number unchanged, so 1 is the **identity element for multiplication.**

EXAMPLE 5   These statements are examples of the identity properties.

(a) $-3 + 0 = -3$

(b) $0 + \dfrac{1}{2} = \dfrac{1}{2}$

(c) $-\dfrac{3}{4} \cdot 1 = -\dfrac{3}{4}$

(d) $1 \cdot 25 = 25$

Inverse properties   The inverse properties say that, for any number x, there is exactly one number $-x$ that we can add to x to get 0, and for any nonzero number x, we can multiply by exactly one number $\dfrac{1}{x}$ to get 1.

$$x + (-x) = 0 \quad \text{and} \quad -x + x = 0$$
$$x \cdot \dfrac{1}{x} = 1 \quad \text{and} \quad \dfrac{1}{x} \cdot x = 1 \qquad (x \neq 0)$$

We call $-x$ the **additive inverse** of x, and we call $\dfrac{1}{x}$ the **multiplicative inverse** of x.

EXAMPLE 6   These statements are examples of the inverse properties.

(a) $\dfrac{2}{3} \cdot \dfrac{3}{2} = 1$

(b) $(-5)\left(-\dfrac{1}{5}\right) = 1$

(c) $-\dfrac{1}{2} + \dfrac{1}{2} = 0$

(d) $4 + (-4) = 0$

The final property of real numbers is one that relates addition or subtraction to multiplication. Using the distributive property, we change a product to a sum or a difference.

Distributive property   The distributive property tells us that we can multiply a number x by a sum of numbers $y + z$ by multiplying x by each number in the sum and then adding the resulting products.

$$x(y + z) = xy + xz \quad \text{and} \quad (y + z)x = yx + zx$$

Another form of the distributive property is valid for subtraction.

$$x(y - z) = xy - xz \quad \text{and} \quad (y - z)x = yx - zx$$

The distributive property can also be extended to more than two numbers.

$$a(b + c + d) = ab + ac + ad$$

EXAMPLE 7 Simplify using the distributive property.

(a) $5(9 + 6) = 5 \cdot 9 + 5 \cdot 6$
$= 45 + 30$
$= 75$

(b) $4(x + 5) = 4x + 4 \cdot 5$
$= 4x + 20$

(c) $-2(x + 3) = -2x + (-2)(3)$
$= -2x - 6$

(d) $3(k - 9) = 3k - 3 \cdot 9$
$= 3k - 27$

(e) $6 \cdot 8 + 6 \cdot 2 = 6(8 + 2)$
$= 6(10)$
$= 60$

(f) $4x - 4m = 4(x - m)$

(g) $8(3r + 5z) = 8(3r) + 8(5z)$
$= (8 \cdot 3)r + (8 \cdot 5)z \quad$ Associative property
$= 24r + 40z$

One important use of the distributive property is to simplify expressions such as $-(2y + 3)$. This is done by writing $-(2y + 3)$ as $-1 \cdot (2y + 3)$:

$$-(2y + 3) = -1 \cdot (2y + 3)$$
$$= -1 \cdot (2y) + (-1) \cdot (3)$$
$$= -2y - 3$$

EXAMPLE 8 Simplify.

(a) $-(7r - 8) = -1(7r) + (-1)(-8)$
$= -7r + 8$

(b) $-(-9w + 2) = 9w - 2$

We can now summarize these properties of the real numbers.

For all real numbers x, y, and z:

	Addition	*Multiplication*
Closure	$x + y$ is a real number	xy is a real number
Commutative	$x + y = y + x$	$xy = yx$
Associative	$(x + y) + z = x + (y + z)$	$(xy)z = x(yz)$
Identity	$x + 0 = x$ and $0 + x = x$	$x \cdot 1 = x$ and $1 \cdot x = x$
Inverse	$x + (-x) = 0$ and $-x + x = 0$	$x \cdot \dfrac{1}{x} = 1$ and $\dfrac{1}{x} \cdot x = 1,$ $(x \neq 0)$
Distributive	$x(y + z) = xy + xz$ and $(y + z)x = yx + zx$	

EXERCISES 1.9 *Label each statement as an example of the commutative, associative, closure, identity, inverse, or distributive property. See Example 4.*

1. $6 + 15 = 15 + 6$

2. $9 + (11 + 4) = (9 + 11) + 4$

3. $5(15 \cdot 8) = (5 \cdot 15)8$

4. $(23)(9) = (9)(23)$

5. $12(-8) = (-8)(12)$

6. $(-9)[6(-2)] = [-9(6)](-2)$

7. $2 + (p + r) = (p + r) + 2$

8. $(m + n) + 4 = (n + m) + 4$

9. $-6 + 12$ is a real number

10. $(-9)(-11)$ is a real number

11. $6 + (-6) = 0$

12. $-8 + 8 = 0$

13. $-4 + 0 = -4$

14. $0 + (-9) = -9$

15. $3\left(\dfrac{1}{3}\right) = 1$

16. $-7\left(-\dfrac{1}{7}\right) = 1$

17. $\dfrac{2}{3} \cdot 1 = \dfrac{2}{3}$

18. $-\dfrac{9}{4} \cdot 1 = -\dfrac{9}{4}$

19. $6(5 - 2x) = 6 \cdot 5 - 6(2x)$

20. $5(2m) + 5(7n) = 5(2m + 7n)$

Use the indicated property to write a new expression that is equal to the given expression. Simplify the new expression if possible. See Examples 2, 3, 5, and 6.

21. $9 + k$; commutative

22. $z + 5$; commutative

23. $m + 0$; identity

24. $(-9) + 0$; identity

25. $3(r + m)$; distributive

26. $11(k + z)$; distributive

27. $8 \cdot \dfrac{1}{8}$; inverse

28. $\dfrac{1}{6} \cdot 6$; inverse

29. $12 + (-12)$; inverse

30. $-8 + 8$; inverse

31. $5 + (-5)$; commutative

32. $-9 + 9$; commutative

33. $-3(r + 2)$; distributive

34. $4(k - 5)$; distributive

35. $9 \cdot 1$; identity

36. $1(-4)$; identity

37. $(k + 5) + (-6)$; associative

38. $(m + 4) + (-2)$; associative

39. $(4z + 2r) + 3k$; associative

40. $(6m + 2n) + 5r$; associative

Use the distributive property to rewrite each expression. See Example 7.

41. $5(m + 2)$

42. $6(k + 5)$

43. $-4(r + 2)$

44. $-3(m + 5)$

45. $-8(k - 2)$

46. $-4(z - 5)$

47. $-9(a + 3)$

48. $-3(p + 5)$

49. $(r + 8)4$

50. $(m + 12)6$

51. $(8 - k)(-2)$

52. $(9 - r)(-3)$

53. $2(5r + 6m)$

54. $5(2a + 4b)$

55. $-4(3x - 4y)$

56. $-9(5k - 12m)$

57. $5 \cdot 8 + 5 \cdot 9$

58. $4 \cdot 3 + 4 \cdot 9$

59. $7 \cdot 2 + 7 \cdot 8$

60. $6x + 6m$

61. $9p + 9q$

62. $8(2x) + 8(3x)$

63. $5(7z) + 5(8w)$

64. $11(2r) + 11(3s)$

Use the distributive property to simplify each of the following. See Example 8.

65. $-(3k + 5)$

66. $-(2z + 12)$

67. $-(4y - 8)$

68. $-(3r - 15)$

69. $-(-4 + p)$

70. $-(-12 + 3a)$

71. $-(-1 - 15r)$ **72.** $-(-14 - 6y)$

Decide whether or not each set of numbers has the closure property for (a) addition, (b) subtraction, (c) multiplication. See Example 1.

EXAMPLE $\{0, 2, 4, 6, 8, \ldots\}$

This set contains all the even numbers that are not negative. The sum of two even numbers is even, so the answer for part (a) is *yes*. When two even numbers are subtracted, the answer might well be negative ($8 - 12$, for example), and there are no negative numbers in the set. Thus, the answer for (b) is *no*. For (c), the answer is *yes*.

73. $\{0, 1, 2, 3, 4, 5, 6, 7, \ldots\}$

74. $\{\ldots, -5, -4, -3, -2, -1, 0\}$

75. $\{\ldots, -4, -3, -2, -1, 0, 1, 2, 3, \ldots\}$

76. $\{\ldots, -6, -4, -2, 0, 2, 4, 6, \ldots\}$

77. $\{0, 5, 10, 15, 20, 25, \ldots\}$

78. $\{0, 3, 6, 9, 12, 15, 18, \ldots\}$

79. $\{1, 3, 5, 7, 9, 11, \ldots\}$

80. $\{\ldots, -7, -5, -3, -1, 1, 3, 5, 7, \ldots\}$

Chapter 1 Test

[1.1]   *Answer* true *or* false *for the following.*

1. $8 \le 17$ **2.** $5 \ne 3 + 2$

3. $6 > 6$

[1.2]   **4.** $5 \cdot 9 + 6 \ge 51$ **5.** $4[5(1) - 3] < 8$

6. $\dfrac{9(4) + 3(2)}{5 \cdot 4 + 1} < 3$ **7.** $2 + 3 \cdot 4 \ge 20$

8. $3^2 + 2^2 = 25$

[1.3]   *Find the numerical value of the given expression if* $m = 6$ *and* $n = 2$.

9. $5m + 2n$ **10.** $\dfrac{7m - n}{m + 4}$

[1.4]   *Select the smaller number from each pair.*

11. $-3, -5$ **12.** $3, |-5|$

13. $6, -|-8|$ **14.** $|-4|, 0$

[1.5] *Perform each operation.*

  15. $-6 + 10$ **16.** $-2 + (-7)$

[1.6] **17.** $27 - (-5)$ **18.** $-1 - 3$

  19. $(-6 + 3) - (-1 - 4)$ **20.** $-8 - [(-7) + (-2)]$

[1.7] **21.** $-2(-3)$ **22.** $12(-6)$

  23. $(-3 - 2)(-5) + (-7)$ **24.** $8 - (3)(-6) + (-1)$

  25. $(3 - 8)(-1 + 4)$

[1.8] **26.** $\dfrac{27}{-3}$

  27. $\dfrac{-8 - (-6)}{-1 - 1}$

  28. $\dfrac{-7 - (-5 + 1)}{-4 - (-3)}$

[1.9] *Match the property in Column I with all examples of it from Column II.*

Column I	Column II
29. Commutative	A. $-2 + 2 = 0$
30. Associative	B. $3 + (7 + x) = (3 + 7) + x$
31. Identity	C. $8 + 0 = 8$
32. Inverse	D. $17 \cdot 1 = 17$
33. Distributive	E. $3(x + y) = 3x + 3y$
	F. $8 + m = m + 8$
	G. $-5\left(\dfrac{1}{-5}\right) = 1$
	H. $mn = nm$

2

Solving Equations and Inequalities

2.1 Simplifying Expressions

- **Identify numerical coefficients.**
- **Identify like terms.**
- **Combine like terms.**

When solving equations, it is often necessary to simplify the equation before proceeding to solve it. We see how to simplify expressions in this section, and then in the next section we begin solving equations.

EXAMPLE 1   Simplify the following expressions.

(a) $4x + 8 + 9$

Since $8 + 9 = 17$, we have

$$4x + 8 + 9 = 4x + 17$$

(b) $4(3m - 2n)$

Use the distributive property.

$$4(3m - 2n) = 4(3m) - 4(2n)$$
$$= 12m - 8n$$

(c) $6 + 3(4k + 5) = 6 + 3(4k) + 3(5)$
$$= 6 + 12k + 15$$
$$= 21 + 12k$$

(d) $5 - (2y - 8) = 5 - 1 \cdot (2y - 8)$
$$= 5 - 2y + 8$$
$$= 13 - 2y$$

A **term** is a single number, or a product of a number and one or more variables raised to powers. Examples of terms include

$$-9x^2, \qquad 15y, \qquad -3, \qquad 8m^2n, \qquad \text{and} \qquad k.$$

The **numerical coefficient** of the term $9m$ is 9, the numerical coefficient of $-15x^3y^2$ is -15, and the numerical coefficient of 8 is 8.

EXAMPLE 2   Give the numerical coefficient for the following terms.

Term	Numerical coefficient
$-7y$	-7
$8p$	8
$34r^3$	34
$-26x^5yz^4$	-26
$-k$	-1

Terms with exactly the same variables (including the same exponents) are called **like terms.** For example, $9m$ and $4m$ have the same variables, and are like terms. Also, $6x^3$ and $-5x^3$ are like terms. The terms $-4y^3$ and $4y^2$ have different exponents and are **unlike terms.**

Like terms may be added or subtracted by using the distributive property. For example,

$$3x + 5x = (3 + 5)x$$
$$= 8x.$$

EXAMPLE 3   Simplify the following expressions.

(a) $9m + 5m$

Use the distributive property to add like terms.

$$9m + 5m = (9 + 5)m$$
$$= 14m$$

(b) $6r + 3r + 2r = 11r$

(c) $4x + x = 4x + 1x$

$\quad\quad\quad\;\; = 5x$

(Note: $x = 1x$)

(d) $16y - 9y = (16 - 9)y$

$\quad\quad\quad\quad\;\; = 7y$

(e) $32y + 10y^2$ cannot be simplified since $32y$ and $10y^2$ are unlike terms.

EXAMPLE 4 Simplify the following expressions.

(a) $14y + 2(6 + 3y) = 14y + 2(6) + 2(3y)$ Distributive property

$\quad\quad\quad\quad\quad\quad\;\; = 14y + 12 + 6y$ Add like terms

$\quad\quad\quad\quad\quad\quad\;\; = 20y + 12$

(b) $9k - 6 - 3(2 - 5k) = 9k - 6 - 3(2) - 3(-5k)$

$\quad\quad\quad\quad\quad\quad\quad\quad\; = 9k - 6 - 6 + 15k$

$\quad\quad\quad\quad\quad\quad\quad\quad\; = 24k - 12$

(c) $-(2 - r) + 10r = -1(2 - r) + 10r$

$\quad\quad\quad\quad\quad\quad\;\; = -1(2) - 1(-r) + 10r$

$\quad\quad\quad\quad\quad\quad\;\; = -2 + r + 10r$

$\quad\quad\quad\quad\quad\quad\;\; = -2 + 11r$

(d) $5(2a - 6) - 3(4a - 9) = 10a - 30 - 12a + 27$

$\quad\quad\quad\quad\quad\quad\quad\quad\quad\; = -2a - 3$

Carrying out the addition or subtraction of like terms is called **combining terms.** We emphasize that

only *like terms* may be added or subtracted.

EXERCISES 2.1 *Give the numerical coefficient of the following terms. See Example 2.*

1. $15y$ **2.** $7z$ **3.** $-22m^4$ **4.** $-2k^7$

5. $35a^4b^2$ **6.** $12m^5n^4$ **7.** -9 **8.** 21

9. y^2 **10.** x^4 **11.** $-r$ **12.** $-z$

Write like *or* unlike *for the following groups of terms.*

13. $6m, -14m$ **14.** $-2a, 5a$

15. $7z^3, 7z^2$ **16.** $10m^5, 10m^6$

17. $25y, -14y, 8y$ **18.** $-11x, 5x, 7x$

19. 2, 5, −2

20. −8, 3, 9

21. p, −5p, 12p

22. 15k, 7k, k

23. 5, −5r

24. 10, −10y

Simplify the following expressions by combining terms. See Examples 1 and 3.

25. $9y + 8y$

26. $15m + 12m$

27. $-4a - 2a$

28. $-3z - 9z$

29. $12b + b$

30. $30x + x$

31. $2k + 9 + 5k + 6$

32. $2 + 17z + 1 + 2z$

33. $m + 1 - m + 2 + m - 4$

34. $12 - 13x - 27 + 2x - x$

35. $-5y + 3 - 1 + 5 + y - 7$

36. $2k - 7 - 5k + 7k - 3 - k$

37. $-2x + 3 + 4x - 17 + 20$

38. $r - 6 - 12r - 4 + 6r$

39. $16 - 5m - 4m - 2 + 2m + 6$

40. $6 - 3z - 2z - 5 + z - 3z - 3$

41. $-3z + 7 - 3z + 7z + 31 - 18$

42. $15 - 2 + 4 - 4 + 1 - 5k + 7k - k$

43. $-10 + x + 4x - 7 - 4x + 21 - 19$

44. $-p + 10p - 3p - 4 - 5p + 2 + 10$

45. $1 + 7x + 11x - 1 + 5x - 2 - 6$

46. $-r + 2 - 5r + 3 + 4r + 3r - 8$

47. $6y^2 + 11y^2 - 8y^2$

48. $-9m^3 + 3m^3 - 7m^3$

49. $2p^2 + 3p^2 - 8p^3 - 6p^3 + 4p^2$

50. $5y^3 + 6y^3 - 3y^2 - 4y^2 + 9y^2$

Use the distributive property to simplify the following expressions. See Example 4.

51. $6(5t + 11)$

52. $2(3x + 4)$

53. $-3(n + 5)$

54. $-4(y - 8)$

55. $7(3r - 5) - 5r$

56. $3(2m - 6) + 5m$

57. $-3(2r - 3) + 2(5r + 3)$

58. $-4(5y - 7) + 3(2y - 5)$

59. $8(2k - 1) - (4k - 3)$

60. $6(3p - 2) - (5p + 1)$

61. $-2(-3k + 2) - (5k - 6) - 3k - 5$

62. $-2(3r - 4) - (6 - r) + 2r - 5$

Convert the following word phrases into mathematical expressions. Use x as the variable. Combine terms whenever possible.

EXAMPLE   Five times a number, four times a number, and six times a number are added to 9.

$$5x + 4x + 6x + 9 \quad \text{Write as a mathematical expression}$$
$$= 15x + 9 \quad \text{Simplify}$$

63. Two times a number is subtracted from the sum of a number and 2.

64. Four times a number is added to the sum of the number and -15.

65. Three times a number is subtracted from twice the number. This result is subtracted from 9 times the number.

66. A number is subtracted from 4 times the number, with this result subtracted from the sum of 6 and five times the number.

67. Nine is multiplied times the sum of five times a number and 4, with the result subtracted from the difference of 4 and twice the number.

68. Seven times a number is added to -9. This result is subtracted from four times the sum of three times the number and 5.

2.2   The Addition Property of Equality

- **Identify linear equations.**
- **Use the addition property of equality.**
- **Simplify equations, then use the addition property of equality.**

In this section we begin to study the methods of solving a linear equation. A **linear equation** has the form

$$ax + b = c,$$

where a, b, and c are real numbers, with $a \neq 0$.

To solve such an equation, we go through a series of steps, ending up with a simpler equation of the form

$$x = \text{a number.}$$

Let's see how to solve the equation

$$x + 5 = 12.$$

We know that "$x + 5$" and "12" represent the same number, since this is the meaning of the equals sign. We want to change the left side from $x + 5$ to just x. We could do this if we add -5 to $x + 5$. However, we can maintain the equals sign only if we do the same thing on the right side:

$$x + 5 = 12 \qquad \text{Given equation}$$
$$x + 5 + (-5) = 12 + (-5) \quad \text{Add } -5 \text{ to both sides}$$

Here we added -5 to both sides of the equation. Now simplify each side separately to get

$$x = 7$$

The solution of the given equation is 7. To check, replace x with 7 in the given equation.

$$x + 5 = 12 \qquad \text{Given equation}$$
$$7 + 5 = 12 \qquad \text{Let } x = 7$$
$$12 = 12 \qquad \text{True}$$

Since this final result is true, 7 checks as the solution.

To solve the equations above, we added the same number to both sides. The property that justifies this is the **addition property of equality.**

If A, B, and C are algebraic expressions, then the equations

$$A = B$$

and

$$A + C = B + C$$

have the same solutions. The same number may be added to both sides of an equation.

EXAMPLE 1 Solve the equation $x - 16 = 7$.

If x were alone on the left, we would have the solution. So use the addition property of equality to add 16 to both sides.

$$x - 16 = 7$$
$$(x - 16) + 16 = 7 + 16 \quad \text{Add 16 to both sides}$$
$$x = 23$$

To check, substitute 23 for x in the original equation.

$$x - 16 = 7 \qquad \text{Given equation}$$
$$23 - 16 = 7 \qquad \text{Let } x = 23$$
$$7 = 7 \qquad \text{True}$$

Since the check results in a true statement, 23 is the correct solution.

In this example, how did we know to add 16 to both sides of the equation $x - 16 = 7$? We want one side of the equation to contain only the variable term and the other side to contain only a number. We know that $x + 0 = x$, so we need to get $x + 0$. What number must be added to $x - 16$ to get $x + 0$? Since the sum of any number and its additive inverse is 0, we must add the additive inverse of -16, which is 16, to both sides of the equation.

EXAMPLE 2   Solve the equation $3k + 17 = 4k$.

In order to find the solution, we need to get all terms that contain variables on the same side of the equation. One way to do this is to use the addition property of equality, and add $-3k$ to both sides.

$$3k + 17 = 4k$$
$$3k + 17 + (-3k) = 4k + (-3k)$$
$$17 = k$$

The solution is 17.

The equation $3k + 17 = 4k$ could also be solved by first adding $-4k$ to both sides as follows.

$$3k + 17 = 4k$$
$$3k + 17 + (-4k) = 4k + (-4k)$$
$$17 - k = 0$$

Now add -17 to both sides.

$$17 - k + (-17) = 0 + (-17)$$
$$-k = -17$$

This result gives the value of $-k$, but not of k itself. However, we know that the additive inverse of k is -17. Then k must be 17.

$$-k = -17$$
$$k = 17.$$

This answer agrees with the first one.

EXAMPLE 3   Solve the equation $4r + 5r - 3 + 8 - 3r - 5r = 12 + 8$.

First, simplify the equation by combining terms.

$$4r + 5r - 3r - 5r - 3 + 8 = 12 + 8$$
$$r + 5 = 20$$

Add -5 to both sides of this equation.

$$r + 5 + (-5) = 20 + (-5)$$
$$r = 15$$

The solution of the given equation is 15.

EXAMPLE 4   Solve $3(2 + 5x) - (1 + 14x) = 6$
Simplify the equation:

$$3(2 + 5x) - (1 + 14x) = 6$$
$$3(2) + 3(5x) - 1(1) - 1(14x) = 6$$
$$6 + 15x - 1 - 14x = 6$$
$$x + 5 = 6$$

Add -5 to both sides of the equation to end up with

$$x = 1.$$

EXERCISES 2.2   *Solve each equation by using the addition property of equality. Check each solution. See Examples 1 and 2.*

1. $x - 3 = 7$ **2.** $x + 5 = 13$

3. $7 + k = 5$ **4.** $9 + m = 4$

5. $3r - 10 = 2r$ **6.** $2p = p + 3$

7. $7z = -8 + 6z$ **8.** $4y = 3y - 5$

9. $m + 5 = 0$ **10.** $k - 7 = 0$

11. $2 + 3x = 2x$ **12.** $10 + r = 2r$

13. $2p + 6 = 10 + p$ **14.** $5r + 2 = -1 + 4r$

15. $2k + 2 = -3 + k$ **16.** $6 + 7x = 6x + 3$

17. $x - 5 = 2x + 6$ **18.** $-3r + 7 = -4r - 19$

19. $6z + 3 = 5z - 3$ **20.** $6t + 5 = 5t + 7$

21. $2p = p + \dfrac{1}{2}$ **22.** $5m = 4m + \dfrac{2}{3}$

23. $\dfrac{4}{3}z = \dfrac{1}{3}z - 5$ **24.** $\dfrac{9}{5}m = \dfrac{4}{5}m + 6$

25. $-2 - \dfrac{3}{4}y = \dfrac{1}{4}y$ **26.** $-11 - \dfrac{7}{9}p = \dfrac{2}{9}p$

27. $\dfrac{11}{4}r - \dfrac{1}{2} = \dfrac{7}{4}r + \dfrac{2}{3}$ **28.** $\dfrac{9}{2}y - \dfrac{3}{4} = \dfrac{7}{2}y + \dfrac{5}{8}$

29. $2.7a + 5 = 1.7a$ **30.** $4.7p - 3 = 3.7p$

Solve the following equations. First simplify each side of the equation as much as possible. Check each solution. See Example 3.

31. $4x + 3 + 2x - 5x = 2 + 8$

32. $3x + 2x - 6 + x - 5x = 9 + 4$

33. $9r + 4r + 6 - 8 = 10r + 6 + 2r$

34. $-3t + 5t - 6t + 4 - 3 = -3t + 2$

35. $11z + 2 + 4z - 3z = 5z - 8 + 6z$

36. $2k + 8k + 6k - 4k - 8 + 2 = 3k + 2 + 10k$

37. $4m + 8m - 9m + 2 - 5 = 4m + 6$

38. $15y - 4y + 8 - 2 + 7 - 4 = 4y + 2 + 8y$

39. $-9p + 4p - 3p + 2p - 6 = -5p - 6$

40. $5x - 2x + 3x - 4x + 8 - 2 + 4 = x + 10$

Solve the following equations. Check each solution. See Example 4.

41. $(5y + 6) - (3 + 4y) = 9$

42. $(8p - 3) - (7p + 1) = -2$

43. $2(r + 5) - (9 + r) = -1$

44. $4(y - 6) - (3y + 2) = 8$

45. $-6(2a + 1) + (13a - 7) = 4$

46. $-5(3k - 3) + (1 + 16k) = 2$

47. $4(7x - 1) + 3(2 - 5x) = 4(3x + 5)$

48. $9(2m - 3) - 4(5 + 3m) = 5(4 + m)$

49. $-2(8p + 7) - 3(4 - 7p) = 2(3 + 2p) - 6$

50. $-5(8 - 2z) + 4(7 - z) = 7(8 + z) - 3$

Write an equation using the following information. Then solve the equation.

51. Three times a number is 17 more than twice the number. Find the number.

52. If six times a number is subtracted from seven times a number, the result is -9. Find the number.

53. If five times a number is added to three times the number, the result is the sum of seven times the number and 9. Find the number.

54. If nine times a number is subtracted from eleven times the number, the result is −4 more than three times the number. Find the number.

55. The sum of twice a number and 5 is multiplied by 6. The result is 8 less than 13 times the number. Find the number.

56. Four times a number is subtracted from 7. The result is multiplied by 5, giving 3 more than −19 times the number. Find the number.

2.3 The Multiplication Property of Equality

- **Use the multiplication property of equality.**
- **Simplify equations, then use the multiplication property of equality.**
- **Solve equations such as $-r = 4$.**
- **Solve equations with decimals.**

The addition property of equality by itself is not enough to solve an equation like $3x + 2 = 17$.

$$3x + 2 = 17$$
$$3x + 2 + (-2) = 17 + (-2) \quad \text{Add } -2 \text{ to both sides}$$
$$3x = 15 \qquad\qquad \text{Simplify}$$

We do not have the variable x alone on one side of the equation; we have $3x$ instead. To go from $3x = 15$ to $x =$ a number, we need another property similar to the addition property.

If $3x = 15$, then $3x$ and 15 both represent the same number. Multiplying both $3x$ and 15 by the same number will also result in an equality. The **multiplication property of equality** states that both sides of an equation can be multiplied by the same term.

If A, B, and C represent algebraic expressions, the equations

$$A = B$$

and

$$AC = BC$$

have exactly the same solution. (Assume that $C \neq 0$.) Both sides of an equation may be multiplied by the same non-zero number.

Now we go back and solve $3x = 15$. On the left, we have $3x$. We need $1x$, or x, instead of $3x$. To get x, multiply both sides of the equation by $\frac{1}{3}$. This works because $3 \cdot \frac{1}{3} = \frac{3}{3} = 1$.

$$3x = 15$$

$$\frac{1}{3}(3x) = \frac{1}{3} \cdot 15 \quad \text{Multiply both sides by } \frac{1}{3}$$

$$\left(\frac{1}{3} \cdot 3\right)x = \frac{1}{3} \cdot 15 \quad \text{Simplify}$$

$$1x = 5$$

$$x = 5$$

The solution of the equation is 5.

EXAMPLE 1 Solve the equation $5p = 30$.

To get p alone on the left, use the multiplication property of equality and multiply both sides of the equation by $\frac{1}{5}$.

$$5p = 30$$

$$\frac{1}{5} \cdot 5p = \frac{1}{5} \cdot 30$$

$$1p = 6$$

$$p = 6$$

The solution is 6.

EXAMPLE 2 Solve the equation $\frac{a}{4} = 3$.

We can replace $\frac{a}{4}$ by $\frac{1}{4}a$, since division by 4 is the same as multiplication by its reciprocal $\frac{1}{4}$. To get a alone on the left, multiply both sides by 4.

$$\frac{a}{4} = 3$$

$$\frac{1}{4}a = 3$$

$$4 \cdot \frac{1}{4}a = 4 \cdot 3 \quad \text{Multiply both sides by 4}$$

$$1a = 12$$

$$a = 12$$

We multiplied by 4 since $4 \cdot \frac{1}{4} = 1$, and we want $1a$ on the left.

Check the answer:

$$\frac{a}{4} = 3 \qquad \text{Given equation}$$

$$\frac{12}{4} = 3 \qquad \text{Let } a = 12$$

$$3 = 3$$

The solution 12 is correct.

EXAMPLE 3 Solve the equation $\frac{3}{4}h = 6$.

To get h alone on the left, multiply both sides of the equation by $\frac{4}{3}$. We use $\frac{4}{3}$ because $\frac{4}{3} \cdot \frac{3}{4} = 1$.

$$\frac{3}{4}h = 6$$

$$\frac{4}{3}\left(\frac{3}{4}h\right) = \frac{4}{3} \cdot 6$$

$$1 \cdot h = \frac{4}{3} \cdot \frac{6}{1}$$

$$h = \frac{24}{3}$$

$$h = 8$$

The solution is 8.

EXAMPLE 4 Solve the equation $5m + 6m = 33$.

First, use the distributive property to combine terms.

$$5m + 6m = 33$$

$$11m = 33$$

Now multiply both sides by the reciprocal of 11, which is $\frac{1}{11}$.

$$\frac{1}{11} \cdot 11m = \frac{1}{11} \cdot 33$$

$$m = 3$$

The solution is 3.

EXAMPLE 5   Solve the equation $-r = 4$.

To find the solution for this equation, we need to get r itself, and not $-r$, on one side of the equals sign. To do this, first write $-r$ as $-1 \cdot r$. (Remember that multiplying any positive number by -1 will give you the additive inverse of that number.)

$$-r = 4$$
$$-1 \cdot r = 4$$

Multiplying both sides of this last equation by -1 will remove the minus sign from r, since the product of two negative numbers is positive.

$$-1(-1 \cdot r) = -1 \cdot 4$$
$$(-1)(-1) \cdot r = -4$$
$$1 \cdot r = -4$$
$$r = -4$$

The solution of the equation $-r = 4$ is thus -4.

EXAMPLE 6   Solve the equation $2.3x = 6.9$.

Multiply both sides by $\frac{1}{2.3}$.

$$\frac{1}{2.3}(2.3x) = \frac{1}{2.3}(6.9)$$
$$1x = \frac{6.9}{2.3}$$
$$x = 3$$

EXERCISES 2.3   *Solve each equation. Check each solution. See Examples 1-6.*

1. $5x = 25$
2. $7x = 28$
3. $2m = 50$
4. $6y = 72$
5. $3a = -24$
6. $5k = -60$
7. $8s = -56$
8. $9t = -36$
9. $-4x = 16$
10. $-6x = 24$
11. $-12z = 108$
12. $-11p = 77$
13. $5r = 0$
14. $2x = 0$
15. $-y = 6$
16. $-m = 2$
17. $-n = -4$
18. $-p = -8$
19. $2x + 3x = 20$
20. $3k + 4k = 14$

21. $5m + 6m - 2m = 72$

22. $11r - 5r + 6r = 84$

23. $k + k + 2k = 80$

24. $4z + z + 2z = 28$

25. $3r - 5r = 6$

26. $9p - 13p = 12$

27. $7r - 13r = -24$

28. $12a - 18a = -36$

29. $6y + 8y - 17y = 9$

30. $14a - 19a + 2a = 15$

31. $-7y + 8y - 9y = -56$

32. $-11b + 7b + 2b = -100$

33. $\dfrac{m}{2} = 16$

34. $\dfrac{p}{5} = 3$

35. $\dfrac{x}{7} = 7$

36. $\dfrac{k}{8} = 2$

37. $\dfrac{2}{3}t = 6$

38. $\dfrac{3}{4}m = 18$

39. $\dfrac{5}{2}z = 20$

40. $\dfrac{9}{5}r = 18$

41. $\dfrac{3}{4}p = -60$

42. $\dfrac{5}{8}z = -40$

43. $\dfrac{2}{3}k = 5$

44. $\dfrac{5}{3}m = 6$

45. $\dfrac{-2}{7}p = -7$

46. $-\dfrac{3}{11}y = -2$

47. $1.7p = 5.1$

48. $2.3k = 11.5$

49. $-4.2m = 25.2$

50. $-3.9a = -15.6$

Write an equation for each problem. Then solve the equation.

51. When a number is divided by 4, the result is 6. Find the number.

52. The quotient of a number and -5 is 2. Find the quotient.

53. Chuck decided to divide a sum of money equally among four relatives, Dennis, Mike, Ed, and Joyce. Each relative received $62. Find the sum that was originally divided.

54. If twice a number is divided by 5, the result is 4. Find the number.

2.4 Solving Linear Equations

- **Learn to use the four steps for solving a linear equation.**

We now combine the methods we have used to help us solve more complicated equations.

To Solve a Linear Equation

Step 1   Combine terms to simplify. Use the commutative, associative, and distributive properties as needed.

Step 2   If necessary, use the addition property of equality to simplify further, so that the variable term is on one side of the equals sign, and the number term is on the other.

Step 3   If necessary, use the multiplication property of equality to simplify further. This gives an equation of the form $x = a$ number.

Step 4   Check the solution by substituting into the original equation. (Do *not* substitute into an intermediate step.)

EXAMPLE 1   Solve the equation $2x + 3x + 3 = 38$. Follow the four steps of the summary above.

Step 1   Combine terms.

$$2x + 3x + 3 = 38$$
$$5x + 3 = 38$$

Step 2   Use the addition property of equality. Add -3 to both sides.

$$5x + 3 + (-3) = 38 + (-3)$$
$$5x = 35$$

Step 3   Use the multiplication property of equality. Multiply both sides by $\frac{1}{5}$.

$$\frac{1}{5} \cdot 5x = \frac{1}{5} \cdot 35$$
$$x = 7$$

Step 4   Check the solution. Substitute 7 for x in the original equation.

$$2x + 3x + 3 = 38$$
$$2(7) + 3(7) + 3 = 38 \qquad \text{Let } x = 7$$
$$14 + 21 + 3 = 38$$
$$38 = 38$$

Since the final statement is true, 7 is the correct solution.

EXAMPLE 2   Solve the equation $3r + 4 - 2r - 7 = 4r + 3$.

Step 1 $3r + 4 - 2r - 7 = 4r + 3$

$r - 3 = 4r + 3$ Combine terms

Step 2 $r - 3 + 3 = 4r + 3 + 3$ Add 3

$r = 4r + 6$

$r + (-4r) = 4r + 6 + (-4r)$ Add $-4r$

$-3r = 6$

Step 3 $-\frac{1}{3}(-3r) = -\frac{1}{3} \cdot 6$ Multiply by $-\frac{1}{3}$

$r = -2$

Step 4   Substitute -2 for r in the original equation.

$3r + 4 - 2r - 7 = 4r + 3$

$3(-2) + 4 - 2(-2) - 7 = 4(-2) + 3$

$-6 + 4 + 4 - 7 = -8 + 3$

$-5 = -5$

The correct solution for the equation is -2.

EXAMPLE 3   Solve the equation $4(k-3) - k = k - 6$.

Step 1   Before combining terms, use the distributive property to simplify $4(k-3)$.

$4(k - 3) = 4k - 4 \cdot 3$

$= 4k - 12$

Now combine terms.

$4k - 12 - k = k - 6$

$3k - 12 = k - 6$

Step 2 $3k - 12 + 12 = k - 6 + 12$ Add 12

$3k = k + 6$

$3k + (-k) = k + 6 + (-k)$ Add $-k$

$2k = 6$

Step 3 $\frac{1}{2}(2k) = \frac{1}{2} \cdot 6$ Multiply by $\frac{1}{2}$

$k = 3$

Step 4   Check your answer by substituting 3 for k in the original equation. Remember to do all the work inside the parentheses first.

$$4(k - 3) - k = k - 6$$
$$4(3 - 3) - 3 = 3 - 6$$
$$4(0) - 3 = 3 - 6$$
$$0 - 3 = 3 - 6$$
$$-3 = -3$$

The correct solution of the equation is 3.

EXAMPLE 4   Solve the equation $6a - (3 + 2a) = 3a + 1$.

Step 1   Simplify.

$$6a - (3 + 2a) = 3a + 1$$
$$6a - 1 \cdot (3 + 2a) = 3a + 1$$
$$6a - 3 - 2a = 3a + 1$$
$$4a - 3 = 3a + 1$$

Step 2   First, add 3 to both sides, then do the same with $-3a$.

$$4a - 3 + 3 = 3a + 1 + 3$$
$$4a = 3a + 4$$
$$4a + (-3a) = 3a + 4 + (-3a)$$
$$a = 4.$$

There is no reason to go further; check that the solution is 4.

EXAMPLE 5   Solve.

$$4(8 - 3t) = 32 - 8(t + 2)$$

Step 1   Simplify.

$$4(8 - 3t) = 32 - 8(t + 2)$$
$$32 - 12t = 32 - 8t - 16$$
$$32 - 12t = 16 - 8t$$

Step 2   Add -32 to both sides and then add $8t$ to both sides.

$$32 - 12t + (-32) = 16 - 8t + (-32)$$
$$-12t = -16 - 8t$$
$$-12t + 8t = -16 - 8t + 8t$$
$$-4t = -16$$

Step 3   Multiply both sides by $-\dfrac{1}{4}$.

$$-\frac{1}{4}(-4t) = -\frac{1}{4}(-16)$$

$$t = 4$$

Step 4   Check this solution back in the original equation.

EXERCISES 2.4   *Solve each equation. Check your solutions. See Examples 1-5.*

1. $4h + 8 = 16$

2. $3x - 15 = 9$

3. $6k + 12 = -12$

4. $2m - 6 = 6$

5. $12p + 18 = 14p$

6. $10m - 15 = 7m$

7. $3x + 9 = -3(2x + 3)$

8. $4z + 2 = -2(z + 2)$

9. $2(2r - 1) = -3(r + 3)$

10. $3(3k + 5) = 2(5k + 5)$

11. $2(3x + 4) = 8(2 + x)$

12. $4(3p + 3) = 3(3p - 1)$

13. $3(5 + 1.4x) = 3x$

14. $2(-3 + 2.1x) = 2x + x$

15. $\frac{1}{2}(4x - 1) = \frac{2}{3}(6x + 9)$

16. $\frac{3}{4}(8x - 3) = \frac{5}{8}(8x + 16)$

Combine terms as necessary. Then solve the equation. See Examples 3-5.

17. $-4 - 3(2x + 1) = 11$

18. $8 - 2(3x - 4) = 2x$

19. $3k - 5 = 2(k + 6) + 1$

20. $4a - 7 = 3(2a + 5) - 2$

21. $5(2m - 1) = 4(2m + 1) + 7$

22. $3(3k - 5) = 4(2k - 5) + 7$

23. $5(4t + 3) = 6(3t + 2) - 1$

24. $7(2y + 6) = 9(y + 3) + 5$

25. $5(x - 3) + 2 = 5(2x - 8) - 3$

26. $6(2v - 1) - 5 = 7(3v - 2) - 24$

27. $-2(3s + 9) - 6 = -3(3s + 11) - 6$

28. $-3(5z + 24) + 2 = 2(3 - 2z) - 10$

29. $6(2p - 8) + 24 = 3(5p - 6) - 6$

30. $2(5x + 3) - 3 = 6(2x - 3) + 15$

31. $3(m - 4) - (2m - 3) = -4$

32. $4(2a + 6) - (7a - 5) = 2$

33. $-(4m + 2) - (-3m - 5) = 3$

34. $-(6k - 5) - (-5k + 8) = -4$

35. $2x + 2(3x + 2) - 9 = 3x - 9 + 3$

36. $3(z - 2) + 4z = 8 + z + 1 - z$

37. $2(r - 3) + 5(r + 4) = 9$

38. $-4(m - 8) + 3(2m + 1) = 6$

39. $1.2(x + 5) = 3(2x - 8) + 23.28$

40. $4.7(m - 1) = 2(3m + 5) - 17.69$

41. $5.1(p + 6) - 3.8p = 4.9(p + 3) + 34.62$

42. $2.7(k - 3) + 1.1k = 3.4(k + 1) - 10.54$

43. $\frac{1}{2}(4r - 6) + \frac{2}{3}(r - 6) = 5$

44. $\frac{1}{3}(6y - 9) + \frac{3}{2}(y + 7) = \frac{19}{2}$

45. $-\frac{2}{3}(6a - 3) + \frac{1}{2}(a - 4) = -\frac{3}{2}$

46. $-\frac{3}{4}(8m + 1) - \frac{1}{2}(m + 2) = -\frac{11}{4}$

Use the given information to write an equation. Then solve it.

47. If 17 is subtracted from a number, and the result is multiplied by 3, the product is 102. What is the number?

48. A teacher says, "If I had three times as many students in my class, I would have 46 more than I have now." How many students are presently in the class?

49. If three times the sum of a number and 4 is subtracted from 8, the result is 2. Find the number.

50. If five times the sum of a number and 3 is added to 5, the result is −5. Find the number.

2.5 From Word Problems to Equations

- **Write verbal phrases as mathematical phrases.**
- **Translate phrases into equations and solve the equations.**

In this section we see how to solve many common types of word problems. To get the answer to a word problem, you must first read it and determine what facts are given and what you are asked to find. Then go through the following five steps.

To Solve a Word Problem

Step 1   Choose a variable to represent the numerical value that you are asked to find—the unknown number.

Step 2   Translate the problem into an equation.

Step 3   Solve the equation.

Step 4   Answer the question asked in the problem.

Step 5   Check your solution by using the original words of the problem.

The second step is often the hardest. To translate the problem into an equation, we must write facts stated in words as mathematical expressions.

You are likely to see some of the same words again and again in word problems. Some of these are explained in the next few examples.

EXAMPLE 1   Write the following as mathematical expressions. Use x to represent the unknown. (We could use other letters to represent this unknown quantity.)

(a) 5 plus a number

The word *plus* indicates addition. If x represents the unknown number, then "5 plus a number" can be written as either

$$5 + x \quad \text{or} \quad x + 5.$$

(b) Add 20 to a number.

If x represents the unknown number, then "add 20 to a number" becomes

$$20 + x \quad \text{or} \quad x + 20.$$

(c) "The sum of a number and 12" is $x + 12$ or $12 + x$.

(d) "7 more than a number" is $7 + x$ or $x + 7$.

EXAMPLE 2   Write each of the following as a mathematical expression. Use x as the variable.

(a) 3 less than a number

"Less than" indicates subtraction. "3 less than a number" is

$$x - 3.$$

(Note: $3 - x$ would *not* be correct.)

(b) "A number decreased by 14" is $x - 14$.

(c) "Ten fewer than x" is $x - 10$.

EXAMPLE 3   Write the following as mathematical expressions. Use x as the variable.

(a) "The product of a number and 3" is written $3 \cdot x$ or just $3x$, since *product* indicates multiplication.

(b) "Three times a number" is also $3x$.

(c) "Two thirds of a number" is $\frac{2}{3}x$.

(d) "The quotient of a number and 2" is $\frac{x}{2}$. (The word *quotient* indicates division; use a fraction bar instead of $\div$.)

(e) "The reciprocal of a number" is $\frac{1}{x}$.

Some word problems must be translated with a combination of symbols, as the next example shows.

EXAMPLE 4   Write the following as mathematical expressions. Use x as the variable.

(a) "7, subtracted from 4 times a number" is written $4x - 7$.

(b) "A number plus its reciprocal" is $x + \dfrac{1}{x}$.

(c) "The sum of a number and 2, multiplied by 5" is $(x + 2) \cdot 5$, or the preferred form, $5(x + 2)$.

(d) "The quotient of a number, and 4 plus the number" is $\dfrac{x}{4 + x}$.

Since equal mathematical expressions are names for the same number, any words that mean *equals* or *same* translate as $=$. The $=$ sign gives us an equation which we can then solve.

EXAMPLE 5   Translate "the product of 4, and a number decreased by 7 is 100" into an equation. Use x as the variable. Solve the equation.
Translate as follows:

The product of 4	and a number	decreased by	7	is	100.
↓	↓	↓	↓	↓	↓
$4 \cdot$	$(x$	$-$	$7)$	$=$	100

Simplify:

$$4 \cdot (x - 7) = 100$$
$$4x - 28 = 100$$
$$4x = 128 \qquad \text{Add 28 to both sides}$$
$$x = 32 \qquad \text{Multiply by } \tfrac{1}{4}$$

Now check the answer by substituting $x = 32$ into the original equation.
$$4(32 - 7) = 100$$
$$4(25) = 100$$
$$100 = 100$$

Since the last statement is true, $x = 32$ is the correct answer.

EXAMPLE 6   If three times the sum of a number and 4 is decreased by twice the number, the result is -6. Find the number.

Let x represent the unknown number. "Three times the sum of a number and 4" translates into symbols as $3(x + 4)$. "Twice the number" is $2x$. Now write an equation using the information of the problem.

Three times the sum of a number and 4	decreased by	twice the number	is	−6.
↓	↓	↓	↓	↓
$3(x + 4)$	−	$2x$	=	−6

We can now solve the equation.

$$3(x + 4) - 2x = -6$$
$$3x + 12 - 2x = -6$$
$$x + 12 = -6$$
$$x = -18$$

Check that $x = -18$ is the correct answer by substituting this value into the original equation.

$$3(-18 + 4) - 2(-18) = -6$$
$$3(-14) - (-36) = -6$$
$$-42 + 36 = -6$$
$$-6 = -6$$

EXAMPLE 7 If the smaller of two consecutive odd integers is doubled, the result is 7 more than the larger of the two integers. Find the two integers.

Let x be the smaller integer. Since the two numbers are consecutive *odd* integers, then $x + 2$ is the larger. Now write an equation from the statement of the problem:

If the smaller is doubled	the result is	7	more than	the larger.
↓	↓	↓	↓	↓
$2x$	=	7	+	$x + 2$

Solve the equation.

$$2x = 7 + x + 2$$
$$2x = 9 + x$$
$$2x + (-x) = 9 + x + (-x)$$
$$x = 9$$

The first integer is 9 and the second is $9 + 2 = 11$.

EXAMPLE 8 At a concert, there were 25 more women than men. The total number of people at the concert was 139. Find the number of men.

Let x represent the number of men. Then the number of women is $x + 25$. The total number of people at the concert was 139, so that

The total	is	the number of men	plus	the number of women.
↓	↓	↓	↓	↓
139	=	x	+	$x + 25$

Solve the equation.

$$139 = 2x + 25$$
$$139 + (-25) = 2x + 25 + (-25)$$
$$114 = 2x$$
$$57 = x$$

There were 57 men at the concert.

EXERCISES 2.5   *Write the following as mathematical expressions. Use* x *as the variable. See Examples 1-4.*

1. 8 plus a number
2. a number added to −6
3. −1 added to a number
4. the sum of a number and 12
5. a quantity is increased by −18
6. the total of x and 12
7. 5 less than a number
8. a number decreased by 6
9. subtract 9 from a number
10. 16 fewer than a number
11. the product of a number and 9
12. double a number
13. triple a number
14. three fifths of a number
15. the quotient of a number and 6
16. the quotient of −9 and a number
17. a number divided by −4
18. 7 divided by a number
19. the product of 8 and the sum of a number and 3
20. a number is added to twice the number
21. a number is subtracted from its reciprocal
22. three times the quotient of a number and 2
23. 8 times the difference of a number and 8
24. the difference of a number and 2, multiplied by −7

Solve the following word problems. Follow steps 1-5. See Examples 5 and 6.

(1) Choose a variable to represent the unknown quantity.
(2) Translate the problem into an equation.
(3) Solve the equation.
(4) Answer the question asked in the problem.
(5) Check your solution by using the original words of the problem.

25. If three times a number is decreased by 2, the result is 22. Find the number.

26. When 6 is added to four times a number, the result is 42. Find the number.

27. The sum of a number and 3 is multiplied by 4, giving 36 as a result. Find the number.

28. The sum of a number and 8 is multiplied by 5, giving 60 as the answer. Find the number.

29. Twice a number is added to the number, giving 90. Find the number.

30. If the sum of a number and 8 is multiplied by −2, the result is −8. Find the number.

31. When 6 is subtracted from a number, the result is 7 times the number. Find the number.

32. If 4 is subtracted from twice a number, the result is 4 less than the number. Find the number.

33. When five times a number is added to twice the number, the result is 10. Find the number.

34. If seven times a number is subtracted from eleven times a number, the result is 9. Find the number.

Solve the following word problems. See Example 7.

35. When the smaller of two consecutive integers is added to three times the larger, the result is 43. Find the integers.

36. If five times the smaller of two consecutive integers is added to three times the larger, the result is 59. Find the integers.

37. The smaller of three consecutive integers is added to twice the larger, producing a result 15 less than four times the middle integer. Find the integers.

38. If the middle of three consecutive integers is added to 100, the result is 1 less than the sum of the third integer and twice the smaller. Find the integers.

39. If 6 is subtracted from the larger of three consecutive odd integers, with this result multiplied by 2, the answer is 23 less than the sum of the first and twice the second of the integers. Find the integers.

40. If the first and third of three consecutive even integers are added, the result is 22 less than three times the second integer. Find the integers.

Solve the following word problems. See Example 8.

41. Tony has a board 44 inches long. He wishes to cut it into two pieces so that one piece will be six inches longer than the other. How long should the shorter piece be?

42. Nevarez and Smith were opposing candidates in the school board election. Nevarez received 30 more votes than did Smith, with 516 total votes cast. How many votes did Smith receive?

43. On an algebra test, the highest grade was 42 points more than the lowest grade. The sum of the two grades was 138. Find the lowest grade.

44. In a physical fitness test, Rolfe did 25 more pushups than Chuck did. The total number of pushups for both men was 173. Find the number of pushups that Chuck did.

45. A pharmacist found that at the end of the day she had 12 more prescriptions for antibiotics than she had for tranquilizers. She had 84 prescriptions altogether for these two types of drugs. How many did she have for tranquilizers?

46. Mark White gives glass-bottom boat rides in the Bahama Islands. One day he noticed that the boat contained 17 more men (counting himself) than women, with a total of 165 people on the boat. How many women were on the boat?

47. Joann McKillip runs a dairy farm. Last year, her cow Bessie gave 238 more gallons of milk than one of her other cows, Bossie. Between them, the two cows gave 1464 gallons of milk. How many gallons of milk did Bossie give?

48. Kevin is three times as old as Bob. Three years ago the sum of their ages was 22 years. How old is each now? (Hint: First write an expression for the age of each now, then for the age of each three years ago.)

The following two problems are real "head-scratchers."

49. A store has 39 quarts of milk, some in pint cartons and some in quart cartons. There are six times as many quart cartons as pint cartons. How many quart cartons are there? (Hint: 1 quart = 2 pints.)

50. A table is three times as long as it is wide. If it were three feet shorter and three feet wider, it would be square (with all sides equal). How long and how wide is it?

2.6 Formulas

- **Identify the formulas needed to solve a problem.**
- **Use a formula to give an equation.**
- **Solve a formula for a specified variable.**

Many word problems can be solved if you know a formula giving the relationships between certain dimensions, amounts, or quantities. Formulas exist for geometric figures such as squares and circles, for distance, for money earned on bank savings, or for converting English measurements to metric measurements. A list of the formulas you will need in this book is given inside the back cover.

EXAMPLE 1   The perimeter of a rectangle is 80 meters, and the length is 25 meters.* (See Figure 2.1.) Find the width of the rectangle.

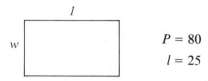

$P = 80$

$l = 25$

Figure 2.1

The distance around a rectangle is called the **perimeter** of the rectangle. The formula for perimeter is

$$P = 2l + 2w.$$

In this formula, P stands for the perimeter, l stands for the length of the long side, and w is the width (the short side).

To find the width, substitute 80 for P and 25 for l in the formula $P = 2l + 2w$.

$$P = 2l + 2w$$
$$80 = 2(25) + 2w$$

Solve this equation to find w. First simplify it.

$$80 = 50 + 2w$$

Add -50 to both sides.

$$80 + (-50) = 50 + 2w + (-50)$$
$$30 = 2w$$

Multiply both sides by $\frac{1}{2}$.

$$15 = w$$

The width of the rectangle is 15 meters.

EXAMPLE 2   The perimeter of a square is 96 inches. Find the length of a side.

You need to know the formula for the perimeter of a square. From the list inside the back cover, you can get the formula $P = 4s$, where s is the length of a side of a square.

The perimeter is given as 96 inches, so that $P = 96$. Substitute 96 for P in the formula.

---

*A meter is a unit of length in the metric system, which is explained in an appendix in the back of the book.

$$P = 4s$$
$$96 = 4s \qquad P = 96$$
$$\frac{1}{4}(96) = \frac{1}{4}(4s) \qquad \text{Multiply by } \frac{1}{4}$$
$$24 = s$$

Each side of the square is 24 inches long.

EXAMPLE 3   The area of a triangle is 126 square meters. The base of the triangle is 21 meters. Find the height.

The formula for the area of a triangle is $A = \frac{1}{2}bh$, where A is area, b is the base, and h is the height. Substitute 126 for A and 21 for b in the formula.

$$A = \frac{1}{2}bh$$

$$126 = \frac{1}{2}(21)h \qquad A = 126, b = 21$$

Simplify the problem by eliminating the fraction $\frac{1}{2}$. Multiply both sides of the equation by 2.

$$2(126) = 2\left(\frac{1}{2}\right)(21)h$$
$$252 = 21h$$

Now multiply both sides by $\frac{1}{21}$.

$$\frac{1}{21}(252) = \frac{1}{21}(21h)$$
$$12 = h$$

The height of the triangle is 12 meters.

Sometimes it is necessary to solve a large number of problems which use the same formula. For example, we might be taking a surveying class and need to solve several problems which involve the formula for the area of a rectangle, $A = lw$. Suppose that in each problem we are given the area (A), and the length (l) of a rectangle and want to find the width (w). We save time in the long run by rewriting the formula $A = lw$ so that the value we do not know, w, is alone on one side of the equals sign. The next example shows how to do this. The process of isolating one letter from a formula is called **solving for a specified variable.**

EXAMPLE 4   Solve $A = lw$ for w.

We need to get w alone on one side of the equals sign. To do this, multiply both sides of $A = lw$ by $\frac{1}{l}$.

$$A = lw$$

$$\frac{1}{l}(A) = \frac{1}{l}(lw)$$

$$\frac{A}{l} = w$$

The formula is now solved for w.

The formula that is used for converting temperatures expressed in degrees Fahrenheit to degrees Celsius is

$$F = \frac{9}{5}C + 32.$$

In Example 5 we see how to solve this formula for C.

EXAMPLE 5   Solve $F = \frac{9}{5}C + 32$ for C.

First, get $\frac{9}{5}C$ alone on one side of the equals sign. Do this by adding -32 on both sides.

$$F = \frac{9}{5}C + 32$$

$$F + (-32) = \frac{9}{5}C + 32 + (-32)$$

$$F - 32 = \frac{9}{5}C$$

Now, multiply both sides by $\frac{5}{9}$.

$$\frac{5}{9}(F - 32) = \frac{5}{9} \cdot \frac{9}{5}C$$

$$\frac{5}{9}(F - 32) = C$$

EXERCISES 2.6   *In the following exercises, a formula is given, along with the values of all but one of the variables in the formula. Find the value of the missing variable. See Examples 1 and 2.*

1. $P = 4s$; $s = 32$

2. $P = 2l + 2w$; $l = 5, w = 3$

3. $A = \frac{1}{2}bh$; $b = 6, h = 12$

4. $A = \frac{1}{2}bh$; $b = 9, h = 24$

5. $V = \frac{1}{3}Bh$; $B = 20, h = 9$

6. $V = \frac{1}{3}Bh$; $B = 82, h = 12$

7. $d = rt$; $d = 8, r = 2$

8. $d = rt$; $d = 100, t = 5$

9. $A = \frac{1}{2}bh$; $A = 20, b = 5$

10. $A = \frac{1}{2}bh$; $A = 30, b = 6$

11. $P = 2l + 2w$; $P = 40, w = 6$

12. $P = 2l + 2w$; $P = 180, l = 50$

13. $V = \frac{1}{3}Bh$; $V = 80, B = 24$

14. $V = \frac{1}{3}Bh$; $V = 52, h = 13$

15. $A = \frac{1}{2}(b + B)h$; $b = 6, B = 8, h = 3$

16. $A = \frac{1}{2}(b + B)h$; $b = 10, B = 12, h = 3$

17. $C = 2\pi r$; $C = 9.42, \pi = 3.14$*

18. $C = 2\pi r$; $C = 25.12, \pi = 3.14$

19. $A = \pi r^2$; $r = 9, \pi = 3.14$

20. $A = \pi r^2$; $r = 15, \pi = 3.14$

21. $V = \frac{4}{3}\pi r^3$; $r = 3, \pi = 3.14$

22. $V = \frac{4}{3}\pi r^3$; $r = 6, \pi = 3.14$

23. $I = prt$; $I = 100, p = 500, r = .10$

24. $I = prt$; $I = 60, p = 150, r = .08$

25. $V = lwh$; $V = 150, l = 10, w = 5$

26. $V = lwh$; $V = 800, l = 40, w = 10$

27. $A = \frac{1}{2}(b + B)h$; $A = 42, b = 5, B = 7$

28. $A = \frac{1}{2}(b + B)h$; $A = 70, b = 15, B = 20$

29. $V = \frac{1}{3}\pi r^2 h$; $V = 9.42, \pi = 3.14, r = 3$

30. $V = \frac{1}{3}\pi r^2 h$; $V = 37.68, \pi = 3.14, r = 6$

Solve the given formula for the indicated variable. See Examples 4 and 5.

31. $A = lw$;   for l

32. $d = rt$;   for r

33. $d = rt$;   for t

34. $V = lwh$;   for w

35. $V = lwh$;   for h

36. $I = prt$;   for p

37. $I = prt$;   for t

38. $C = 2\pi r$;   for r

39. $A = \frac{1}{2}bh$;   for b

40. $A = \frac{1}{2}bh$;   for h

41. $P = 2l + 2w$;   for w

42. $a + b + c = P$;   for b

*Actually, π is *approximately* equal to 3.14, not *exactly* equal to 3.14.

43. $A = \frac{1}{2}(b + B)h$;   for b

44. $C = \frac{5}{9}(F - 32)$;   for F

45. $A = \frac{r}{2l}$;   for l

46. $R = \frac{E}{I}$;   for I

47. $k = \frac{mv^2}{2g}$;   for g

48. $S = 2\pi rh + 2\pi r^2$;   for h

49. $S = \frac{a}{1-r}$;   for r

50. $A = p + prt$;   for p

51. $A = 4\pi r^2$;   for r^2

52. $c^2 = a^2 + b^2$;   for a^2

53. $V = \pi r^2 h$;   for r^2

54. $V = \frac{1}{3}\pi r^2 h$;   for r^2

Write an equation for each word problem and then solve it. Check the solution in the words of the original problem. The necessary formulas are listed at the back of this book. See Example 3.

55. The area of a rectangle is 60 square meters and the width is 6 meters. Find the length.

56. The perimeter of a square is 80 centimeters. Find the length of a side.

57. The radius of a circle is 6 feet. Find the circumference. (Let π be approximated by 3.14.)

58. The length of a rectangle is 15 inches, and the perimeter is 50 inches. Find the width.

59. The perimeter of a triangle is 72 kilometers. One side is 16 kilometers, and another side is 32 kilometers. Find the third side.

60. The shorter base of a trapezoid is 16 and the longer base is 20. The height is 6. Find the area.

2.7 Further Word Problems

- **Learn to solve word problems about geometric figures, money, interest, distance, and mixtures.**

In this section, we look at further types of word problems. As you read through these examples, pay careful attention to the way that we start each solution by saying what the variable represents.

EXAMPLE 1   The length of a rectangle is 2 meters more than the width. The perimeter is 40 meters. (See Figure 2.2.) Find the width and length of the rectangle.

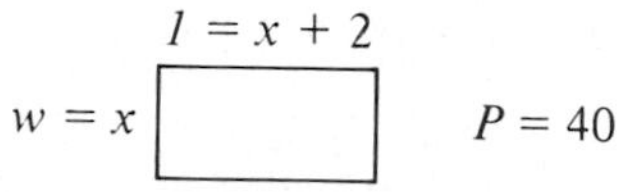

$$l = x + 2$$

$w = x$ $\boxed{}$ $P = 40$

Figure 2.2

Let x represent the width of the rectangle. Since the length is 2 meters more, we use $x + 2$ for the length. The formula for the perimeter of a rectangle is $P = 2l + 2w$. Substitute x for w, $x + 2$ for l, and 40 for P.

$$P = 2l + 2w$$
$$40 = 2(x + 2) + 2x \qquad P = 40, l = x + 2, w = x$$
$$40 = 2x + 4 + 2x \qquad \text{Simplify}$$
$$40 = 4x + 4$$
$$36 = 4x \qquad \text{Add } -4 \text{ to both sides}$$
$$9 = x \qquad \text{Multiply by } \frac{1}{4}$$

The width of the rectangle is 9 meters and the length is $9 + 2 = 11$ meters.

EXAMPLE 2 A bank teller has 25 more five-dollar bills than ten-dollar bills. The total value of all the money that the teller has is $200. How many of each type of bill does he have?

Let x be the number of ten-dollar bills, so that $x + 25$ is the number of fives. The value of all the tens is given by the number of tens (x) times the value per bill (10), or

$$\text{value of tens} = 10x$$

In the same way,

$$\text{value of fives} = 5(x + 25)$$

The total value of all the money is $200.

The value of fives	plus	the value of tens	is	$200.
↓	↓	↓	↓	↓
$5(x + 25)$	$+$	$10x$	$=$	200

Solve this equation.

$$5x + 125 + 10x = 200$$
$$15x + 125 = 200$$
$$15x = 75 \qquad \text{Add } -125$$
$$x = 5 \qquad \text{Multiply by } \frac{1}{15}$$

Since x represents the number of tens, the teller has 5 tens and $5 + 25 = 30$ fives.

EXAMPLE 3 Elizabeth Thornton receives an inheritance. She invests part of it at 9% and $2000 more than this amount at 10%. Altogether, she makes $1150 per year in interest. How much does she have invested at each rate?

Let x be the amount invested at 9%, and $x + 2000$ the amount at 10%. The formula for simple interest is $i = prt$. For the money at 9%, we have $p = x$, $r = 9\% = .09$, and $t = 1$, so that

$$\text{interest at } 9\% = x(.09)(1) = .09x$$
$$\text{interest at } 10\% = .10(x + 2000)$$

The total interest is $1150:

The interest at 9%	plus	the interest at 10%	is	the total interest.
↓	↓	↓	↓	↓
.09x	+	.10(x + 2000)	=	1150

Solve:

$$.09x + .10x + 200 = 1150$$
$$.19x + 200 = 1150$$
$$.19x = 950 \qquad \text{Add } -200$$
$$x = 5000 \qquad \frac{950}{.19} = 5000$$

She has $5000 invested at 9% and $5000 + $2000 = $7000 invested at 10%.

For the next example, we need the formula for distance,

$$d = rt$$

where d represents distance, r is the rate or speed, and t is the time.

EXAMPLE 4 Two cars start from the same point at the same time and travel in the same direction at constant speeds of 34 and 45 miles per hour, respectively. In how many hours will they be 33 miles apart? (See Figure 2.3.)

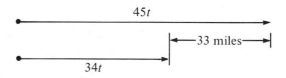

Figure 2.3

Let t represent the unknown number of hours. The distance traveled by the slower car is its rate multiplied by its time, or $34t$. The distance traveled by the faster car is $45t$. The numbers $34t$ and $45t$ represent different distances. From the information of the problem, we know that these distances differ by 33 miles, or

$$45t - 34t = 33$$

Solve:

$$11t = 33$$
$$t = 3$$

In 3 hours the two cars will be 33 miles apart.

EXAMPLE 5   A chemist needs to mix 20 liters of 40% salt solution with some 70% solution to get a mixture which is 50% salt. How many liters of the 70% solution should be used?

Let x represent the number of liters of 70% solution that are needed. The amount of pure salt in this solution will be given by the product of the percent of strength and the number of liters of solution, or

liters of pure salt in 70%: $.70x$.

The amount of pure salt in the 20 liters of 40% solution is

liters of pure salt in 40%: $.40(20) = 8$.

The final solution will contain $20 + x$ liters of 50% solution. This solution will have

liters of pure salt in 50%: $.50(20 + x)$

liters of pure salt. Since the amount of pure salt before and after mixing the solutions must be equal, our equation is

The pure salt in 70%	plus	the pure salt in 40%	is	the pure salt in 50%
↓	↓	↓	↓	↓
$.70x$	$+$	$.40(20)$	$=$	$.50(20 + x)$

Solve:

$$.70x + 8 = 10 + .50x \qquad \text{Simplify}$$
$$.20x + 8 = 10 \qquad \text{Add } -.50x$$
$$.20x = 2 \qquad \text{Add } -8$$
$$x = 10 \qquad \frac{2}{.20} = 10$$

The chemist needs to use 10 liters of the 70% salt solution.

EXERCISES 2.7   *Work the following word problems. See Example 1.*

1. The perimeter of a certain square is seven times the length of a side, decreased by 12. Find the length of a side.

2. The perimeter of a certain rectangle is 16 times the width. The length is 12 centimeters more than the width. Find the length and width of the rectangle.

3. The width of a certain rectangle is one less than the length. The perimeter is five times the length, decreased by 5. Find the length of the rectangle.

4. The length of a certain rectangle is 8 more than the width. The perimeter of the rectangle is 6 more than five times the width. Find the length and width of the rectangle.

5. The longest side of a triangle is 5 meters longer than the shortest side, and the medium side is 2 meters longer than the shortest side. The perimeter of the triangle is 55 meters. Find the lengths of the sides of the triangle.

6. One side of a triangle is 10 centimeters longer than the shortest side. A third side is 20 centimeters longer than the shortest side. The perimeter of the triangle is 120 meters. Find the lengths of the three sides of the triangle.

7. The numerical value of the area of a certain triangle is five times the length of the base. The height is fifty times the reciprocal of the base. Find the length of the base.

8. The circumference of a certain circle is five times the radius, increased by 2.56 meters. Find the radius of the circle. (Use 3.14 as an approximation for π.)

Work the following word problems. See Example 2.

9. A bank teller has some five-dollar bills and some twenty-dollar bills. The teller has 5 more of the twenties. The total value of the money is $725. Find the number of each kind of bill that the teller has.

10. A woman has $1.70 in dimes and nickels; she has two more dimes than nickels. How many of each of these coins does she have?

11. A stamp collector buys some 16¢ stamps and some 29¢ stamps, paying $8.68 for them. He buys 2 more 29¢ stamps than 16¢ stamps. How many of each does he buy?

12. For a retirement party, a person buys some 32¢ favors and some 50¢ favors, paying $46 in total. If she buys 10 more of the 50¢ favors, how many of each were bought?

13. A cashier has a total of 83 bills. He has twice as many fives as tens, with the rest of the bills twenties. The total value of the money is $660. How many of each type of bill does he have?

14. A convention manager finds that she has twice as many twenty-dollar bills as fifties, with a total of 52 bills, including twenties, fifties, and hundreds. The total value of the money is $1840. How many of each kind of bill did the manager have?

Work the following word problems. See Example 3.

15. Nancy Liskar inherited a sum of money from a relative. She deposits some of the money at 8%, with $4000 more at 12%. She earns $2080 in interest per year. Find the amount she has at each rate.

16. Adda McDowell invested some money at 9%, with $3000 less invested at 10%. In total, the investments produce $1600 per year interest. How much is deposited at each rate?

17. Two investments produce an annual interest income of $2430. The amount invested at 7% is $6000 less than the amount invested at 12%. Find the amount invested at each rate.

18. Carol Foresman invested money at 10%, with $5000 more invested at 14%. Her total annual income from these investments is $3100. How much does she have invested at each rate?

19. With income earned by selling a patent, an engineer invests some money at 8%, with $3000 more than twice as much invested at 10%. The total annual income from the investments is $2540. Find the amount invested at each rate.

20. An actor invests his earnings in two ways: some goes into a 5% tax-free bond, while $5000 more than twice as much goes into an apartment house paying 10%. His total annual income from the investments is $4600. Find the amount he has invested at each rate.

Work the following word problems. See Example 4.

21. Two trains leave a city at the same time. One travels north at 60 miles per hour, and the other travels south at 80 miles per hour. In how many hours will they be 280 miles apart?

22. Two planes leave an airport at the same time. One flies east at 300 miles per hour, while the other flies west at 450 miles per hour. In how many hours will they be 2250 miles apart?

23. From a point on a straight road, John and Fred ride bicycles in opposite directions. John rides 10 miles per hour and Fred rides 12 miles per hour. In how many hours will they be 55 miles apart?

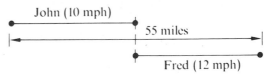

24. Two cars are 400 miles apart. Both start at the same time and travel toward one another. They meet four hours later. If the speed of one car is 20 miles per hour faster than the other, what is the speed of each car?

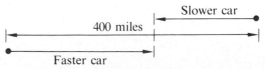

25. Two runners start from the same point and run in the same direction. One runner goes at 8 miles per hour, while the other runs at 11 miles per hour. In how many hours will the runners be 9 miles apart?

26. At a given hour, two steamboats leave a city in the same direction on a straight canal. One travels at 18 miles per hour, and the other travels at 25 miles per hour. In how many hours will the boats be 35 miles apart?

Work the following word problems. See Example 5.

27. How many gallons of 50% antifreeze must be mixed with 20 gallons of 20% antifreeze to get a mixture which is 40% antifreeze?

28. How many liters of 25% salt solution must be added to 80 liters of 40% solution to get a solution which is 30% salt?

29. A merchant wishes to mix candy worth $5 per pound with 40 pounds of candy worth $2 per pound to get a mixture which can be sold for $3 per pound. How many pounds of $5 candy should be used?

30. Ink worth $100 per barrel will be mixed with 30 barrels of ink worth $60 per barrel to get a mixture worth $75 per barrel. How many barrels of $100 ink should be used?

31. A certain metal is 40% tin. How many kilograms of this metal must be mixed with 80 kilograms of a metal which is 70% tin to get a metal which is 50% tin?

32. A pharmacist has 20 liters of a 10% drug solution. How many liters of 5% solution must be added to get a mixture which is 8%?

Work the following miscellaneous word problems. Some of these are difficult.

33. Ann has saved $163 for a trip to Disneyland. Transportation will cost $28, tickets for the park entrance and rides will cost $15 per day, and lodging and meals will cost $30 per day. How many days can she spend there?

34. At Irv's Burgerville, hamburgers cost 90 cents each, and a bag of french fries costs 40 cents. How many hamburgers and how many bags of french fries can Ted buy with $8.80 if he wants twice as many hamburgers as bags of french fries?

35. Ms. Sullivan has $10,000 to invest. She wants to invest part at 5½% interest and part at 6½%. The total annual interest would be $625. How much should she invest at each rate?

36. Mr. Johnson received $16,000 from his mother's estate. He invested part at 8% per year. He put $2000 less than twice that amount in a safe 5% bond. His total annual income from interest is $980. How much did he invest at each rate?

37. A boat travels upstream for three hours. The return trip requires two

hours. If the speed of the current is five miles per hour, find the speed of the boat in still water.

38. In an automobile race, a driver was 120 miles from the finish line after five hours. Another driver, who was in a later race, traveled at the same speed as the first driver. After three hours, the second driver was 250 miles from the finish. Find the speed of each driver.

2.8 The Addition Property of Inequality

- **Graph intervals on a number line.**
- **Learn the addition property of inequality.**
- **Solve inequalities.**

Inequalities are statements in which algebraic expressions are related by

$<$	"is less than"
$\leq$	"is less than or equal to"
$>$	"is greater than"
$\geq$	"is greater than or equal to."

We assume that the domain of any inequality we study is the set of all real numbers. So, when you solve an inequality, you must find all real number solutions for it. For example, $x \leq 2$ represents all real numbers that are less than or equal to 2, and not just the integers less than or equal to 2.

A good way to show the solution of an inequality is by graphing. To graph all real numbers satisfying $x \leq 2$, place a dot at 2 on a number line and draw an arrow extending from the dot to the left (to represent the fact that all numbers less than 2 are also part of the graph). The graph is shown in Figure 2.4.

$$2$$

Figure 2.4

EXAMPLE 1 Graph $x > -5$.

The statement $x > -5$ says that x can represent numbers greater than -5, but x cannot equal -5 itself. To show this on a graph, place an open circle at -5 and draw an arrow to the right, as in the graph shown in Figure 2.5. The open circle at -5 shows that -5 is not part of the graph.

$$-5$$

Figure 2.5

EXAMPLE 2   Graph $3 > x$.

The statement $3 > x$ means the same as $x < 3$. The graph of $x < 3$ is shown in Figure 2.6.

Figure 2.6

EXAMPLE 3   Graph $-3 \leq x < 2$.

The statement $-3 \leq x < 2$ is read "-3 is less than or equal to x and x is less than 2." To graph this inequality, place a heavy dot at -3 (because -3 is part of the graph), and an open circle at 2 (because 2 is not part of the graph). Then draw a line segment between the two circles, as in Figure 2.7.

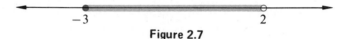

Figure 2.7

Inequalities such as $x + 4 \leq 9$ can be solved in much the same way that we solved equations. We first use the **addition property of inequality,** which states that the same term can be added to both sides of an inequality.

For any expressions A, B, and C, the inequalities

$$A < B$$

and

$$A + C < B + C$$

have exactly the same solutions. The same number may be added to both sides of an inequality.

The addition property of inequality also works with $>$, $\leq$, or $\geq$.

EXAMPLE 4   Solve the inequality $7 + 3k > 2k - 5$.

Use the addition property of inequality twice—once to get the terms containing k on one side of the inequality, and a second time to get the integers together on the other side.

$$7 + 3k > 2k - 5$$

$$7 + 3k + (-2k) > 2k - 5 + (-2k) \qquad \text{Add } -2k \text{ to both sides}$$

$$7 + k > -5$$

$$7 + k + (-7) > -5 + (-7) \qquad \text{Add } -7 \text{ to both sides}$$
$$k > -12$$

The graph of the solution $k > -12$ is shown in Figure 2.8.

-12

Figure 2.8

EXAMPLE 5   Solve $6 + 3y \geq 4y - 5$.

First add $-3y$ to both sides.

$$6 + 3y + (-3y) \geq 4y - 5 + (-3y)$$
$$6 \geq y - 5$$

Then add 5 to both sides.

$$6 + 5 \geq y - 5 + 5$$
$$11 \geq y$$

This solution is perfectly correct, but it is customary to write the solution to an inequality with the variable on the left. The statement $11 \geq y$ says that 11 is greater than or equal to y. We can say the same thing in another way by saying that y is less than or equal to 11, or

$$y \leq 11.$$

The graph of the solution $y \leq 11$ is shown in Figure 2.9.

11

Figure 2.9

If the inequality $6 + 3y \geq 4y - 5$ in Example 5 were solved by first adding the term $-4y$ to both sides, then

$$6 + 3y + (-4y) \geq 4y - 5 + (-4y)$$
$$6 - y \geq -5$$
$$6 - y + (-6) \geq -5 + (-6)$$
$$-y \geq -11.$$

To complete the solution, add y to both sides and add 11 to both sides.

$$-y \geq -11$$
$$-y + y \geq -11 + y \qquad \text{Add } y$$
$$0 \geq -11 + y$$
$$0 + 11 \geq -11 + y + 11 \qquad \text{Add } 11$$
$$11 \geq y$$

This solution can be rewritten as $y \leq 11$ if desired.

EXAMPLE 6   If 2 is added to five times a number, the result is greater than or equal to 5 more than four times the number. Find the number.

We first translate this word problem into an inequality. Let x represent the number you want to find. The "2 is added to five times a number" is expressed as $5x + 2$. And "5 more than four times the number" is $4x + 5$. The two expressions are related by "greater than or equal to."

$$5x + 2 \geq 4x + 5$$

To solve the inequality $5x + 2 \geq 4x + 5$, first add $-4x$ to both sides.

$$5x + 2 + (-4x) \geq 4x + 5 + (-4x)$$
$$x + 2 \geq 5$$

Then add -2 to both sides.

$$x + 2 + (-2) \geq 5 + (-2)$$
$$x \geq 3$$

The number we want is greater than or equal to 3.

Inequalities which say that one number is between two other numbers can also be solved using the addition property of inequality.

EXAMPLE 7   Solve each inequality.

(a) $4 \leq x + 5 \leq 15$

Add -5 to each part of the inequality.

$$4 \leq x + 5 \leq 15$$
$$4 + (-5) \leq x + 5 + (-5) \leq 15 + (-5)$$
$$-1 \leq x \leq 10$$

A graph of this result is shown in Figure 2.10.

$$-1 \qquad\qquad\qquad 10$$

Figure 2.10

(b) $24 < y - 5 < 32$

Add 5 throughout.

$$24 + 5 < y - 5 + 5 < 32 + 5$$
$$29 < y < 37$$

The graph is in Figure 2.11.

$$29 \qquad\qquad\qquad 37$$

Figure 2.11

EXERCISES 2.8 *Graph each inequality on a number line. See Examples 1-3.*

1. $x \le 4$

2. $x \le -3$

3. $k \ge -5$

4. $m \ge 6$

5. $a < 3$

6. $p > 4$

7. $-2 \le x \le 5$

8. $8 \le m \le 10$

9. $3 \le y < 5$

10. $0 < y \le 10$

Solve each inequality. See Examples 4 and 5.

11. $a + 6 < 8$

12. $k - 4 < 2$

13. $z - 3 \ge -2$

14. $p + 2 \ge -6$

15. $p - 8 \le 4$

16. $2 + m \ge 5$

17. $-3 + k \ge 2$

18. $-8 + y < -10$

19. $x + 6 \le 6$

20. $x + 5 > 5$

21. $4x < 3x + 6$

22. $5x \le 4x - 8$

23. $9k \le 8k - 9$

24. $12p > 11p + 5$

Solve each inequality and then graph your solution. See Examples 4 and 5.

25. $3n + 5 \le 2n - 6$

26. $5x - 2 < 4x - 5$

27. $2z - 8 > z - 3$

28. $4x + 6 \le 3x - 5$

29. $3(y - 5) + 2 < 2(y - 4)$

30. $4(x + 6) - 5 > 3(x + 1)$

31. $-6(k + 2) + 3 \ge -7(k - 5)$

32. $-3(m - 5) + 8 < -4(m + 2)$

33. $5(2k + 3) - 2(k - 8) > 3(2k + 4) + k - 2$

34. $2(3z - 5) + 4(z + 6) \ge 2(3z + 2) + 3(z - 5)$

Solve each inequality and then graph your solution. See Example 7.

35. $8 \le p + 2 \le 15$

36. $4 \le k - 1 \le 10$

37. $-3 < y - 8 < 4$

38. $-6 < r - 1 < -2$

39. $-10 \le p + 11 \le -2$

40. $0 \le x + 7 \le 8$

In Exercises 41–46, write an inequality using the information given in the problem and then solve it. See Example 6.

41. If four times a number is added to 8, the result is less than three times the number added to 5. Find all possible values of the number.

42. The product of 7 and a number is added to 4, giving a result which is greater than or equal to six times the number. Find all possible values of the number.

43. If the length of a rectangle is to be twice the width, and the difference between the two dimensions is to be less than or equal to 7 meters, what is the largest possible value for the width?

44. The perimeter of a triangle must be no more than 55 centimeters. One side of the triangle is 18 centimeters, and a second side is 13 centimeters. Find the largest possible length for the third side.

45. The length of a rectangle is four times the width. If three times the width is subtracted from the length, the result is at least 15. Find the smallest possible values for the length and width of the rectangle.

46. The perimeter of a triangle cannot be more than 25 meters. One side is 7 meters. A second side is 9 meters. Find the longest possible length of the third side.

2.9 The Multiplication Property of Inequality

- **Learn the multiplication property of inequality.**
- **Solve inequalities.**

Using only the addition property of inequality, we cannot solve inequalities such as $3y \geq 12$. We need the **multiplication property of inequality.** To see how this property works, let's look at some examples.

First take the inequality $3 < 7$ and multiply both sides by the positive number 2.

$$3 < 7$$
$$2(3) < 2(7) \qquad \text{Multiply both sides by 2}$$
$$6 < 14 \qquad \text{True}$$

Multiply both sides of $3 < 7$ by the negative number -5.

$$3 < 7$$
$$-5(3) < -5(7) \qquad \text{Multiply both sides by } -5$$
$$-15 < -35 \qquad \text{False}$$

To get a true statement when we multiply both sides by -5, we would have to reverse the direction of the inequality symbol.

$$3 < 7$$
$$-5(3) > -5(7) \qquad \text{Multiply by } -5; \text{ reverse the symbol}$$
$$-15 > -35 \qquad \text{True}$$

Take the inequality $-6 < 2$ as another example. Multiply both sides by the positive number 4.

$$-6 < 2$$
$$4(-6) < 4(2)$$
$$-24 < 8 \qquad \text{True}$$

If we multiply both sides of $-6 < 2$ by -5, *and at the same time reverse the direction of the inequality symbol,* we get

$$-6 < 2$$
$$(-5)(-6) > (-5)(2)$$
$$30 > -10 \qquad \text{True}$$

In summary, we have the two parts of the **multiplication property of inequality.**

---

(1)   For any expressions A, B, and C,
        if C is *positive,* then the inequalities

$$A < B$$

and

$$AC < BC$$

have exactly the same solutions;

(2)   if C is *negative,* then the inequalities

$$A < B$$

and

$$AC > BC$$

have exactly the same solutions. (Assume that $C \neq 0$.) Both sides of an inequality may be multiplied by the same nonzero number. If the number is negative, reverse the inequality symbol.

The multiplication property of inequality also works with $>$, $\leq$, or $\geq$.

Important: (1) When you multiply both sides of an inequality by a positive number, the direction of the inequality symbol does not change. Also, adding terms to both sides does not change the symbol.

(2) When you multiply both sides of an inequality by a negative number, the direction of the symbol does change. *You reverse the symbol of inequality only when multiplying by a negative number.*

EXAMPLE 1 Solve the inequality $3r < 18$.

To simplify this inequality, use the multiplication property of inequality and multiply both sides by $\frac{1}{3}$. Since $\frac{1}{3}$ is a positive number, the direction of the inequality symbol does not change.

$$3r < 18$$

$$\frac{1}{3}(3r) < \frac{1}{3}(18)$$

$$r < 6$$

The graph of this solution is shown in Figure 2.12.

6

Figure 2.12

EXAMPLE 2 Solve the inequality $-4t \geq 8$.

Here we need to multiply both sides of the inequality by $-\frac{1}{4}$, a negative number. This does change the direction of the inequality symbol.

$$-4t \geq 8$$

$$\left(-\frac{1}{4}\right)(-4t) \leq \left(-\frac{1}{4}\right)(8)$$

$$t \leq -2$$

The solution is graphed in Figure 2.13.

-2

Figure 2.13

EXAMPLE 3 Solve the inequality $-x \leq -11$.

Use the multiplication property of inequality and multiply both sides by -1. Since -1 is negative, change the direction of the inequality symbol.

$$-x \leq -11$$

$$(-1)(-x) \geq (-1)(-11)$$

$$x \geq 11$$

The solution is graphed in Figure 2.14.

11

Figure 2.14

We can now summarize the steps involved in solving an inequality. (Remember that $<$ can be replaced with $>$, $\leq$, or $\geq$ in this summary.)

To Solve an Inequality

Step 1   Use the associative, commutative, and distributive properties to combine terms on both sides of the inequality.

Step 2   Use the addition property of inequality to simplify the inequality to one of the form $ax < b$, where a and b are real numbers.

Step 3   Use the multiplication property of inequality to simplify further to an inequality of the form $x < c$ or $x > c$, where c is a real number.

EXAMPLE 4   Solve the inequality $3z + 2 - 5 > -z + 7 + 2z$.

Step 1   Simplify and combine terms.

$$3z + 2 - 5 > -z + 7 + 2z$$
$$3z - 3 > z + 7$$

Step 2   Use the addition property of inequality.

$$3z - 3 + 3 > z + 7 + 3$$
$$3z > z + 10$$
$$3z + (-z) > z + 10 + (-z)$$
$$2z > 10$$

Step 3   Use the multiplication property of inequality.

$$\frac{1}{2}(2z) > \frac{1}{2}(10)$$
$$z > 5$$

Since $\dfrac{1}{2}$ is positive, the direction of the inequality symbol was not changed in the third step. A graph of the solution is shown in Figure 2.15.

5

Figure 2.15

EXAMPLE 5   Solve $5(k - 3) - 7k \geq 4(k - 3) + 9$.

Step 1   Combine terms.

$$5(k - 3) - 7k \geq 4(k - 3) + 9$$
$$5k - 15 - 7k \geq 4k - 12 + 9$$
$$-2k - 15 \geq 4k - 3$$

Step 2   Use the addition property.

$$-2k - 15 + (-4k) \geq 4k - 3 + (-4k)$$
$$-6k - 15 \geq -3$$
$$-6k - 15 + 15 \geq -3 + 15$$
$$-6k \geq 12$$

Step 3   Multiply both sides by $-\frac{1}{6}$, a negative number. Change the direction of the inequality symbol.

$$\left(-\frac{1}{6}\right)(-6k) \leq \left(-\frac{1}{6}\right)(12)$$
$$k \leq -2$$

A graph of the solution is shown in Figure 2.16.

$$-2$$

Figure 2.16

EXAMPLE 6   Solve $4 \leq 3x - 5 < 6$

First add 5 to each part.

$$4 \leq 3x - 5 < 6$$
$$4 + 5 \leq 3x - 5 + 5 < 6 + 5$$
$$9 \leq 3x < 11$$

Now multiply by the positive number $\frac{1}{3}$.

$$\frac{1}{3} \cdot 9 \leq \frac{1}{3} \cdot 3x < \frac{1}{3} \cdot 11$$

$$3 \leq x < \frac{11}{3}$$

A graph of the solution is in Figure 2.17.

$$3 \qquad\qquad\qquad\qquad \frac{11}{3}$$

Figure 2.17

EXERCISES 2.9   *Solve each inequality and graph the solution. See Examples 1-5.*

1. $3x < 27$ 2. $5h \geq 20$

3. $4r \geq -12$ 4. $6a < -18$

5. $-2k \leq 12$ 6. $-3v > 6$

7. $-8y > 72$ 8. $-5z \leq 40$

9. $-5m > -35$
10. $-8x \le -16$
11. $-6r < -16$
12. $-9a \ge -63$
13. $4k + 1 \ge 2k - 9$
14. $5y + 3 < 2y + 12$
15. $3 + 2r > 5r - 27$
16. $8 + 6t \le 8t + 12$
17. $4q + 1 - 5 < 8q + 4$
18. $5x - 2 \le 2x + 6 - x$
19. $10p + 20 - p > p + 3 - 23$
20. $-3v + 6 + 3 - 2 > -5v - 19$
21. $-k + 4 + 5k \le -1 + 3k + 5$
22. $6y - 2y - 4 + 7y > 3y - 4 + 7y$
23. $2(x - 5) + 3x < 4(x - 6) + 3$
24. $5(t + 3) - 6t \le 3(2t + 1) - 4t$
25. $5 - (2 - r) \le 3r + 5$
26. $-9 + (8 + y) > 7y - 4$
27. $3(p + 1) - 2(p - 4) \ge 5(2p - 3) + 2$
28. $-5(m - 3) + 4(m + 6) < 2(m - 3) + 4$

Solve each inequality. Graph your solution. See Example 6.

29. $-5 \le 2x - 3 \le 9$
30. $-7 \le 3x - 4 \le 8$
31. $5 < 6m - 1 < 12$
32. $10 < 7p + 3 < 24$
33. $-1 \le 5q - 1 \le 16$
34. $-8 \le 3r - 1 \le -1$
35. $-12 \le \frac{1}{2}z + 1 \le 4$
36. $-6 \le \frac{1}{3}a - 3 \le 5$

In Exercises 37–48, write an inequality using the information given in the problem. Then solve it.

37. A student has test grades of 75 and 82. What must he score on a third test to have an average of 80 or higher?

38. In Exercise 37, if 100 is the highest score possible on the third test, how high an average (to the nearest tenth) can the student make? What is the lowest average possible for the three tests?

39. Twice a number added to three times the sum of the number and 2 is more than 17. Find the numbers that satisfy this condition.

40. Mr. Odjakjian earned $200 at odd jobs during July, $300 during August, and $225 during September. If his average salary for the four

months from July through October is to be at least $250, how much must he earn during October?

41. The perimeter of a rectangle must be no greater than 120 meters. The width of the rectangle must be 22 meters. Find the longest possible value for the length of the rectangle.

42. One side of a triangle is twice as long as a second side. The third side of the triangle is 17 feet long. The perimeter of the triangle cannot be more than 50 feet. Find the longest possible values for the other two sides of the triangle.

43. In order to qualify for a company pension plan, an employee must average at least $500 per month in earnings. During the first four months of the year, an employee made $450, $600, $520, and $380. What amount of earnings during the fifth month will qualify the employee?

44. When four times a number is subtracted from 8, the result is less than 15. Find all numbers that satisfy this condition.

45. If half a number is added to 5, the result is greater than or equal to −3. Find all such numbers.

46. If two thirds of a number is added to −3, the result is no more than 2. Find all such numbers.

47. One side of a rectangle is 8 meters long. The area of the rectangle must be at least 240 square meters. Find the shortest possible length for the rectangle.

48. A triangle has a height of 20 meters. The area of the triangle must be less than or equal to 40 square meters. Find the longest possible length for the base of the triangle.

Chapter 2 Test

[2.1] *Simplify by combining like terms.*

1. $2x + 5 + 5x - 3x - 3$ **2.** $k - 3k + 5k - 6k + 4k$

3. $9r + 3r - 4r - r - 8r$ **4.** $3z - 6z + 8 - 9 + 4z - 9$

5. $4(2m + 1) - (m + 5)$

[2.2-2.4] *Solve each equation.*

6. $2m - 5 = 3$ **7.** $6v + 3 = 8v - 7$

8. $3(a + 12) = 1 - 2(a - 5)$

9. $4k - 6k + 8(k - 3) = -2(k + 12)$

10. $\dfrac{m}{5} = 2$

11. $4 - (3 - m) = 12 + 3m$

12. $-(r + 4) = 2 + r$

[2.5] **13.** If 8 is added to 4 times a number, the result is -12. Find the number.

14. Vern paid $57 more to tune up his Bronco than for his Oldsmobile. He paid $257 in total. How much did it cost for the tune-up on the Oldsmobile?

[2.6] **15.** Solve the formula $I = prt$ for p.

16. Solve the formula $A = \frac{1}{2}(b + B)h$ for h.

Write an equation for each problem, then solve.

17. A rectangle has a perimeter which is two inches less than three times the length. The perimeter is 190 inches. Find the length and width of the rectangle.

[2.7] **18.** Dick's lunch cost $2.40. Sandwiches are 70¢ each and milk is 30¢ per glass. He bought one glass of milk. How many sandwiches did he buy?

19. Joe bicycled a distance of 21 miles in five hours. During the last two hours, he became tired and slowed down by two miles per hour. What was his speed for the first three hours?

20. Don is now twenty years older than Hank. In five years Don will be twice as old as Hank. What are their ages now?

[2.8-2.9] *Solve each inequality. Graph the solution.*

21. $x + 4 \le 8$ **22.** $-2m < -14$

23. $-3k < k - 8$ **24.** $5(k - 2) + 3 \le 2(k - 3) + 2k$

25. One of the regulations of the Post Office says that a package can be mailed only if the length plus the distance around at the widest point does not exceed 72 inches. That is, if l represents the length of the package, w the width, and h the height, then

$$l + 2w + 2h \le 72.$$

Find the longest acceptable package with width 10 inches and height 6 inches.

3

Exponents and Polynomials

3.1 Exponents

- **Use exponents.**
- **Learn the product rule for exponentials.**
- **Use zero as an exponent.**
- **Use negative numbers as exponents.**
- **Learn the quotient rule for exponentials.**

In Chapter 1 we used exponents to write repeated products:

$$5^2 = 5 \cdot 5$$
$$= 25$$
$$4^3 = 4 \cdot 4 \cdot 4$$
$$= 64$$
$$9^1 = 9,$$

and so on. In the expression 5^2, the number 5 is called the **base,** while 2 is the **exponent.** The expression 5^2 is called an **exponential.**

EXAMPLE 1   Write $3 \cdot 3 \cdot 3 \cdot 3 \cdot 3$ in exponential form. Evaluate the exponential.
Since 3 occurs as a factor five times, the base is 3 and the exponent is 5.

The exponential is 3^5. The value is

$$3^5 = 3 \cdot 3 \cdot 3 \cdot 3 \cdot 3$$
$$= 243.$$

EXAMPLE 2 Evaluate each exponential. Name the base and the exponent.

(a) $5^4 = 5 \cdot 5 \cdot 5 \cdot 5$
$= 625$. The base is 5; the exponent is 4.

(b) $-(5^4) = -(5 \cdot 5 \cdot 5 \cdot 5)$
$= -625$. The base is 5; the exponent is 4.

(c) $(-5)^4 = (-5)(-5)(-5)(-5)$
$= 625$. The base is -5; the exponent is 4.

(d) $(-5^4) = -(5^4)$
$= -625$

The base is 5 and the exponent is 4.

By the definition of exponents,

$$2^4 \cdot 2^3 = (2 \cdot 2 \cdot 2 \cdot 2)(2 \cdot 2 \cdot 2)$$
$$= 2 \cdot 2 \cdot 2 \cdot 2 \cdot 2 \cdot 2 \cdot 2$$
$$= 2^7.$$

In general, for positive integers m and n, we have the **product rule for exponentials.**

$$a^m \cdot a^n = a^{m+n}$$

The bases must be the same before the product rule for exponentials can be applied.

EXAMPLE 3 Use the product rule for exponentials to find each product.

(a) $6^3 \cdot 6^5 = 6^{3+5}$
$= 6^8$ by the product rule.

(b) $(-4)^5(-4)^3 = (-4)^{5+3}$
$= (-4)^8$ by the product rule.

(c) There is no shortcut way to find the product $2^3 \cdot 3^2$, since the bases are different. The only thing we can do is to actually work out the multiplication:

$$2^3 \cdot 3^2 = 2 \cdot 2 \cdot 2 \cdot 3 \cdot 3$$
$$= 72.$$

EXAMPLE 4 Multiply $2x^3$ by $3x^7$.

Since $2x^3$ means $2 \cdot x^3$ and $3x^7$ means $3 \cdot x^7$,

$$2x^3 \cdot 3x^7 = 2 \cdot 3 \cdot x^3 \cdot x^7$$
$$= 6x^{10}.$$

The rule for division of exponentials is similar to the product rule. For example,

$$\frac{6^5}{6^2} = \frac{6 \cdot 6 \cdot 6 \cdot 6 \cdot 6}{6 \cdot 6}$$

$$= 6 \cdot 6 \cdot 6$$

$$= 6^3.$$

The difference of the exponents, $5 - 2$, gives the exponent of the answer, 3.

$$\frac{3^4}{3^6} = \frac{3 \cdot 3 \cdot 3 \cdot 3}{3 \cdot 3 \cdot 3 \cdot 3 \cdot 3 \cdot 3}$$

$$= \frac{1}{3 \cdot 3}$$

$$= \frac{1}{3^2}$$

In this example, the difference $6 - 4$ gives the new exponent, 2.

There is one other possibility. If the exponents in the numerator and denominator are equal, we have

$$\frac{6^5}{6^5} = \frac{6 \cdot 6 \cdot 6 \cdot 6 \cdot 6}{6 \cdot 6 \cdot 6 \cdot 6 \cdot 6}$$

$$= 1.$$

However, if we subtract the exponents as we did above,

$$\frac{6^5}{6^5} = 6^{5-5}$$

$$= 6^0.$$

This means that $6^0 = 1$. In general, for any number a, except 0,

$$a^0 = 1.$$

EXAMPLE 5 Evaluate each exponential.

(a) $60^0 = 1$

(b) $(-60)^0 = 1$

(c) $-(60^0) = -(1) = -1$

Note the difference between Examples 5(b) and 5(c). In Example 5(b) the base is -60 and the exponent is 0. Any nonzero base raised to a zero exponent is 1. But in Example 5(c), the base is 60. Then $60^0 = 1$, so that $-60^0 = -1$.

In the discussion above, we found that

$$\frac{6^5}{6^2} = 6^3, \qquad \text{while} \qquad \frac{3^4}{3^6} = \frac{1}{3^2}.$$

In the first of these examples, we subtracted the bottom exponent from the top exponent; in the other we subtracted the top from the bottom exponent. To get around the problem of trying to decide which way to subtract, we use **negative exponents.** For any nonzero real number a and any integer n,

$$a^{-n} = \frac{1}{a^n}.$$

EXAMPLE 6 Simplify each term using the definition of negative exponents.

(a) $3^{-2} = \dfrac{1}{3^2}$

$\phantom{(a)\ 3^{-2}} = \dfrac{1}{9}$

(b) $5^{-3} = \dfrac{1}{5^3}$

$\phantom{(b)\ 5^{-3}} = \dfrac{1}{125}$

(c) $\left(\dfrac{1}{2}\right)^{-3} = \dfrac{1}{\left(\dfrac{1}{2}\right)^3}$

$ = \dfrac{1}{\dfrac{1}{8}}$

$ = 1 \cdot \dfrac{8}{1}$

$ = 8$

(d) $4^{-1} - 2^{-1} = \dfrac{1}{4} - \dfrac{1}{2}$

$\phantom{(d)\ 4^{-1} - 2^{-1}} = \dfrac{1}{4} - \dfrac{2}{4}$

$\phantom{(d)\ 4^{-1} - 2^{-1}} = -\dfrac{1}{4}$

Using the definition of negative exponent, we can now give the **quotient rule for exponentials:** for any integers m and n, and nonzero real number a,

$$\frac{a^m}{a^n} = a^{m-n}.$$

EXAMPLE 7 Simplify, using the quotient rule for exponentials.

(a) $\dfrac{5^8}{5^6} = 5^{8-6}$

$ = 5^2$

(b) $\dfrac{4^2}{4^9} = 4^{2-9}$

$ = 4^{-7}$

$ = \dfrac{1}{4^7}$

(c) $\dfrac{5^{-3}}{5^{-7}} = 5^{-3-(-7)}$

$= 5^4$

(d) $\dfrac{3^2 x^5}{3^4 x^3} = 3^{2-4} x^{5-3}$

$= 3^{-2} x^2$

$= \dfrac{1}{3^2} \cdot x^2$

$= \dfrac{x^2}{3^2}$ or $\dfrac{x^2}{9}$

Using the definition of negative exponent, the product rule for exponentials is also true for negative integer exponents. We can now summarize our rules for exponentials.

Product rule:	$a^m \cdot a^n = a^{m+n}$	
Zero exponent:	$a^0 = 1$	$(a \neq 0)$
Negative exponent:	$a^{-n} = \dfrac{1}{a^n}$	$(a \neq 0)$
Quotient rule:	$\dfrac{a^m}{a^n} = a^{m-n}$	$(a \neq 0)$

EXAMPLE 8 Simplify, using the rules for exponentials.

(a) $5^{-4} \cdot 5^7 = 5^{-4+7} = 5^3$

(b) $x^{-8} \cdot x^7 \cdot x^{-3} = x^{-8+7+(-3)} = x^{-4} = \dfrac{1}{x^4}$

EXERCISES 3.1 *Identify the base and exponent for each exponential. See Example 2.*

1. 5^{12} 2. a^6 3. $(3m)^4$ 4. -2^4

5. -125^3 6. $(-1)^8$ 7. $(-24)^2$ 8. $-(-3)^5$

9. $3m^2$ 10. $5y^3$

Write each expression using exponents. See Example 1.

11. $3 \cdot 3 \cdot 3 \cdot 3 \cdot 3$ 12. $4 \cdot 4 \cdot 4$

13. $5 \cdot 5 \cdot 5 \cdot 5$ 14. $3 \cdot 3 \cdot 3 \cdot 3 \cdot 3 \cdot 3 \cdot 3 \cdot 3 \cdot 3$

15. $(-2)(-2)(-2)(-2)(-2)$ 16. $(-1)(-1)(-1)(-1)$

17. $\dfrac{1}{4 \cdot 4 \cdot 4 \cdot 4 \cdot 4}$ 18. $\dfrac{1}{(-2)(-2)(-2)}$

19. $\dfrac{1}{3 \cdot 3 \cdot 3 \cdot 3}$ **20.** $\dfrac{1}{2 \cdot 2 \cdot 2 \cdot 2 \cdot 2}$

Evaluate each expression. For example, $5^2 + 5^3 = 25 + 125 = 150$.

21. $3^2 + 3^4$ **22.** $2^8 - 2^6$

23. $4^2 + 4^3$ **24.** $3^3 + 3^4$

25. $2^2 + 2^5$ **26.** $4^2 + 4^1$

27. $4^0 + 5^0$ **28.** $3^0 + 8^0$

29. $(-9)^0 + 9^0$ **30.** $(-8)^0 + (-8)^0$

Evaluate each expression. See Example 6.

31. 3^{-3} **32.** 4^{-2}

33. 5^{-2} **34.** 2^{-5}

35. 9^{-1} **36.** $(-12)^{-1}$

37. $(-6)^{-2}$ **38.** 8^{-3}

39. 7^{-1} **40.** 12^{-2}

41. $\left(\dfrac{1}{2}\right)^{-5}$ **42.** $\left(\dfrac{1}{5}\right)^{-2}$

43. $\left(\dfrac{1}{2}\right)^{-1}$ **44.** $\left(\dfrac{3}{4}\right)^{-1}$

45. $\left(\dfrac{2}{3}\right)^{-3}$ **46.** $\left(\dfrac{5}{4}\right)^{-2}$

47. $2^{-1} + 3^{-1}$ **48.** $3^{-1} - 4^{-1}$

49. $5^{-1} + 4^{-1}$ **50.** $3^{-1} + 6^{-1}$

Use the product rule to simplify each expression. Write each answer in exponential form. See Example 3.

51. $4^2 \cdot 4^3$ **52.** $3^5 \cdot 3^4$

53. $9^5 \cdot 9^3$ **54.** $8^6 \cdot 8^4$

55. $3^4 \cdot 3^{-7}$ **56.** $2^{-5} \cdot 2^{15}$

57. $4^3 \cdot 4^5 \cdot 4^{-10}$ **58.** $2^3 \cdot 2^4 \cdot 2^{-6}$

59. $(-3)^3(-3)^2$ **60.** $(-4)^5(-4)^3$

61. $(-2)^3(-2)^6$ **62.** $(-3)^4(-3)^6$

Use the quotient rule to simplify each expression. Leave each answer in exponential form. See Example 7.

63. $\dfrac{4^7}{4^2}$ **64.** $\dfrac{11^5}{11^3}$ **65.** $\dfrac{4^2}{4^4}$ **66.** $\dfrac{14^{11}}{14^{15}}$

67. $\dfrac{8^3}{8^9}$ **68.** $\dfrac{5^4}{5^{10}}$ **69.** $\dfrac{6^{-4}}{6^2}$ **70.** $\dfrac{7^{-5}}{7^3}$

71. $\dfrac{14^{-2}}{14^{-5}}$ **72.** $\dfrac{3^{-6}}{3^{-9}}$ **73.** $\dfrac{8}{8^{-1}}$ **74.** $\dfrac{12}{12^{-1}}$

75. $\dfrac{3^{-1}}{3}$ **76.** $\dfrac{15^{-1}}{15}$

3.2 Further Rules for Exponents

- **Learn the power rule for exponentials.**
- **Use** $(ab)^m = a^m b^m$.
- **Use** $\left(\dfrac{a}{b}\right)^m = \dfrac{a^m}{b^m}$.

In this section we shall develop further rules of exponents to go with the product rule and quotient rule of the previous section.

To simplify an expression such as $(8^3)^2$, use the definition of an exponent:

$$(8^3)^2 = (8^3)(8^3)$$
$$= (8 \cdot 8 \cdot 8)(8 \cdot 8 \cdot 8)$$
$$= 8^6$$

Looking at just the exponents of $(8^3)^2$, we see $3 \cdot 2 = 6$. In general, to find $(a^m)^n$, where m and n are integers, use the **power rule for exponentials:**

$$(a^m)^n = a^{mn}$$

EXAMPLE 1 Use the power rule for exponentials to simplify each expression.

(a) $(2^5)^3 = 2^{5 \cdot 3}$
$= 2^{15}$

(b) $(5^7)^{-2} = 5^{7(-2)}$
$= 5^{-14}$
$= \dfrac{1}{5^{14}}$

(c) $(8^{-2})^{-5} = 8^{(-2)(-5)}$
$= 8^{10}$

We can use the properties studied in Chapter 1 to develop two more rules for exponentials. By definition,

$$(4 \cdot 8)^3 = (4 \cdot 8)(4 \cdot 8)(4 \cdot 8)$$
$$= 4 \cdot 4 \cdot 4 \cdot 8 \cdot 8 \cdot 8 \quad \text{(Commutative and associative properties)}$$
$$= 4^3 \cdot 8^3.$$

Based on this example, we have the following rule. For any integer m,

$$(ab)^m = a^m b^m.$$

EXAMPLE 2 Use the rule given above to simplify each exponential.

(a) $(3xy)^2 = 3^2 x^2 y^2$

$\qquad = 9x^2 y^2$

(b) $9(pq)^2 = 9(p^2 q^2)$

$\qquad = 9p^2 q^2$

(c) $(2m^2 p^3)^4 = 2^4 (m^2)^4 (p^3)^4$

$\qquad = 2^4 m^8 p^{12}$

$\qquad = 16 m^8 p^{12}$

(d) $(3k^{-2})^{-3} = 3^{-3} k^{(-2)(-3)}$

$\qquad = 3^{-3} k^6$

$\qquad = \dfrac{k^6}{3^3}$

Since $\dfrac{a}{b}$ can be written as $a\left(\dfrac{1}{b}\right)$, the rule above, together with some of the properties of real numbers, gives us the final rule for exponentials. For any integer m, and for real numbers a and b, with $b \neq 0$,

$$\left(\frac{a}{b}\right)^m = \frac{a^m}{b^m}.$$

EXAMPLE 3 Use the rule given above to simplify each expression.

(a) $\left(\dfrac{2}{3}\right)^5 = \dfrac{2^5}{3^5}$ or $\dfrac{32}{243}$

(b) $\left(\dfrac{4}{5}\right)^{-2} = \dfrac{4^{-2}}{5^{-2}}$

$\qquad = \dfrac{\dfrac{1}{4^2}}{\dfrac{1}{5^2}}$

$\qquad = \dfrac{1}{4^2} \cdot \dfrac{5^2}{1}$

$\qquad = \dfrac{5^2}{4^2}$ or $\dfrac{25}{16}$

EXAMPLE 4 Use a combination of the rules for exponentials to simplify each expression.

(a) $\dfrac{(4^2)^3}{4^5}$

Use the power rule and then the quotient rule.

$$\frac{(4^2)^3}{4^5} = \frac{4^6}{4^5}$$
$$= 4^1$$
$$= 4.$$

(b) $(2x)^3(2x)^2$

Use the product rule first.

$$(2x)^3(2x)^2 = (2x)^5$$
$$= 2^5x^5$$
$$= 32x^5$$

(c) $\left(\dfrac{2x^3}{5}\right)^4$

By the last two rules given above,

$$\left(\frac{2x^3}{5}\right)^4 = \frac{2^4x^{12}}{5^4}$$
$$= \frac{16x^{12}}{625}.$$

(d) $\left(\dfrac{3x^{-2}}{4^{-1}y^3}\right)^{-3} = \dfrac{3^{-3}x^6}{4^3y^{-9}}$

$$= \frac{\dfrac{1}{3^3} \cdot x^6}{4^3 \cdot \dfrac{1}{y^9}}$$

$$= \frac{\dfrac{x^6}{3^3}}{\dfrac{4^3}{y^9}}$$

$$= \frac{x^6}{3^3} \cdot \frac{y^9}{4^3}$$

$$= \frac{x^6y^9}{27 \cdot 64}$$

$$= \frac{x^6y^9}{1728}$$

We again summarize the rules for exponentials, adding the three rules we learned in this section.

If m and n are integers, then

Product rule: $\qquad a^m \cdot a^n = a^{m+n}$

Zero exponent: $\qquad a^0 = 1 \qquad\qquad (a \neq 0)$

Negative exponent: $\quad a^{-n} = \dfrac{1}{a^n} \qquad\quad (a \neq 0)$

Quotient rule: $\qquad \dfrac{a^m}{a^n} = a^{m-n} \qquad (a \neq 0)$

Power rule: $\qquad (a^m)^n = a^{mn}$

$\qquad\qquad\qquad (ab)^m = a^m b^m$

$\qquad\qquad\qquad \left(\dfrac{a}{b}\right)^m = \dfrac{a^m}{b^m} \qquad (b \neq 0)$

EXERCISES 3.2 *Use the rules for exponentials to simplify each expression. Write each answer in exponential form. See Examples 1–4.*

1. $(6^3)^2$ $\qquad\qquad\qquad\qquad$ **2.** $(8^4)^6$

3. $(9^{-3})^2$ $\qquad\qquad\qquad\quad$ **4.** $(2^{-3})^4$

5. $(3^{-5})^{-2}$ $\qquad\qquad\qquad$ **6.** $(8^{-4})^{-1}$

7. $\dfrac{(y^3)^3}{(y^2)^2}$ $\qquad\qquad\qquad$ **8.** $\dfrac{(r^2)^4}{(r^3)^2}$

9. $\dfrac{a^6 \cdot a^5}{(a^2)^4}$ $\qquad\qquad\quad$ **10.** $\dfrac{s^7 \cdot s^9}{(s^5)^2}$

11. $\dfrac{(k^2)^4}{(k^6)^2}$ $\qquad\qquad\quad$ **12.** $\dfrac{(w^4)^2}{(w^7)^3}$

13. $\dfrac{4^3 \cdot 4^{-5}}{4^7}$ $\qquad\qquad$ **14.** $\dfrac{2^5 \cdot 2^{-4}}{2^{-1}}$

15. $\dfrac{5^{-3} \cdot 5^{-2}}{5^4}$ $\qquad\qquad$ **16.** $\dfrac{8^{-2} \cdot 8^5}{8^6}$

17. $\dfrac{m^4 \cdot m^{-5}}{m^{-6}}$ $\qquad\qquad$ **18.** $\dfrac{p^3 \cdot p^{-5}}{p^5}$

19. $\dfrac{m^{11} \cdot m^{-7}}{m^5}$ $\qquad\qquad$ **20.** $\dfrac{z^3 \cdot z^{-5}}{z^{10}}$

21. $\dfrac{r^5 \cdot r^{-8}}{r^{-6} \cdot r^4}$ $\qquad\qquad$ **22.** $\dfrac{x^3 \cdot x^{-1}}{x^8 \cdot x^{-2}}$

23. $\dfrac{a^6 \cdot a^{-3}}{a^{-5} \cdot a}$

24. $\dfrac{b^{10} \cdot b^{-2}}{b^{-8} \cdot b^6}$

25. $(5m)^3$

26. $(2xy)^4$

27. $(3mn)^4$

28. $(-2ab)^5$

29. $(-3x^5)^2$

30. $(4m^3n^2)^4$

31. $(5p^2q)^3$

32. $(2p^2a^4)^5$

33. $(3x^{-5})^2$

34. $(5p^{-4})^{-2}$

35. $(9^{-1}y^5)^{-2}$

36. $(4^{-2}m^{-3})^{-2}$

37. $\left(\dfrac{a}{5}\right)^3$

38. $\left(\dfrac{9}{x}\right)^2$

39. $\left(\dfrac{3mn}{2}\right)^5$

40. $\left(\dfrac{2x}{5y}\right)^4$

41. $\left(\dfrac{a}{b}\right)^{-1}$

42. $\left(\dfrac{2a}{3}\right)^{-2}$

43. $\left(\dfrac{5m^{-2}}{m^{-1}}\right)^2$

44. $\left(\dfrac{4x^3}{3^{-1}}\right)^{-1}$

45. $\dfrac{x^7x^8(x^3)^2}{x^9x^7}$

46. $\dfrac{(m^3)^2(m^2)^4m^8}{(m^9)^3}$

47. $\dfrac{b^{11}(b^2)^4}{(b^3)^3(b^2)^6}$

48. $\dfrac{(8m^2)^3(8m^4)^2}{(8m^3)^4}$

49. $\dfrac{(3x^2)^{-2}(5x^{-1})^3}{3x^{-5}}$

50. $\dfrac{(2m^3)^{-1}(3m^{-2})^2}{2m^{-4}}$

51. $\dfrac{(4a^2b^3)^{-2}(2ab^{-1})^3}{(a^3b)^{-4}}$

52. $\dfrac{(m^6n)^{-2}(m^2n^{-2})^3}{m^{-1}n^{-2}}$

53. $\dfrac{(2y^{-1}z^2)^2(3y^{-2}z^{-3})^3}{(y^3z^2)^{-1}}$

54. $\dfrac{(3p^{-2}q^3)^2(5p^{-1}q^{-4})^{-1}}{(p^2q^{-2})^{-3}}$

55. $\dfrac{(9^{-1}z^{-2}x)^{-1}(4z^2x^4)^{-2}}{(5z^{-2}x^{-3})^2}$

56. $\dfrac{(4^{-3}a^{-1}b^{-2})^{-2}(5a^{-3}b^4)^{-2}}{(3a^{-3}b^{-5})^2}$

3.3   An Application of Exponentials: Scientific Notation

- **Express numbers in scientific notation.**
- **Convert numbers in scientific notation to numbers without exponents.**

One example of the use of exponentials comes from the field of science. The numbers occurring in science are often extremely large (such as the distance from the earth to the sun, which is 93,000,000 miles) or extremely small (the wavelength of yellow-green light is approximately .0000006 meters). Because of the difficulty of working with many zeros, scientists often express such numbers as exponentials. Each number is written as the product of a number *a* (where $1 \leq a < 10$) and an integer power of 10. This form is called **scientific notation.** There is always one nonzero digit to the left of the decimal point. For example, 35 is written 3.5×10^1, or 3.5×10; while 56,200 is written 5.62×10^4, since

$$56,200 = 5.62 \times 10,000$$
$$= 5.62 \times 10^4.$$

EXAMPLE 1   Express in scientific notation.

(a) 93,000,000

Count from the left of the first nonzero digit, to the decimal point.

93,000,000   7 places

Thus, $93,000,000 = 9.3 \times 10^7$

(b) 463,000,000,000,000   14 places

463,000,000,000,000 $= 4.63 \times 10^{14}$

(c) $63,200,000,000 = 6.32 \times 10^{10}$

(d) $302,100 = 3.021 \times 10^5$

EXAMPLE 2   Write each number without exponents.

(a) 6.2×10^3

The number 6.2×10^3 is in scientific notation. We write

$$6.2 \times 10^3 = 6.2 \times 1000$$
$$= 6200.$$

(b) $4.283 \times 10^5 = 4.283 \times 100,000$
$$= 428,300$$

By using negative exponents, we can also use scientific notation for very small numbers.

EXAMPLE 3   Write in scientific notation.

(a) .00462

Count from the left of the first nonzero digit, to the decimal point.

.00462   3 places

Since we are counting from right to left, the exponent will be negative.

$$.00462 = 4.62 \times 10^{-3}$$

(b) $.0000762 = 7.62 \times 10^{-5}$

(c) $.000000000834 = 8.34 \times 10^{-10}$

EXAMPLE 4   Write each number without exponents.

(a) $9.73 \times 10^{-2} = .0973$

(b) $(6 \times 10^3)(5 \times 10^{-4})$

   First find the product.

$$(6 \times 10^3)(5 \times 10^{-4}) = (6 \times 5)(10^3 \times 10^{-4})$$
$$= 30 \times 10^{-1}$$

Then express the result without exponents as 3.0.

(c) $\dfrac{4 \times 10^{-5}}{2 \times 10^3} = \dfrac{4}{2} \times \dfrac{10^{-5}}{10^3}$

$$= 2 \times 10^{-8}$$
$$= .00000002$$

EXERCISES 3.3   *Express each number in scientific notation. See Examples 1 and 3.*

1. 6,835,000,000
2. 321,000,000,000,000
3. 8,360,000,000,000
4. 6850
5. 215
6. 683
7. 25,000
8. 110,000,000
9. .035
10. .005
11. .0101
12. .0000006
13. .000012
14. .000000982

Write each number without exponents. See Examples 2 and 4.

15. 8.1×10^9
16. 3.5×10^2
17. 9.132×10^6
18. 2.14×10^0
19. 3.24×10^8
20. 4.35×10^4
21. 3.2×10^{-4}
22. 5.76×10^{-5}
23. 4.1×10^{-2}
24. 1.79×10^{-3}
25. $(2 \times 10^8) \times (4 \times 10^{-3})$
26. $(5 \times 10^4) \times (3 \times 10^{-2})$
27. $(4 \times 10^{-1}) \times (1 \times 10^{-5})$
28. $(6 \times 10^{-5}) \times (2 \times 10^4)$
29. $(7 \times 10^3) \times (2 \times 10^2) \times (3 \times 10^{-4})$
30. $(3 \times 10^{-5}) \times (3 \times 10^2) \times (5 \times 10^{-2})$
31. $(1.2 \times 10^2) \times (5 \times 10^{-3}) \times (2.4 \times 10^3)$
32. $(4.6 \times 10^{-3}) \times (2 \times 10^{-1}) \times (4 \times 10^5)$

33. $\dfrac{9 \times 10^5}{3 \times 10^{-1}}$ **34.** $\dfrac{12 \times 10^{-4}}{4 \times 10^4}$

35. $\dfrac{4 \times 10^{-3}}{2 \times 10^{-2}}$ **36.** $\dfrac{5 \times 10^{-1}}{1 \times 10^{-5}}$

37. $\dfrac{2.6 \times 10^5}{2 \times 10^2}$ **38.** $\dfrac{9.5 \times 10^{-1}}{5 \times 10^3}$

39. $\dfrac{7.2 \times 10^{-3}}{4 \times 10^{-2}}$ **40.** $\dfrac{8.7 \times 10^{-2}}{3 \times 10^{-4}}$

Write the numbers in each statement in scientific notation. See Examples 1 and 3.

41. Light visible to the human eye has a wavelength between .0004 mm and .0008 mm.

42. In the ocean, the amount of oxygen per cubic mile of water is 4,037,000,000 tons, while the amount of radium is .0003 tons.

43. Each tide in the Bay of Fundy carries more than 3,680,000,000,000,000 cubic feet of water into the bay.

44. The mean (average) diameter of the sun is about 865,000 miles.

Write the numbers in each statement without exponents. See Examples 2 and 4.

45. 1×10^3 cubic millimeters equals 6.102×10^{-2} cubic inches.

46. In the food chain which links the largest sea creature, the whale, to the smallest, the diatom, 4×10^{14} diatoms sustain a medium-sized whale for only a few hours.

47. Many ocean trenches have a depth of 3.5×10^4 feet.

48. The average lifespan of a human is 1×10^9 seconds.

3.4 Polynomials

- Identify coefficients.
- Combine like terms.
- Know the vocabulary concerning polynomials.
- Find the value of a polynomial for a given value of the variable.

Recall that in an expression such as

$$4x^3 + 6x^2 + 5x,$$

the quantities $4x^3, 6x^2$, and $5x$ are called **terms.** In the term $4x^3$, the number 4 is called the **numerical coefficient,** or simply the **coefficient,** of x^3. In the same way, 6 is the coefficient of x^2 in the term $6x^2$, and 5 is the coefficient of x in the term $5x$.

EXAMPLE 1 Name the coefficient of each term in these expressions.

(a) $4x^3$

The coefficient is 4.

(b) $x - 6x^4$

The coefficient of x is 1 because $x = 1 \cdot x$. The coefficient of x^4 is -6, since $x - 6x^4$ can be written as the sum $x + (-6x^4)$.

(c) $5 - v^3$

The coefficient of 5 is 5 since $5 = 5v^0$. If $5 - v^3$ is written as a sum, $5 + (-v^3)$, and if v^3 is written as $1 \cdot v^3$, we have

$$5 - v^3 = 5 + (-v^3)$$
$$= 5 + (-1v^3).$$

Thus the coefficent of v^3 is -1.

Recall that **like terms** have exactly the same combination of variables with the same exponent. Only the coefficients may be different. Examples include

$$19m^5 \quad \text{and} \quad 14m^5,$$
$$6y^9, \quad -37y^9, \quad \text{and} \quad y^9,$$
$$3pq \quad \text{and} \quad -2pq.$$

To add like terms, use the distributive property.

EXAMPLE 2 Simplify each expression using the distributive property.

(a) $-4x^3 + 6x^3 = (-4 + 6)x^3$
$$= 2x^3$$

(b) $3x^4 + 5x^4 = (3 + 5)x^4$
$$= 8x^4$$

(c) $9x^6 - 14x^6 + x^6 = (9 - 14 + 1)x^6$
$$= -4x^6$$

(d) $12m^2 + 5m + 4m^2 = (12 + 4)m^2 + 5m$
$$= 16m^2 + 5m$$

(e) $3x^2y + 4x^2y - x^2y = (3 + 4 - 1)x^2y$
$$= 6x^2y$$

Example 2(d) shows that it is not possible to add $16m^2$ and $5m$. These two terms are unlike because the exponents on the variables are different. **Unlike terms** have different variables or different exponents on the same variables.

EXAMPLE 3   Simplify each expression, if possible.

(a) $4m^2 - 5m^3$ cannot be combined or simplified any further, because the exponents differ.

(b) $8x^4 + 9y^4$ cannot be combined or simplified, because the variables are not the same.

(c) $3z^2 + 3z + 3$ cannot be combined or simplified, because the exponents are different and the last term, 3, has no variable associated with it.

One of the basic ideas of algebra is the polynomial. A **polynomial** is defined as any finite sum of terms which are the product of a number and a variable or variables raised to a whole number, such as

$$4y^3 + 3x^2 - 2m.$$

[Recall that $4y^3 + 3x^2 - 2m = 4y^3 + 3x^2 + (-2)m$.] On the other hand,

$$2x^3 - x^2 + \frac{4}{x^4}$$

is not a polynomial because the last term is the quotient (not the product) of a number and a variable raised to a power.

In general, we shall be concerned only with polynomials containing a single variable, such as x. A **polynomial in x** is a polynomial whose terms contain only variables which are whole number powers of x (including the zero power of x). Thus

$$16x^8 - 7x^6 + 5x^5 + 5x^3 - 3x + 2$$

is a polynomial in x. (Note that $2 = 2x^0$.) This last polynomial is written in **descending powers** of the variable, since the exponents on x decrease from left to right.

EXAMPLE 4   Examine these expressions.

$$x^2 + 3x^3 + 4x^4$$
$$2m + 5$$
$$p^3 - p^5$$
$$3k^2 - 2k + \frac{1}{k}$$

(a) Which are polynomials?

The first three are polynomials, since each one is the sum of terms which are the product of a number and a variable raised to a whole number power.

(b) Which are polynomials in x?

The first expression is a polynomial in x.

(c) Which are polynomials in descending powers?

$2m + 5$ is written in descending powers.

The **degree** of a term with one variable is the exponent on the variable. Thus $3x^4$ has degree 4, $6x^{17}$ has degree 17, $5x$ has degree 1, and -7 has degree 0 (since -7 can be written as $-7x^0$). The **degree of a polynomial** in one variable is the highest exponent found in any nonzero term of the polynomial. Thus $3x^4 - 5x^2 + 6$ is of degree 4, while $5x$ is of degree 1, and 3 (or $3x^0$) is of degree 0.

Three types of polynomials are very common and are given special names. A polynomial with exactly three terms is called a **trinomial.** (Tri- means "three," as in *tri*angle.) Examples are:

$$9m^3 - 4m^2 + 6, \qquad 19y^2 + 8y + 5, \qquad -3m^5 - 9m^2 + 2.$$

A polynomial with exactly two terms is called a **binomial.** (Bi- means "two," as in *bi*cycle.) Examples are:

$$-9x^4 + 9x^3, \qquad 8m^2 + 6m, \qquad 3m^5 - 9m^2.$$

A polynomial with only one term is called a **monomial.** [Mon(o)- means "one," as in *mono*rail.] Examples are:

$$9m, \qquad -6y^5, \qquad a^2, \qquad 6.$$

EXAMPLE 5   For each polynomial, first simplify if possible by combining like terms. Then give the degree and tell whether it is a monomial, a binomial, a trinomial, or none of these.

(a) $2x^3 + 5$

The polynomial cannot be simplified. The degree is 3. The polynomial is a binomial.

(b) $4x - 5x + 2x$

Add like terms to simplify: $4x - 5x + 2x = x$. The degree is 1. The polynomial is a monomial.

A polynomial represents different numbers for different values of the variable as shown in the next examples.

EXAMPLE 6   Find the value of $3x^4 - 5x^3 - 4x - 4$ when $x = 1$.
Substitute 1 for x.

$$3x^4 - 5x^3 - 4x - 4 = 3(1)^4 - 5(1)^3 - 4(1) - 4$$
$$= 3(1) - 5(1) - 4 - 4$$
$$= 3 - 5 - 4 - 4$$
$$= -10$$

We sometimes use a capital letter to represent a polynomial. For example, if we let $P(x)$ represent the polynomial

$$3x^4 - 5x^3 - 4x - 4,$$

then $P(x) = 3x^4 - 5x^3 - 4x - 4$ where $P(x)$ is read "P of x." We sometimes express the fact that $P(x) = 92$ when $x = -2$ by writing $P(-2) = 92$. [Read $P(-2)$ as "P of -2."]

EXAMPLE 7 If $P(x) = 9x^3 - 8x + 6$, find

(a) $P(-3)$

If we replace x by -3, we have

$$P(-3) = 9(-3)^3 - 8(-3) + 6$$
$$= 9(-27) + 24 + 6$$
$$= -243 + 30$$
$$P(-3) = -213.$$

(b) $P(1)$

$$P(1) = 9(1)^3 - 8(1) + 6$$
$$= 9 - 8 + 6 = 7$$

EXERCISES 3.4 *In each polynomial, combine terms whenever possible. Write the results in descending powers of the variable. See Examples 2 and 3.*

1. $3m^5 + 5m^5$

2. $-4y^3 + 3y^3$

3. $2r^5 + (-3r^5)$

4. $-19y^2 + 9y^2$

5. $2m^5 - 5m^2$

6. $-9y + 9y^2$

7. $3x^5 + 2x^5 - 4x^5$

8. $6x^3 - 8x^7 - 9x^3$

9. $-4p^7 + 8p^7 - 5p^7$

10. $-3a^8 + 4a^8 - 3a^8 + 2a^8$

11. $4y^2 + 3y^2 - 2y^2 + y^2$

12. $3r^5 - 8r^5 + r^5 - 2r^5$

13. $-5p^5 + 8p^5 - 2p^5 - p^5$

14. $6k^3 - 9k^3 + 8k^3 - 2k^3$

15. $y^4 + 8y^4 - 9y^2 + 6y^2 + 10y^2$

16. $11a^2 - 10a^2 + 2a^2 - a^6 + 2a^6$

17. $4z^5 - 9z^3 + 8z^2 + 10z^5$

18. $-9m^3 + 2m^3 - 11m^3 + 15m^2 - 9m$

19. $2p^7 - 8p^6 + 5p^4 - 9p$

20. $7y^3 - 8y^2 + 6y + 2$

For each polynomial, first simplify, if possible, then give the degree of the polynomial and tell whether it is (a) a monomial, (b) a binomial, (c) a trinomial, (d) none of these. See Example 5.

21. $5x^4 - 8x$

22. $4y - 8y$

23. $23x^9 - \dfrac{1}{2}x^2 + x$

24. $2m^7 - 3m^6 + 2m^5 + m$

25. $x^8 + 3x^7 - 5x^4$

26. $2x - 2x^2$

27. $\dfrac{3}{5}x^5 + \dfrac{2}{5}x^5$

28. $\dfrac{9}{11}x^2$

29. -8

30. $2m^8 - 5m^9$

Find the value of each polynomial (a) when $x = 2$ and (b) when $x = -1$. See Example 6.

31. $2x^2 - 4x$

32. $8x + 5x^2 + 2$

33. $2x^5 - 4x^4 + 5x^3 - x^2$

34. $9x + 1$

35. $2x^2 + 5x + 1$

36. $-3x^2 + 14x - 2$

37. $-2x^2 + 3$

38. $-5x^2 + 4x + 5$

39. $-x^2 - 8x$

40. $-x^2 + 7x + 2$

Let $P(x) = x^3 - 3x^2 + 2x - 3$ and $Q(x) = x^4 - 1$. Find each value. See Example 7.

41. $P(-1)$

42. $P(0)$

43. $P(2)$

44. $Q(2)$

45. $P(-2)$

46. $Q(1)$

47. $Q(-2) + Q(-4)$

48. $P(-2) + Q(-2)$

49. $P(-1) \cdot Q(-2)$

50. $P(0) \cdot Q(0)$

For each statement, write always, sometimes, *or* never.

51. A binomial is a polynomial.

52. A polynomial is a trinomial.

53. A trinomial is a binomial.

54. A monomial has no coefficient.

55. A binomial is a trinomial.

55. A polynomial of degree 4 has 4 terms.

3.5 Addition and Subtraction of Polynomials

- **Add polynomials.**
- **Subtract polynomials.**
- **Work problems with both addition and subtraction of polynomials.**

To add two polynomials, add like terms, as shown in Example 1.

EXAMPLE 1   Add $6x^3 - 4x^2 + 3$ and $-2x^3 + 7x^2 - 5$.

Write like terms in columns.

$$6x^3 - 4x^2 + 3$$
$$-2x^3 + 7x^2 - 5$$

Now add, column by column.

$$
\begin{array}{ccc}
6x^3 & -4x^2 & 3 \\
-2x^3 & 7x^2 & -5 \\
\hline
4x^3 & 3x^2 & -2
\end{array}
$$

Add the three sums together.

$$4x^3 + 3x^2 + (-2) = 4x^3 + 3x^2 - 2$$

We can also add these same polynomials when they are written horizontally on a line.

EXAMPLE 2   Add $6x^3 - 4x^2 + 3$ and $-2x^3 + 7x^2 - 5$.
Write the sum.

$$(6x^3 - 4x^2 + 3) + (-2x^3 + 7x^2 - 5).$$

Rewrite this sum with the parentheses removed and with subtractions changed to additions of inverses.

$$6x^3 + (-4x^2) + 3 + (-2x^3) + 7x^2 + (-5)$$

Place like terms together.

$$6x^3 + (-2x^3) + (-4x^2) + 7x^2 + 3 + (-5)$$

Combine like terms to get

$$4x^3 + 3x^2 + (-2)$$

or simply

$$4x^3 + 3x^2 - 2.$$

This is the same answer we found in Example 1.

Earlier, we defined the difference $x - y$ as $x + (-y)$. For example,

$$7 - 2 = 7 + (-2)$$
$$= 5$$
$$\text{and } -8 - (-2) = -8 + 2$$
$$= -6$$

We use this same method to subtract polynomials.

EXAMPLE 3 Subtract: $(5x - 2) - (3x - 8)$.
By the definition of subtraction,

$$(5x - 2) - (3x - 8) = (5x - 2) + [-(3x - 8)]$$

From our work in Chapter 2,

$$-(3x - 8) = -1(3x - 8)$$
$$= -3x + 8.$$

Now we have

$$(5x - 2) - (3x - 8) = (5x - 2) + (-3x + 8)$$
$$= 2x + 6$$

As a general rule,

to subtract two polynomials, change all the signs on the second polynomial and add.

EXAMPLE 4 Subtract $6x^3 - 4x^2 + 2$ from $11x^3 + 2x^2 - 8$.
Write the problem.

$$(11x^3 + 2x^2 - 8) - (6x^3 - 4x^2 + 2)$$

Change all the signs on the second polynomial and add.

$$(11x^3 + 2x^2 - 8) + (-6x^3 + 4x^2 - 2) = 5x^3 + 6x^2 - 10$$

To check a subtraction problem such as this, use the fact that if $a - b = c$, then $a = b + c$. For example, $6 - 2 = 4$. To check this, write $6 = 2 + 4$, which is correct. For the polynomials, to check the subtraction above, add $6x^3 - 4x^2 + 2$ and $5x^3 + 6x^2 - 10$. Since the sum is $11x^3 + 2x^2 - 8$, the subtraction was performed correctly.
Subtraction can also be done in columns.

EXAMPLE 5 Use the method of subtracting by columns to find $(14y^3 - 6y^2 + 2y - 5) - (2y^3 - 7y^2 - 4y + 6)$.

Step 1 Arrange like terms in columns.

$$\begin{array}{r} 14y^3 - 6y^2 + 2y - 5 \\ \underline{2y^3 - 7y^2 - 4y + 6} \end{array}$$

Step 2 Change all signs in the second row, and then add. (*Step 3*).

$$\begin{array}{r} 14y^3 - 6y^2 + 2y - 5 \\ \underline{-2y^3 + 7y^2 + 4y - 6} \\ 12y^3 + y^2 + 6y - 11 \end{array}$$

Either the horizontal or the vertical method may be used for adding and subtracting polynomials. The choice is a personal preference.

EXERCISES 3.5 *Add or subtract as indicated. See Examples 1 and 5.*

1. Add:

$3m^2 + 5m$
$2m^2 - 2m$

2. Add:

$4a^3 - 4a^2$
$6a^3 + 5a^2$

3. Subtract:

$12x^4 - x^2$
$8x^4 + 3x^2$

4. Subtract:

$2a + 5d$
$3a - 6d$

5. Subtract:

$2n^5 - 5n^3 + 6$
$3n^5 + 7n^3 + 8$

6. Subtract:

$3r^2 - 4r + 2$
$7r^2 + 2r - 3$

7. Add:

$9m^3 - 5m^2 + 4m - 8$
$3m^3 + 6m^2 + 8m - 6$

8. Add:

$12r^5 + 11r^4 - 7r^3 - 2r^2 - 5r - 3$
$-8r^5 - 10r^4 + 3r^3 + 2r^2 - 5r + 7$

9. Add:

$12m^2 - 8m + 6$
$3m^2 + 5m - 2$

10. Subtract:

$5a^4 - 3a^3 + 2a^2$
$a^3 - a^2 + a - 1$

11. Add:

$5b^2 + 6b + 2$
$3b^2 - 4b + 5$

12. Add:

$3w^2 - 5w + 2$
$4w^2 + 6w - 5$
$8w^2 + 7w - 2$

Perform the indicated operations. See Examples 2–4.

13. $(2r^2 + 3r) - (3r^2 + 5r)$

14. $(3r^2 + 5r - 6) + (2r - 5r^2)$

15. $(8m^2 - 7m) - (3m^2 + 7m)$

16. $(x^2 + x) - (3x^2 + 2x - 1)$

17. $8 - (6s^2 - 5s + 7)$

18. $2 - [3 - (4 + s)]$

19. $(8s - 3s^2) + (-4s + 5s^2)$

20. $(3x^2 + 2x + 5) + (8x^2 - 5x - 4)$

21. $(16x^3 - x^2 + 3x) + (-12x^3 + 3x^2 + 2x)$

22. $(-2b^6 + 3b^4 - b^2) - (b^6 + 2b^4 + 2b^2)$

23. $(7y^4 + 3y^2 + 2y) - (18y^4 - 5y^2 - y)$

24. $(3x^2 + 2x + 5) + (-7x^2 - 8x + 2) + (3x^2 - 4x + 7)$

25. $(9a^4 - 3a^2 + 2) + (4a^4 - 4a^2 + 2) + (-12a^4 + 6a^2 - 3)$

26. $(4m^2 - 3m + 2) + (5m^2 + 13m - 4) - (16m^2 + 4m - 3)$

27. $[(8m^2 + 4m - 7) - (2m^2 - 5m + 2)] - (m^2 + m + 1)$

28. $[(9b^3 - 4b^2 + 3b + 2) - (-2b^3 - 3b^2 + b)] - (8b^3 + 6b + 4)$

Write each statement as an equation or an inequality. Do not solve.

29. When $4 + x^2$ is added to $-9x + 2$, the result is larger than 8.

30. When $6 + 3x$ is subtracted from $5 + 2x$, the difference is larger than $8x + x^2$.

31. The sum of $5 + x^2$ and $3 - 2x$ is not equal to 5.

32. The sum of $3 - 2x + x^2$ and $8 - 9x + 3x^2$ is negative.

3.6 Multiplication of Polynomials

- **Multiply a monomial and a polynomial.**
- **Multiply two polynomials.**

The product of two monomials is found by using the rules for exponents and the commutative and associative properties. For example,

$$(6x^3)(4x^4) = 6 \cdot 4 \cdot x^3 \cdot x^4 = 24x^7.$$

Also,

$$(-8m^6)(-9n^6) = (-8)(-9)(m^6)(n^6) = 72m^6n^6.$$

To use this method to find the product of a monomial and a polynomial with more than one term, use the distributive property, as shown in Examples 1 and 2.

EXAMPLE 1 Use the distributive property to multiply $4x^2(3x + 5)$.

$$4x^2(3x + 5) = (4x^2)(3x) + (4x^2)(5)$$
$$= 12x^3 + 20x^2$$

EXAMPLE 2 Use the distributive property to multiply $-8m^3(4m^3 + 3m^2 + 2m - 1)$.

$-8m^3(4m^3 + 3m^2 + 2m - 1)$

$= (-8m^3)(4m^3) + (-8m^3)(3m^2) + (-8m^3)(2m) + (-8m^3)(-1)$

$= -32m^6 - 24m^5 - 16m^4 + 8m^3$

The distributive property is also used to find the product of any two polynomials. Suppose we want to find the product of the polynomials $x + 1$

and $x - 4$. If we work with $x + 1$ as a single quantity, we can use the distributive property:

$$(x + 1)(x - 4) = (x + 1)x - (x + 1)4$$

Now use the distributive property to multiply $(x + 1)x$ and $(x + 1)4$.

$$[(x + 1)x] - [(x + 1)4] = [x(x) + 1(x)] - [x(4) + 1(4)]$$
$$= x^2 + x - 4x - 4$$
$$= x^2 - 3x - 4$$

EXAMPLE 3   Multiply $(2x + 1)(3x - 5)$.

$$(2x + 1)(3x - 5) = (2x + 1)(3x) - (2x + 1)5$$
$$= (2x)(3x) + (1)(3x) - (2x)(5) - (1)(5)$$
$$= 6x^2 + 3x - 10x - 5$$
$$= 6x^2 - 7x - 5$$

The work involved in multiplication can also be done by writing one polynomial above the other.

$$\begin{array}{r} 2x + 1 \\ \underline{3x - 5} \end{array}$$

To begin, multiply each term in the top row by -5.

Step 1
$$\begin{array}{r} 2x + 1 \\ \underline{3x - 5} \\ -10x - 5 \end{array}$$

This is similar to ordinary multiplication. Then multiply $3x$ times each term in the top row. Be careful to place the like terms in columns, since the final step will involve addition (as in multiplying two whole numbers).

Step 2
$$\begin{array}{r} 2x + 1 \\ \underline{3x - 5} \\ -10x - 5 \\ \underline{6x^2 + 3x} \\ 6x^2 - 7x - 5 \end{array}$$

Thus, $(2x + 1)(3x - 5) = 6x^2 - 7x - 5$.

EXAMPLE 4   Multiply $(3p - 5)(2p + 6)$.

$$\begin{array}{r} 3p - 5 \\ \underline{2p + 6} \\ 18p - 30 \\ \underline{6p^2 - 10p} \\ 6p^2 + 8p - 30 \end{array}$$

EXAMPLE 5 Multiply $(4m^3 - 2m^2 + 4m)(m^2 + 5)$.

$$
\begin{array}{r}
4m^3 - 2m^2 + 4m \\
m^2 + 5 \\
\hline
20m^3 - 10m^2 + 20m \\
4m^5 - 2m^4 + 4m^3 \\
\hline
4m^5 - 2m^4 + 24m^3 - 10m^2 + 20m
\end{array}
$$

EXAMPLE 6 Find $(n + 2)^2$.

We know $(n + 2)^2 = (n + 2)(n + 2)$. We use the vertical method of multiplication.

$$
\begin{array}{r}
n + 2 \\
n + 2 \\
\hline
2n + 4 \\
n^2 + 2n \\
\hline
n^2 + 4n + 4
\end{array}
$$

EXAMPLE 7 Find $(x + 5)^3$.

Since $(x + 5)^3 = (x + 5)(x + 5)(x + 5)$, we begin by finding $(x + 5)(x + 5)$.

$$
\begin{array}{r}
x + 5 \\
x + 5 \\
\hline
5x + 25 \\
x^2 + 5x \\
\hline
x^2 + 10x + 25
\end{array}
$$

Now multiply this result times $x + 5$

$$
\begin{array}{r}
x^2 + 10x + 25 \\
x + 5 \\
\hline
5x^2 + 50x + 125 \\
x^3 + 10x^2 + 25x \\
\hline
x^3 + 15x^2 + 75x + 125
\end{array}
$$

EXERCISES 3.6 *Multiply. See Examples 1 and 2.*

1. $(-4x^5)(8x^2)$

2. $(-3x^7)(2x^5)$

3. $(5y^4)(3y^7)$

4. $(10p^2)(5p^3)$

5. $(15a^4)(2a^5)$

6. $(-3m^6)(-5m^4)$

7. $2m(3m + 2)$

8. $-5p(6 - 3p)$

9. $3p(-2p^3 + 4p^2)$

10. $4x(3 + 2x + 5x^3)$

11. $-8z(2z + 3z^2 + 3z^3)$

12. $7y(3 + 5y^2 - 2y^3)$

13. $2y(3 + 2y + 5y^4)$

14. $-2m^4(3m^2 + 5m + 6)$

Find each binomial product. See Examples 3 and 4.

15. $(m + 7)(m + 5)$ **16.** $(n - 1)(n + 4)$

17. $(x + 5)(x - 5)$ **18.** $(y + 8)(y - 8)$

19. $(t - 4)(t + 4)$ **20.** $(x - 4)(x + 2)$

21. $(6p + 5)(p - 1)$ **22.** $(2x + 3)(6x - 4)$

23. $(4m - 3)(4m + 3)$ **24.** $(3x - 2)(x + 5)$

25. $(b + 8)(6b - 2)$ **26.** $(5a + 1)(2a + 7)$

27. $(8 - 3a)(2 + a)$ **28.** $(6 - 5m)(2 + 3m)$

29. $(-4 + k)(2 - k)$ **30.** $(5 - 3x)(4 + x)$

Find each product. See Example 5.

31. $(6x + 1)(2x^2 + 4x + 1)$ **32.** $(9y - 2)(8y^2 - 6y + 1)$

33. $(9a + 2)(9a^2 + a + 1)$ **34.** $(2r - 1)(3r^2 + 4r - 4)$

35. $(4m + 3)(5m^3 - 4m^2 + m - 5)$

36. $(y + 4)(3y^4 - 2y^2 + 1)$

37. $(2x - 1)(3x^5 - 2x^3 + x^2 - 2x + 3)$

38. $(2a + 3)(a^4 - a^3 + a^2 - a + 1)$

39. $(5x^2 + 2x + 1)(x^2 - 3x + 5)$

40. $(2m^2 + m - 3)(m^2 - 4m + 5)$

Find each product. See Examples 6 and 7.

41. $(x + 7)^2$ **42.** $(m + 6)^2$

43. $(a - 4)^2$ **44.** $(b - 10)^2$

45. $(2p - 5)^2$ **46.** $(3m + 1)^2$

47. $(5k + 8)^2$ **48.** $(8m - 3)^2$

49. $(m - 5)^3$ **50.** $(p + 3)^3$

51. $(2a + 1)^3$ **52.** $(3m - 1)^3$

53. $(k + 1)^4$ **54.** $(r - 1)^4$

3.7 Products of Binomials

- **Multiply binomials by the shortcut method.**
- **Square binomials.**
- **Find the difference of two squares.**

The procedures described in the last section can be used to find the product of any two polynomials and are the only practical methods for multiplying polynomials with three or more terms. We can also use these methods to multiply two binomials. However, in practice, many of the polynomials that must be multiplied are binomials, so for binomials, we need a quick method that eliminates writing out all the steps. To find such a shortcut, let us look carefully at the process of multiplying two binomials. If we multiply $x + 3$ and $x + 5$ using the distributive property, we have

$$(x + 3)(x + 5) = (x + 3)x + (x + 3)5$$
$$= (x)(x) + (3)(x) + (x)(5) + (3)(5)$$
$$= x^2 + 3x + 5x + 15$$
$$= x^2 + 8x + 15.$$

The first term in the second line, $(x)(x)$, is the product of the first term in each binomial.

$(x + 3)(x + 5)$: Multiply the first terms: $(x)(x)$.

The term $(x)(5)$ is the product of the first term of the first binomial and the last term of the second binomial. This is the **outer product.**

$(x + 3)(x + 5)$: Multiply the outer terms: $(x)(5)$

The term $(3)(x)$ is the product of the last term of the first binomial and the first term of the second binomial. The product of these middle terms is called the **inner product.**

$(x + 3)(x + 5)$: Multiply the inner terms: $(3)(x)$.

Finally, $(3)(5)$ is the product of the last term of each binomial.

$(x + 3)(x + 5)$: Multiply the last terms: $(3)(5)$.

In the third step of the multiplication, we add the inner product and the outer product. This step should be performed mentally, so that the three terms of the answer can be written down without any extra steps.

A summary of these steps is given below.

To Multiply Binomials

Step 1   Multiply the first two terms of the binomials to get the first term of the answer.

Step 2   Find the outer product and the inner product and mentally add them to get the middle term of the answer.

Step 3   Multiply the two last terms of the binomials to get the last term of the answer.

This procedure is sometimes called the FOIL method; an abbreviation for *First, Outer, Inner, Last.*

EXAMPLE 1   Multiply $(x + 8)(x - 6)$ by the FOIL method.

Step 1 (F)   Multiply the first terms.

$$x(x) = x^2$$

Step 2 (O)   Find the product of the outer terms.

$$x(-6) = -6x$$

(I)   Find the product of the inner terms.

$$8(x) = 8x$$

Add the outer and inner products mentally:

$$-6x + 8x = 2x$$

Step 3 (L)   Multiply the last terms.

$$8(-6) = -48$$

The product of $(x + 8)$ and $(x - 6)$ is found by finding the sum of these terms, or

$$(x + 8)(x - 6) = x^2 - 6x + 8x - 48$$
$$= x^2 + 2x - 48.$$

As a shortcut, this product can be found in the following manner:

EXAMPLE 2   Multiply $9x - 2$ and $3x + 1$.

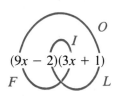

F: $9x(3x) = 27x^2$ O: $9x(1) = 9x$

I: $-2(3x) = -6x$ L: $-2(1) = -2$

The product is the sum of these four results, or

$$27x^2 + 9x - 6x - 2 = 27x^2 + 3x - 2.$$

EXAMPLE 3   Find the following products.

(a) $(2k + 5y)(k + 3y) = (2k)(k) + (2k)(3y) + (5y)(k) + (5y)(3y)$
$$= 2k^2 + 6ky + 5ky + 15y^2$$
$$= 2k^2 + 11ky + 15y^2$$

(b) $(7p + 2q)(3p - q) = 21p^2 - pq - 2q^2$

Special types of binomial products occur so often in practice that the form of the answers should be memorized. For example, we frequently need to find the **square of a binomial,** $(x + y)^2$.

EXAMPLE 4   Find $(2m + 3)^2$.

Squaring $2m + 3$ by the method shown above gives

$$(2m + 3)(2m + 3) = 4m^2 + 12m + 9.$$

In the result, note that we have the square of both the first and the last terms of the binomial:

$$(2m)^2 = 4m^2 \qquad \text{and} \qquad 3^2 = 9.$$

We also have twice the product of the two terms of the binomial, that is,

$$2(2m)(3) = 12 \ m.$$

The general rule is that the square of a binomial is a trinomial composed of the square of the first term, plus twice the product of the two terms, plus the square of the last term of the binomial, or

$$(x + y)^2 = x^2 + 2xy + y^2.$$

Also,

$$(x - y)^2 = x^2 - 2xy + y^2.$$

EXAMPLE 5   Use the formula to square each binomial.

(a) $(5z - 1)^2 = (5z)^2 + 2(5z)(-1) + (-1)^2$
$$= 25z^2 - 10z + 1$$

Recall that $(5z)^2 = 5^2z^2 = 25z^2$.

(b) $(3b + 5r)^2 = (3b)^2 + 2(3b)(5r) + (5r)^2$
$$= 9b^2 + 30br + 25r^2$$

(c) $(2a - 9x)^2 = 4a^2 - 36ax + 81x^2$

Binomial products of the form $(x + y)(x - y)$ also occur frequently. In these products, one binomial is the sum of two terms, while the other is the difference of the same two terms. For example, let us multiply $(a + 2)(a - 2)$.

$$(a + 2)(a - 2) = a^2 - 2a + 2a - 4$$
$$= a^2 - 4$$

In general,

$$(x + y)(x - y) = x^2 - y^2,$$

and the result, $x^2 - y^2$, is called the **difference of two squares**.

EXAMPLE 6   Multiply $(5m + 3)(5m - 3)$.

Use the formula for the difference of two squares.

$$(5m + 3)(5m - 3) = (5m)^2 - 3^2$$
$$= 25m^2 - 9$$

EXAMPLE 7   Multiply $(4x + y)(4x - y)$.

$$(4x + y)(4x - y) = (4x)^2 - y^2$$
$$= 16x^2 - y^2.$$

EXERCISES 3.7   *Find each product. See Examples 1–3.*

1. $(r - 1)(r + 3)$
2. $(x + 2)(x - 5)$
3. $(x - 7)(x - 3)$
4. $(r + 3)(r + 6)$
5. $(2x - 1)(3x + 2)$
6. $(4y - 5)(2y + 1)$
7. $(6z + 5)(z - 3)$
8. $(8a + 3)(6a + 1)$
9. $(a + 4)(2a + 1)$
10. $(3x - 1)(2x + 3)$
11. $(2r - 1)(4r + 3)$
12. $(5m + 2)(3m - 4)$
13. $(2a + 4)(3a - 2)$
14. $(11m - 10)(10m + 11)$
15. $(4 + 5x)(5 - 4x)$
16. $(8 + 3x)(2 - x)$
17. $(-3 + 2r)(4 + r)$
18. $(-5 + 6z)(2 - z)$
19. $(-3 + a)(-5 - 2a)$
20. $(-6 - 3y)(1 - 4y)$
21. $(p + 3q)(p + q)$
22. $(2r - 3s)(3r + s)$
23. $(5y + z)(2y - z)$
24. $(9m + 4k)(2m - 3k)$
25. $(8y - 9z)(y + 5z)$
26. $(3a + 7b)(-4a + b)$
27. $(4r + 9s)(-2r + 5s)$
28. $(7m + 11n)(3m - 8n)$

Find each square. See Examples 4 and 5.

29. $(m + 2)^2$
30. $(x + 8)^2$
31. $(5 + x)^2$
32. $(2 - y)^2$
33. $(x + 2y)^2$
34. $(3m - n)^2$
35. $(2z - 5x)^2$
36. $(6a - b)^2$
37. $(5p + 2q)^2$
38. $(8a - 3b)^2$
39. $(4a + 5b)^2$
40. $(9y + z)^2$

Find the following products. See Examples 6 and 7.

41. $(p + 2)(p - 2)$ **42.** $(a + 8)(a - 8)$

43. $(2b + 5)(2b - 5)$ **44.** $(3x + 4)(3x - 4)$

45. $(m - n)(m + n)$ **46.** $(p + q)(p - q)$

47. $(r + z)(r - z)$ **48.** $(a + b)(a - b)$

49. $(6a - p)(6a + p)$ **50.** $(5y + 3x)(5y - 3x)$

51. $(2m - 5)(2m + 5)$ **52.** $(3a - 5)(3a + 5)$

53. $(7y + 10)(7y - 10)$ **54.** $(6x + 3)(6x - 3)$

Write each statement as an equation or an inequality using x *to represent the unknown number. Do not try to solve.*

55. The square of 3 more than a number is 5.

56. The square of the sum of a number and 6 is less than 3.

57. When 3 plus a number is multiplied by the number less 4, the result is greater than 7.

58. Twice a number plus 4, multiplied by 6 times the number, less 5, gives 8.

3.8   Dividing a Polynomial by a Monomial

- **Divide a polynomial by a monomial.**

To divide a monomial by another monomial, use the quotient rule for exponents. For example,

$$\frac{12x^2}{6x} = 2x, \quad \frac{25m^5}{5m^2} = 5m^3, \quad \text{and} \quad \frac{30a^2b^8}{15a^3b^3} = \frac{2b^5}{a}.$$

To divide a polynomial by a monomial, use the fact that

$$\frac{a}{b} = a \cdot \frac{1}{b}.$$

EXAMPLE 1   Divide $5m^5 - 10m^3$ by $5m^2$.

We multiply by $\frac{1}{5m^2}$.

$$\frac{5m^5 - 10m^3}{5m^2} = (5m^5 - 10m^3)\frac{1}{5m^2}$$

Now use the distributive property and the quotient rule for exponents.

$$(5m^5 - 10m^3)\frac{1}{5m^2} = (5m^5)\frac{1}{5m^2} - (10m^3)\frac{1}{5m^2}$$

$$= \frac{5m^5}{5m^2} - \frac{10m^3}{5m^2}$$

$$= m^3 - 2m$$

Therefore,

$$\frac{5m^5 - 10m^3}{5m^2} = (5m^5 - 10m^3)\frac{1}{5m^2}$$

$$= m^3 - 2m.$$

To check, multiply

$$5m^2(m^3 - 2m) = 5m^5 - 10m^3.$$

Since we cannot divide by 0, the quotient

$$\frac{5m^5 - 10m^3}{5m^2}$$

has no value if $m = 0$. In the rest of the chapter, we assume that no denominators are 0.

EXAMPLE 2   Divide $\dfrac{16a^5 - 12a^4 + 8a^2}{4a^3}$.

$$\frac{16a^5 - 12a^4 + 8a^2}{4a^3} = (16a^5 - 12a^4 + 8a^2)\frac{1}{4a^3}$$

$$= (16a^5)\frac{1}{4a^3} - (12a^4)\frac{1}{4a^3} + (8a^2)\frac{1}{4a^3}$$

$$= \frac{16a^5}{4a^3} - \frac{12a^4}{4a^3} + \frac{8a^2}{4a^3}$$

$$= 4a^2 - 3a + \frac{2}{a}$$

The result is not a polynomial because of the expression $\dfrac{2}{a}$ which has a variable in the denominator. Note that although the sum and the product of two polynomials always result in a polynomial, the quotient of two polynomials may not.

Some of the steps shown in Examples 1 and 2 may be dropped as shown in Example 3.

EXAMPLE 3   Divide: $\dfrac{12x^4 - 7x^3 + x - 4}{4x} = \dfrac{12x^4}{4x} - \dfrac{7x^3}{4x} + \dfrac{x}{4x} - \dfrac{4}{4x}$

$$= 3x^3 - \frac{7x^2}{4} + \frac{1}{4} - \frac{1}{x}$$

$$= 3x^3 - \frac{7}{4}x^2 + \frac{1}{4} - \frac{1}{x}$$

Many of the intermediate steps may be done mentally.

EXAMPLE 4 Divide the polynomial

$$180y^{10} - 150y^8 + 120y^6 - 90y^4 + 100y$$

by the monomial $-30y^2$.

Using the methods of this section, we have

$$\frac{180y^{10} - 150y^8 + 120y^6 - 90y^4 + 100y}{-30y^2}$$

$$= \frac{180y^{10}}{-30y^2} - \frac{150y^8}{-30y^2} + \frac{120y^6}{-30y^2} - \frac{90y^4}{-30y^2} + \frac{100y}{-30y^2}$$

$$= -6y^8 + 5y^6 - 4y^4 + 3y^2 - \frac{10}{3y}.$$

EXERCISES 3.8 *Find each quotient.*

1. $\dfrac{4x^2}{2x}$ 2. $\dfrac{8m^5}{2m}$

3. $\dfrac{10a^3}{5a}$ 4. $\dfrac{36p^8}{4p^3}$

5. $\dfrac{27k^4m^5}{3km^6}$ 6. $\dfrac{18x^5y^6}{3x^2y^2}$

Divide each polynomial by 2m. See Examples 1–4.

7. $60m^4 - 20m^2$ 8. $16m^3 - 8m^2$

9. $120m^6 - 60m^3 + 80m^2$ 10. $10m^5 - 16m^2 + 8m^3$

11. $6m^5 - 4m^3 + 2m^2$ 12. $8m^5 - 4m^3 + 4m^2$

13. $8m^3 - 4m^2 + 6m$ 14. $2m^5 - 4m^2 + 8m$

15. $m^2 + m + 1$ 16. $2m^2 - 2m + 5$

Divide each polynomial by 3x². See Examples 1–4.

17. $3x^4 + 9x^3$ 18. $15x^2 - 9x^3$

19. $12x^4 - 3x^3 + 3x^2$ 20. $45x^3 + 15x^2 - 9x^5$

21. $27x^3 - 9x^4 + 18x^5$ 22. $-12x^6 + 6x^5 + 3x^4 - 9x^3 + 3x$

23. $36x + 24x^2 + 3x^3$ 24. $4x^4 - 3x^3 + 2x$

25. $x^3 + 6x^2 - x$ 26. $6x^5 - 3x^4 + 9x^2 + 27$

Perform each division. See Examples 1–4.

27. $\dfrac{8k^4 - 12k^3 - 2k^2 + 7k - 3}{2k}$ 28. $\dfrac{27r^4 - 36r^3 - 6r^2 + 26r - 2}{3r}$

29. $\dfrac{100p^5 - 50p^4 + 30p^3 - 30p}{-10p^2}$ **30.** $\dfrac{2m^5 - 6m^4 + 8m^2}{-2m^3}$

31. $\dfrac{8x + 16x^2 + 10x^3}{4x^4}$ **32.** $\dfrac{36m^5 - 24m^4 + 16m^3 - 8m^2}{4m^3}$

33. $(16y^5 - 8y^2 + 12y) \div (4y^2)$ **34.** $(20a^4 - 15a^5 + 25a^3) \div (15a^4)$

35. $(120x^{11} - 60x^{10} + 140x^9 - 100x^8) \div (10x^{12})$

36. $(5 + x + 6x^2 + 8x^3) \div (3x^4)$

Solve each problem.

37. What polynomial, when divided by $3x^2$, yields $4x^3 + 3x^2 - 4x + 2$ as a quotient?

38. What polynomial, when divided by $4m^3$, yields $-6m^2 + 4m$ as a quotient?

39. The quotient of a certain polynomial and $-7y^2$ is $9y^2 + 3y + 5 - \dfrac{2}{y}$. Find the polynomial.

40. The quotient of a certain polynomial and a is $2a^2 + 3a + 5$. Find the certain polynomial.

3.9 The Quotient of Two Polynomials

- **Divide a polynomial by a polynomial.**

To divide a polynomial by any other polynomial, we use a method of "long division." This is similar to long division of two whole numbers. We show division of whole numbers alongside the division of polynomials so that you may compare.

Step 1 Divide 27 into 6696.

$$27\,\overline{)6696}$$

Divide $2x + 3$ into $8x^3 - 4x^2 - 14x + 15$.

$$2x + 3\,\overline{)8x^3 - 4x^2 - 14x + 15}$$

Step 2 27 divides into 66 two times; $2 \cdot 27 = 54$.

$$\begin{array}{r} 2 \\ 27\,\overline{)6696} \\ \underline{54} \end{array}$$

$2x$ divides into $8x^3$ ($4x^2$) times; $4x^2(2x + 3) = 8x^3 + 12x^2$.

$$\begin{array}{r} 4x^2 \\ 2x + 3\,\overline{)8x^3 - 4x^2 - 14x + 15} \\ \underline{8x^3 + 12x^2} \end{array}$$

Step 3 Subtract and bring down the next term.

$$
\begin{array}{r}
2 \\
27\overline{)6696} \\
\underline{54} \\
129
\end{array}
$$

Subtract and bring down the next term.

$$
\begin{array}{r}
4x^2 \phantom{{}-4x^2-14x+15} \\
2x + 3\overline{)8x^3 - 4x^2 - 14x + 15} \\
\underline{8x^3 + 12x^2} \\
-16x^2 - 14x
\end{array}
$$

(To subtract two polynomials, change the sign of the second, and add.)

Step 4 27 divides into 129 four times; $4 \cdot 27 = 108$.

$$
\begin{array}{r}
24 \\
27\overline{)6696} \\
\underline{54} \\
129 \\
\underline{108}
\end{array}
$$

$2x$ divides into $-16x^2$ ($-8x$) times; $-8x(2x + 3) = -16x^2 - 24x$.

$$
\begin{array}{r}
4x^2 - 8x \phantom{{}-14x+15} \\
2x + 3\overline{)8x^3 - 4x^2 - 14x + 15} \\
\underline{8x^3 + 12x^2} \\
-16x^2 - 14x \\
-16x^2 - 24x
\end{array}
$$

Step 5 Subtract and bring down the next term.

$$
\begin{array}{r}
24 \\
27\overline{)6696} \\
\underline{54} \\
129 \\
\underline{108} \\
216
\end{array}
$$

Subtract and bring down the next term.

$$
\begin{array}{r}
4x^2 - 8x \phantom{{}-14x+15} \\
2x + 3\overline{)8x^3 - 4x^2 - 14x + 15} \\
\underline{8x^3 + 12x^2} \\
-16x^2 - 14x \\
\underline{-16x^2 - 24x} \\
10x + 15
\end{array}
$$

Step 6 27 divides into 216 eight times; $8 \cdot 27 = 216$.

$$
\begin{array}{r}
248 \\
27\overline{)6696} \\
\underline{54} \\
129 \\
\underline{108} \\
216 \\
\underline{216}
\end{array}
$$

$2x$ divides into $10x$ five times; $5(2x + 3) = 10x + 15$.

$$
\begin{array}{r}
4x^2 - 8x + 5 \\
2x + 3\overline{)8x^3 - 4x^2 - 14x + 15} \\
\underline{8x^3 + 12x^2} \\
-16x^2 - 14x \\
\underline{-16x^2 - 24x} \\
10x + 15 \\
\underline{10x + 15}
\end{array}
$$

6696 divided by 27 is 248. There is no remainder.

$8x^3 - 4x^2 - 14x + 15$ divided by $2x + 3$ is $4x^2 - 8x + 5$. There is no remainder.

Step 7   Check by multiplication.

$27 \cdot 248 = 6696$

Check by multiplication.

$$(2x + 3)(4x^2 - 8x + 5) =$$
$$8x^3 - 4x^2 - 14x + 15$$

EXAMPLE 1   Divide $4x^3 - 4x^2 + 5x - 8$ by $2x - 1$.

$$
\begin{array}{r}
2x^2 - x + 2 \\
2x - 1 \overline{)4x^3 - 4x^2 + 5x - 8} \\
4x^3 - 2x^2 \\
\hline
-2x^2 + 5x \\
-2x^2 + x \\
\hline
4x - 8 \\
4x - 2 \\
\hline
-6
\end{array}
$$

Step 1 $2x$ divides into $4x^3$ ($2x^2$) times; $2x^2(2x - 1) = 4x^3 - 2x^2$.

Step 2   Subtract; bring down the next term.

Step 3 $2x$ divides into $-2x^2$ ($-x$) times; $-x(2x - 1) = -2x^2 + x$.

Step 4   Subtract; bring down the next term.

Step 5 $2x$ divides into $4x$ two times; $2(2x - 1) = 4x - 2$.

Step 6   Subtract. The remainder is -6.

Thus $2x - 1$ divides into $4x^3 - 4x^2 + 5x - 8$ with a quotient of $2x^2 - x + 2$ and a remainder of -6. The result is not a polynomial because of the remainder.

$$\frac{4x^3 - 4x^2 + 5x - 8}{2x - 1} = 2x^2 - x + 2 + \frac{-6}{2x - 1}$$

Step 7   Check by multiplication.

$$(2x - 1)\left(2x^2 - x + 2 + \frac{-6}{2x - 1}\right)$$
$$= 4x^3 - 4x^2 + 5x - 8$$

EXAMPLE 2   Divide $x^3 - 1$ by $x - 1$.

Here the polynomial $x^3 - 1$ is missing the x^2 term and the x term. When this is the case, the polynomial should be filled in with 0 as the coefficient for the missing terms.

$$x^3 - 1 = x^3 + 0x^2 + 0x - 1$$

Now we can rewrite the problem.

$$
\begin{array}{r}
x^2 + x + 1 \\
x - 1 \overline{)x^3 + 0x^2 + 0x - 1} \\
x^3 - x^2 \\
\hline
x^2 + 0x \\
x^2 - x \\
\hline
x - 1 \\
x - 1 \\
\hline
\end{array}
$$

There is no remainder. The quotient is $x^2 + x + 1$. Check by multiplication.

$$(x^2 + x + 1)(x - 1) = x^3 - 1$$

EXAMPLE 3 Divide $x^4 + 2x^3 + 2x^2 - x - 1$ by $x^2 + 1$.

The denominator of $x^2 + 1$ has a missing x term which we fill in with $0x$, since $x^2 + 1 = x^2 + 0x + 1$. We then proceed as usual through the division process.

$$
\begin{array}{r}
x^2 + 2x + 1 \\
x^2 + 0x + 1 \overline{) x^4 + 2x^3 + 2x^2 - x - 1} \\
\underline{x^4 + 0x^3 + x^2} \\
2x^3 + x^2 - x \\
\underline{2x^3 + 0x^2 + 2x} \\
x^2 - 3x - 1 \\
\underline{x^2 + 0x + 1} \\
-3x - 2
\end{array}
$$

When the result of subtracting ($-3x - 2$, in this case) is a polynomial of smaller degree than the divisor ($x^2 + 0x + 1$), that polynomial is the remainder. We write the quotient as

$$x^2 + 2x + 1 + \frac{-3x - 2}{x^2 + 1}.$$

EXERCISES 3.9 *Perform each division. See Example 1.*

1. $\dfrac{x^2 - x - 6}{x - 3}$ 2. $\dfrac{m^2 - 2m - 24}{m + 4}$

3. $\dfrac{2y^2 + 9y - 35}{y + 7}$ 4. $\dfrac{y^2 + 2y + 1}{y + 1}$

5. $\dfrac{p^2 + 2p - 24}{p + 6}$ 6. $\dfrac{x^2 + 11x + 24}{x + 8}$

7. $\dfrac{r^2 - 8r + 15}{r - 3}$ 8. $\dfrac{t^2 - 3t - 10}{t - 5}$

9. $\dfrac{12m^2 - 20m + 3}{2m - 3}$ 10. $\dfrac{2y^2 - 5y - 3}{2y + 1}$

11. $\dfrac{2a^2 - 11a - 21}{2a + 3}$ 12. $\dfrac{9w^2 + 6w - 8}{3w - 2}$

13. $\dfrac{2x^2 + 5x + 3}{2x + 1}$ 14. $\dfrac{4m^2 - 4m + 5}{2m - 1}$

15. $\dfrac{2a^2 - 3a + 4}{2a + 1}$ 16. $\dfrac{4p^2 - 4p + 7}{2p - 1}$

17. $\dfrac{2d^2 - 2d + 5}{2d + 4}$

18. $\dfrac{4m^2 + 11m - 8}{m + 3}$

19. $\dfrac{2x^3 - x^2 + 3x + 2}{2x + 1}$

20. $\dfrac{12t^3 - 11t^2 + 9t + 18}{4t + 3}$

21. $\dfrac{8k^4 - 12k^3 - 2k^2 + 7k - 6}{2k - 3}$

22. $\dfrac{27r^4 - 36r^3 - 6r^2 + 26r - 24}{3r - 4}$

Perform each division. See Examples 2 and 3.

23. $\dfrac{3y^3 + y^2 + 3y + 1}{y^2 + 1}$

24. $\dfrac{2x^5 + 6x^4 - x^3 + 3x^2 - x}{2x^2 + 1}$

25. $\dfrac{x^4 - x^2 - 6x}{x^2 - 2}$

26. $\dfrac{x^4 - 2x^2 + 5}{x^2 - 1}$

27. $\dfrac{x^3 + 1}{x + 1}$

28. $\dfrac{x^4 - 1}{x^2 - 1}$

29. $\dfrac{x^4 - 1}{x^2 + 1}$

30. $\dfrac{x^5 - 1}{x^2 - 1}$

Chapter 3 Test

[3.1-3.2] *Evaluate the following.*

1. 3^{-4}

2. 17^0

Simplify. Write each answer in exponential form, with positive exponents only.

3. $\dfrac{6^8}{6^2}$

4. $5^{-3} \cdot 5^2$

5. $(2^3)^{-4}$

6. $\dfrac{8^0 \cdot 8^5}{8^{-3}}$

7. $\dfrac{(p^{-2})^{-3}(p^4)^2}{(p^{-5})^2}$

[3.3] *Write each number in scientific notation.*

8. 4,000,000

9. 245,000,000

10. .000379

Write without exponents.

11. 4.8×10^{-3}

12. $\dfrac{8 \times 10^{-4}}{2 \times 10^{-6}}$

[3.4] *For each polynomial, combine terms, then give the degree of the polynomial. Finally, select the most specific description from this list.*
(a) trinomial   (b) binomial   (c) monomial   (d) none of these

13. $3x^2 + 6x - 4x^2$

14. $11m^3 - m^2 + m^4 + m^4 - 7m^2$

15. $3x^3 - 4x^2 + 2x - 1$

If $P(x) = x^4 + 2x^2 - 7x + 2$, find each value.

16. $P(2)$

17. $P(-1)$

[3.5] *Perform the indicated operation.*

18. $(3x^3 + 2x^2 - 5x + 3) + (7x^3 - 4x^2 - 3x - 3)$

19. $(2x^5 - 4x + 7) - (x^5 + x^2 - 2x - 5)$

20. $(y^2 - 5y - 3) + (3y^2 + 2y) - (y^2 - y - 1)$

[3.6-3.7] 21. $6m^2(m^3 + 2m^2 - 3m + 7)$

22. $(r - 5)(r + 2)$

23. $(3t + 4)(2t - 3)$

24. $(2k + 7)^2$

25. $(5r - 3s)^2$

26. $(m - 8)(m + 8)$

27. $(6p - 8q)(6p + 8q)$

28. $(2x - 3)(x^2 + 2x - 5)$

[3.8-3.9] 29. $\dfrac{9y^3 - 15y^2 + 6y}{3y}$

30. $(10r^3 + 25r^2 - 15r + 8) \div (5r)$

31. $\dfrac{6a^2 - 11a - 10}{2a - 5}$

32. $\dfrac{12y^2 - 15y - 11}{4y + 3}$

33. $\dfrac{3x^3 - 2x^2 - 6x - 4}{x - 2}$

4

Factoring

4.1 Factors

- **List the factors of a number.**
- **Identify prime numbers.**
- **Find the greatest common factor of a list of numbers.**
- **Factor out the greatest common factor.**

Since the product of 6 and 2 is 12, the numbers 6 and 2 are **factors** of 12. Also, $6 \cdot 2$ is a **factored form** of 12. Other factored forms of 12 include $(-6)(-2)$, $3 \cdot 4$, $(-3)(-4)$, $12 \cdot 1$, and $(-12)(-1)$. Since $\left(\frac{1}{2}\right)(24) = 12$, and $\left(\frac{2}{3}\right)(18) = 12$, we might think of these as factored forms of 12. However, factors of positive integers are usually limited to positive integers. The positive integer factors of 12 are

$$1, 2, 3, 4, 6, 12.$$

In general,

an integer a is a **factor** of an integer b if b can be divided by a with no remainder.

EXAMPLE 1 The positive integer factors of 36 are 1, 2, 3, 4, 6, 9, 12, 18, and 36.

EXAMPLE 2   The positive integer factors of 11 are 1 and 11.

As shown in Example 2, the only positive integer factors of 11 are 11 and 1. A number with only itself and 1 as factors is called a **prime number.** The first few prime numbers are

2, 3, 5, 7, 11, 13, 17, 19, 23, 29, 31, 37, 41, 43,

and so on. (The number 1 is not considered prime.) An integer (other than 1) that is not prime is called **composite.**

EXAMPLE 3   Write *prime* or *composite* for each number,

(a) 33

This number has factors of 3 and 11, as well as 1 and 33, so it is composite.

(b) 53

Try dividing 53 by various integers; it is only divisible by itself and 1, so it is prime.

(c) 14,976,083,922

This number ends in 2, so that it is even. It is composite.

Each composite number may be expressed as a product of primes. For example,

$$30 = 2 \cdot 3 \cdot 5, \qquad 55 = 5 \cdot 11, \qquad \text{and} \qquad 72 = 2^3 \cdot 3^2$$

and so on. When a number is written as a product of primes, it is written in **prime factored form.**

EXAMPLE 4   Write each number in prime factored form.

(a) 50

Divide 50 by the first prime, 2.

$$50 = 2 \cdot 25$$

We can't divide 25 by 2, or by the next prime, 3, but we can divide by 5.

$$50 = 2 \cdot 5 \cdot 5$$
$$50 = 2 \cdot 5^2$$

(b) $300 = 2 \cdot 150$
$$= 2 \cdot 2 \cdot 75$$
$$= 2 \cdot 2 \cdot 3 \cdot 25$$
$$= 2 \cdot 2 \cdot 3 \cdot 5 \cdot 5$$
$$= 2^2 \cdot 3 \cdot 5^2$$

(c) Since 71 is prime, its prime factored form is just 71.

A table giving the prime factored form of all positive integers from 2 through 100 is on page 318 of this book.

An integer which is a factor of two or more other integers is called a **common factor** of those integers. For example, 6 is a common factor of 18 and 24 since 6 is a factor of both 18 and 24. Other common factors of 18 and 24 are 1, 2, and 3. The **greatest common factor** of a list of integers is the largest common factor of the list. Thus, 6 is the greatest common factor of 18 and 24, since it is the largest of the common factors of these numbers.

Greatest common factors of numbers can be found by using prime factored forms, as the next example shows.

EXAMPLE 5   Find the greatest common factor for each group of numbers.

(a) 30, 45

Write each number in prime factored form.

$$30 = 2 \cdot 3 \cdot 5 \qquad 45 = 3^2 \cdot 5$$

To get the greatest common factor, take each prime the *least* number of times it appears in either factored form. There is no 2 in the prime factored form of 45, so that there will be no 2 in the greatest common factor. The least number of times 3 appears is 1, as is the least number of times 5 appears. Thus,

$$\text{greatest common factor} = 3^1 \cdot 5^1 = 3 \cdot 5 = 15$$

(b) 36, 60, 108

Find the prime factored form of each number.

$$36 = 2^2 \cdot 3^2, \qquad 60 = 2^2 \cdot 3 \cdot 5, \qquad 108 = 2^2 \cdot 3^3$$

The least number of times 2 appears is 2, while the least number of times 3 appears is 1. There is no 5 in the prime factored form of either 36 or 108, so that

$$\text{greatest common factor} = 2^2 \cdot 3 = 12$$

(c) 10, 11, 14

Write the prime factored forms:

$$10 = 2 \cdot 5, \qquad 11 = 11, \qquad 14 = 2 \cdot 7$$

There are no primes in common, so that the greatest common factor is 1.

You can find the greatest common factor of a collection of terms. For example, the terms x^4, x^5, x^6, and x^7 have x^4 as the greatest common factor, because x^4 is the highest power of x that is a factor of each of the terms x^4, x^5, x^6, and x^7. To see this, write the terms in factored form.

$$x^4 = x^4 \cdot 1$$
$$x^5 = x^4 \cdot x$$

$$x^6 = x^4 \cdot x^2$$
$$x^7 = x^4 \cdot x^3$$

Generally, the exponent on the greatest common factor is the *smallest* exponent that appears on the terms. In the example above, 4 is the smallest exponent on x^4, x^5, x^6, x^7, so x^4 is the greatest common factor for these terms.

EXAMPLE 6   Find the greatest common factor of the terms

$$y^2, y^5, y^7, \text{ and } y^{15}.$$

Here 2 is the smallest exponent on y, so y^2 is the greatest common factor.

EXAMPLE 7   Find the greatest common factor of the terms

$$21m^7, -18m^6, 45m^8, \text{ and } -24m^5.$$

First, 3 is the greatest common factor of the coefficients 21, -18, 45, and -24. The smallest exponent on m is 5, so the greatest common factor of the terms is $3m^5$.

EXAMPLE 8   Find the greatest common factor of the terms

$$x^4y^2, x^7y^5, x^3y^7, \text{ and } y^{15}.$$

There is no x in the last term, y^{15}, so that x will not appear in the greatest common factor. There is a y in each term, however, with 2 the smallest exponent of y. The greatest common factor is y^2.
In summary,

when finding a greatest common factor, always take each factor the *least* number of times that it appears in any term.

We can use the idea of a greatest common factor to write a polynomial in factored form. For example, the polynomial

$$3m + 12$$

is made up of the two terms $3m$ and 12. The greatest common factor for these two terms is 3. Write $3m + 12$ so that each term is a product with 3 as one factor.

$$3m + 12 = 3 \cdot m + 3 \cdot 4$$

Now use the distributive property.

$$3m + 12 = 3 \cdot m + 3 \cdot 4$$
$$= 3(m + 4)$$

The factored form of $3m + 12$ is $3(m + 4)$. This process is called **factoring out the greatest common factor.**

EXAMPLE 9 Factor out the greatest common factor.

(a) $20m^5 + 10m^4 + 15m^3$

The greatest common factor for the terms of this polynomial is $5m^3$.

$$20m^5 + 10m^4 + 15m^3 = (5m^3)(4m^2) + (5m^3)(2m) + (5m^3)\,3$$
$$= 5m^3(4m^2 + 2m + 3)$$

To check your work, multiply $5m^3$ and $(4m^2 + 2m + 3)$. You should get the original polynomial as your answer.

(b) $48y^{12} - 36y^{10} + 12y^7$

$$= (12y^7)(4y^5) - (12y^7)(3y^3) + (12y^7)1$$
$$= 12y^7(4y^5 - 3y^3 + 1)$$

(c) $x^5 - x^3 = (x^3)x^2 - (x^3)1$
$$= x^3(x^2 - 1)$$

(d) $20m^7p^2 - 36m^3p^4 = 4m^3p^2(5m^4 - 9p^2)$

Throughout this book, always look for a greatest common factor as the first step in factoring a polynomial.

EXERCISES 4.1 *Find all the positive integer factors of each number. See Examples 1 and 2.*

1. 14	**2.** 18	**3.** 27	**4.** 35
5. 45	**6.** 50	**7.** 60	**8.** 72
9. 100	**10.** 130	**11.** 29	**12.** 37

Find the prime factored form for the following. See Example 4.

13. 120	**14.** 150	**15.** 180	**16.** 225
17. 275	**18.** 350	**19.** 475	**20.** 650

Find the greatest common factor for each set of terms. See Examples 5–8.

21. $12y$, 24   **22.** $72m$, 12

23. $30p^2$, $20p^3$, $40p^5$ **24.** $14r^5$, $28r^2$, $56r^8$

25. $18r$, $32y$, $11z$ **26.** $45m^2$, $12n$, $7p^2$

27. $18m^2n^2$, $36m^4n^5$, $12m^3n$ **28.** $50p^5r^2$, $25p^4r^7$, $30p^7r^8$

Complete the factoring.

29. $12 = 6(\quad)$ **30.** $18 = 9(\quad)$

31. $3x^2 = 3x(\quad)$ **32.** $8x^3 = 8x(\quad)$

33. $9m^4 = 3m^2(\quad)$ **34.** $12p^5 = 6p^3(\quad)$

35. $-8z^9 = -4z^5(\quad)$

36. $-15k^{11} = -5k^8(\quad)$

37. $x^2y^3 = xy(\quad)$

38. $a^3b^2 = a^2b(\quad)$

39. $6m^4n^5 = 3m^3n(\quad)$

40. $27a^3b^2 = 9a^2b(\quad)$

41. $14x^4y^3 = 2xy(\quad)$

42. $-16m^3n^3 = 4mn^2(\quad)$

Factor out the greatest common factor. See Example 9.

43. $12x + 24$

44. $18m - 9$

45. $3 + 36d$

46. $15 + 25r$

47. $9a^2 - 18a$

48. $21m^5 - 14m^4$

49. $65y^9 - 35y^5$

50. $100a^4 - 16a^2$

51. $121p^5 - 33p^4$

52. $8p^2 - 4p^4$

53. $11z^2 - 100$

54. $12z^2 - 11y^4$

55. $9m^2 + 90m^3$

56. $16r^2s + 64rs^2$

57. $19y^3p^2 + 38y^2p^3$

58. $4mn^2 - 12m^2n$

59. $18x^2y^3 - 24x^4y$

60. $100m^5 - 50m^3 + 100m^2$

61. $13y^6 + 26y^5 - 39y^3$

62. $5x^4 + 25x^3 - 20x^2$

63. $16a^3 + 8a^2 + 24a$

64. $6a^2 + 8c^2 - 4b^2$

65. $45q^4p^5 - 36qp^6 + 81q^2p^3$

66. $a^5 + 2a^5b + 3a^5b^2 - 4a^5b^3$

67. $a^3b^5 - a^2b^7 + ab^3$

68. $m^6n^5 - 2m^5 + 5m^3n^5$

69. $125z^5a^3 - 60z^4a^5 + 85z^3a^4$

70. $30a^2m^2 + 60a^3m + 180a^3m^2$

71. $33y^8 - 44y^{12} + 77y^3 + 11y^4$

72. $26g^6h^4 + 13g^3h^4 - 39g^4h^3$

4.2 Factoring Trinomials

- **Factor trinomials with a coefficient of 1 for the squared term.**
- **Factor such polynomials after factoring out the greatest common factor.**

The product of two binomials is usually a trinomial. For example,

$$(x + 4)(x - 6) = x^2 - 2x - 24;$$
$$(y + 5)(y - 3) = y^2 + 2y - 15.$$

Exceptions to this rule include $(x + 2)(x - 2) = x^2 - 4$, which is not a trinomial.

In this section our goal is to factor a trinomial as the product of two binomial factors. We limit ourselves to trinomials like $x^2 - 2x - 24$ or $y^2 + 2y - 15$, where the coefficient of the squared term is 1.

Let's try to factor $x^2 + 5x + 6$. We want to find integers a and b such that

$$x^2 + 5x + 6 = (x + a)(x + b)$$

To find these integers a and b, first multiply the right-hand side of the equation.

$$(x + a)(x + b) = x^2 + ax + bx + ab$$

By the distributive property,

$$x^2 + ax + bx + ab = x^2 + (a + b)x + ab.$$

Thus, we want integers a and b such that

$$x^2 + 5x + 6 = x^2 + (a + b)x + ab.$$

The integers a and b must satisfy the conditions

$$a + b = 5$$
$$ab = 6.$$

Can we find two integers whose sum is 5 ($a + b = 5$) and whose product is 6 ($ab = 6$)? Since many pairs of integers can be found which have a sum of 5, it is best to list first those pairs of integers whose product is 6. Both 5 and 6 are positive, so we need consider only pairs having both integers positive.

product	*sum*
$1 \cdot 6 = 6$	$1 + 6 = 7$
$2 \cdot 3 = 6$	$2 + 3 = 5$

Both pairs have a product of 6, but only the pair with 2 and 3 has a sum of 5. So 2 and 3 are the integers we are looking for.

$$x^2 + 5x + 6 = (x + 2)(x + 35)$$

The trinomial $x^2 + 5x + 6$ has been factored into the product of the binomials $x + 2$ and $x + 3$.

To check, multiply the binomials. Make sure that the sum of the outer and inner products produces the correct middle term.

$$(x + 2)(x + 3) = x^2 + 5x + 6$$

with $3x$ (outer) and $2x$ (inner) products indicated.

This method can only be used on trinomials having coefficient of the squared term equal to 1. Methods for other trinomials will be given in the next section.

EXAMPLE 1 To factor $m^2 + 9m + 14$, look for two integers whose product is 14, and whose sum is 9. List the pairs of integers whose products are 14. Then examine the sums. Again, we need only positive integers, because all signs are positive.

14, 1	$14 + 1 = 15$
7, 2	$7 + 2 = 9$

From the list, 7 and 2 are the integers we need, since $7 \cdot 2 = 14$ and $7 + 2 = 9$. Thus the binomial factors of $m^2 + 9m + 14$ are $(m + 2)(m + 7)$. This answer could also have been written as $(m + 7)(m + 2)$. The order of the factors does not matter.

EXAMPLE 2 To factor $p^2 - 2p - 15$, find two integers whose product is -15 and whose sum is -2. If these numbers do not come to mind right away, we can always find them (if they exist) by listing all the pairs of integers whose product is -15. Here we need to consider negative integers as well as positive ones.

$$15, -1 \qquad 15 + (-1) = 14$$
$$5, -3 \qquad 5 + (-3) = 2$$
$$-15, 1 \qquad -15 + 1 = -14$$
$$-5, 3 \qquad -5 + 3 = -2$$

The integers we need are -5 and 3, The factored trinomial is

$$p^2 - 2p - 15 = (p - 5)(p + 3).$$

EXAMPLE 3 To try to factor $x^2 - 5x + 12$, we first list all pairs of integers whose product is 12.

$$12, 1 \qquad 12 + 1 = 13$$
$$6, 2 \qquad 6 + 2 = 8$$
$$3, 4 \qquad 3 + 4 = 7$$
$$-12, -1 \qquad -12 + (-1) = -13$$
$$-6, -2 \qquad -6 + (-2) = -8$$
$$-3, -4 \qquad -3 + (-4) = -7$$

None of the pairs of integers has a sum of -5. Because of this, the trinomial $x^2 - 5x + 12$ *cannot be factored with integer factors,* and is called *prime*.

EXAMPLE 4 There is no pair of integers whose product is 11 and whose sum is -8, so that $k^2 - 8k + 11$ is prime.

EXAMPLE 5 Factor $4x^5 - 28x^4 + 40x^3$.

First, factor out the greatest common factor, $4x^3$.

$$4x^5 - 28x^4 + 40x^3 = 4x^3(x^2 - 7x + 10)$$

Now factor $x^2 - 7x + 10$. The integers -5 and -2 have a product of 10 and a sum of -7. The complete factored form is

$$4x^5 - 28x^4 + 40x^3 = 4x^3(x - 5)(x - 2).$$

When factoring, always remember to first look for a common factor.

EXAMPLE 6   To factor $z^2 - 2bz - 3b^2$, look for two numbers whose product is $-3b^2$ and whose sum is $-2b$. The numbers we need are $-3b$ and b. Thus

$$z^2 - 2bz - 3b^2 = (z - 3b)(z + b).$$

EXERCISES 4.2   *Complete the factoring.*

1. $x^2 + 10x + 21 = (x + 7)($ $)$

2. $p^2 + 11p + 30 = (p + 5)($ $)$

3. $r^2 + 15r + 56 = (r + 7)($ $)$

4. $x^2 + 15x + 44 = (x + 4)($ $)$

5. $t^2 - 14t + 24 = (t - 2)($ $)$

6. $x^2 - 9x + 8 = (x - 1)($ $)$

7. $x^2 - 12x + 32 = (x - 4)($ $)$

8. $y^2 - 2y - 15 = (y + 3)($ $)$

9. $m^2 + 2m - 24 = (m - 4)($ $)$

10. $x^2 + 9x - 22 = (x - 2)($ $)$

11. $p^2 + 7p - 8 = (p + 8)($ $)$

12. $y^2 - 7y - 18 = (y + 2)($ $)$

13. $x^2 - 7x - 30 = (x - 10)($ $)$

14. $k^2 - 3k - 28 = (k - 7)($ $)$

Factor as completely as possible. If a polynomial cannot be factored, write "cannot be factored." See Examples 1–4.

15. $x^2 + 6x + 5$ 16. $y^2 + y - 72$

17. $a^2 + 9a + 20$ 18. $b^2 + 8b + 15$

19. $x^2 - 8x + 7$ 20. $m^2 + m - 20$

21. $p^2 + 4p + 5$ 22. $n^2 - 4n - 12$

23. $y^2 - 6y + 8$ 24. $r^2 - 11r + 30$

25. $s^2 + 2s - 35$ 26. $h^2 + 11h + 12$

27. $n^2 - 12n - 35$ 28. $a^2 - 2a - 99$

29. $b^2 - 11b + 24$ 30. $x^2 - 9x + 20$

31. $y^2 - 4y - 21$ 32. $z^2 - 14z + 49$

33. $y^2 - 12y + 8$ 34. $r^2 + r - 42$

35. $z^2 - 3z - 40$ 36. $p^2 + 5p - 66$

Factor completely. See Example 5.

37. $3m^3 + 12m^2 + 9m$

38. $3y^5 - 18y^4 + 15y^3$

39. $6a^2 - 48a - 120$

40. $h^7 - 5h^6 - 14h^5$

41. $3j^3 - 30j^2 + 72j$

42. $2x^6 - 8x^5 - 42x^4$

43. $3x^4 - 3x^3 - 90x^2$

44. $2y^3 - 8y^2 - 10y$

Factor completely. See Example 6.

45. $x^2 + 4ax + 3a^2$

46. $x^2 - mx - 6m^2$

47. $y^2 - by - 30b^2$

48. $z^2 + 2zx - 15x^2$

49. $x^2 + xy - 30y^2$

50. $a^2 - ay - 56y^2$

51. $r^2 - 2rs + s^2$

52. $m^2 - 2mn - 3n^2$

53. $p^2 - 3pq - 10q^2$

54. $c^2 - 5cd + 4d^2$

55. $a^5 + 3a^4b - 4a^3b^2$

56. $m^3n - 2m^2n^2 - 3mn^3$

57. $y^3z + y^2z^2 - 6yz^3$

58. $k^7 - 2k^6m - 15k^5m^2$

59. $z^{10} - 4z^9y - 21z^8y^2$

60. $x^9 + 5x^8w - 24x^7w^2$

4.3 More About Factoring Trinomials

- **Factor trinomials not having 1 as the coefficient of the squared term.**

In this section, we factor trinomials where the coefficient of the squared term is *not* 1, such as

$$2x^2 + 7x + 6.$$

The possible factors of $2x^2$ are $2x$ and x, or $-2x$ and $-x$. We normally use only positive coefficients for the first factors. If we use $2x$ and x, then the factoring of $2x^2 + 7x + 6$ is started as follows:

$$2x^2 + 7x + 6 = (2x \qquad)(x \qquad).$$

The last term of $2x^2 + 7x + 6$ is 6. There are several possible factors of 6, including 6 and 1. We don't know if these are the correct factors or not; we have to see if we get the correct middle term of $+ 7x$.

$$\overset{\displaystyle\frown}{\underset{x}{(2x + 1)(x + 6)}} \overset{12x}{=} 2x^2 + 13x + 6 \qquad \text{Incorrect}$$

Exchange the 6 and 1, and see if the middle term is correct now.

$$\overset{\displaystyle\frown}{\underset{6x}{(2x + 6)(x + 1)}} \overset{2x}{=} 2x^2 + 8x + 6 \qquad \text{Incorrect}$$

We could have noticed from the beginning that $(2x + 6)(x + 1)$ could not be correct. This is because $2x + 6$ has a common factor, while $2x^2 + 7x + 6$ does not.

If the original polynomial has no common factor, then none of its factors will either.

Let's now try 2 and 3 as factors of 6. We can't use $(2x + 2)(x + 3)$ because of the common factor in $2x + 2$. Let's try $(2x + 3)(x + 2)$.

$$(2x + 3)(x + 2) = 2x^2 + 7x + 6 \qquad \text{Correct}$$

We have now finally factored $2x^2 + 7x + 6$:

$$2x^2 + 7x + 6 = (2x + 3)(x + 2).$$

As you gain experience in factoring, you will be able to do many of these steps in your head.

EXAMPLE 1   Factor $3y^2 + 14y + 8$.

The only factors of $3y^2$ having positive coefficients are $3y$ and y, so that we start with

$$(3y \qquad)(y \qquad)$$

The factors of 8 are 8 and 1, or 4 and 2. Try 4 and 2.

$$(3y + 4)(y + 2) = 3y^2 + 10y + 8 \qquad \text{Incorrect}$$

Try 2 and 4:

$$(3y + 2)(y + 4) = 3y^2 + 14y + 8 \qquad \text{Correct}$$

EXAMPLE 2   Factor $8p^2 + 14p + 5$.

The number 8 has several possible pairs of factors, while 5 has only 1 and 5 or -1 and -5. For this reason, it is easiest to begin by considering the factors of 5. We can ignore the negative factors since all terms of the trinomial have positive coefficients. Thus, if $8p^2 + 14p + 5$ can be factored, it will have to be factored as

$$(\qquad + 5)(\qquad + 1).$$

The possible factors of $8p^2$ are $8p$ and p, or $4p$ and $2p$.

$$(8p + 5)(p + 1) = 8p^2 + 13p + 5 \quad \text{Incorrect}$$

$$(p + 5)(8p + 1) = 8p^2 + 41p + 5 \quad \text{Incorrect}$$

$$(4p + 5)(2p + 1) = 8p^2 + 14p + 5 \quad \text{Correct}$$

Thus, $8p^2 + 14p + 5$ factors as $(4p + 5)(2p + 1)$.

EXAMPLE 3 Factor $6x^2 - 11x + 3$.

There are several possible factors for 6, while 3 has only 1 and 3 or -1 and -3. Thus, we begin by factoring 3. Since the middle term of $6x^2 - 11x + 3$ has a negative coefficient, we have to consider negative factors. Let's try -3 and -1 as factors of 3, so that our first step is

$$(\quad -3)(\quad -1).$$

The factors of $6x^2$ are $6x$ and x, or $2x$ and $3x$. Let's try $2x$ and $3x$.

$$(2x - 3)(3x - 1) = 6x^2 - 11x + 13 \quad \text{Correct}$$

EXAMPLE 4 Factor $8x^2 + 6x - 9$.

The integer 8 has several possible factors, as does -9. Since the coefficient of the middle term is small, it probably would be wise to avoid large factors such as 8 or 9. Let us begin by trying 4 and 2 as factors of 8, and 3 and -3 as factors of -9.

$$(4x + 3)(2x - 3) = 8x^2 - 6x - 9 \quad \text{Incorrect}$$

$$(4x - 3)(2x + 3) = 8x^2 + 6x - 9 \quad \text{Correct}$$

EXAMPLE 5 Factor $12a^2 - ab - 20b^2$.

There are several possible factors of $12a^2$, including $12a$ and a, $6a$ and $2a$, and $3a$ and $4a$, just as there are many possible factors of $-20b^2$, including $-20b$ and b, $10b$ and $-2b$, $-10b$ and $2b$, $4b$ and $-5b$, and $-4b$ and $5b$. Once again, since our desired middle term is small we avoid the larger factors. Let us try as factors $6a$ and $2a$ and $4b$ and $-5b$.

$$(6a + 4b)(2a - 5b)$$

This cannot be correct, as we mentioned before, since $6a + 4b$ has a common factor, while the trinomial itself has none.

Let's try $3a$ and $4a$ with $4b$ and $-5b$.

$$(3a + 4b)(4a - 5b) = 12a^2 + ab - 20b^2 \qquad \text{Incorrect}$$

Here the middle term has the wrong sign, so we change the signs on the factors.

$$(3a - 4b)(4a + 5b) = 12a^2 - ab - 20b^2 \qquad \text{Correct}$$

EXAMPLE 6 Factor $28x^5 - 58x^4 - 30x^3$.

First factor out $2x^3$, the greatest common factor.

$$28x^5 - 58x^4 - 30x^3 = 2x^3(14x^2 - 29x - 15)$$

We must now try to factor $14x^2 - 29x - 15$. Let's try $7x$ and $2x$ as factors of $14x^2$, and -3 and 5 as factors of -15.

$$(7x - 3)(2x + 5) = 14x^2 + 29x - 15 \qquad \text{Incorrect}$$

The middle term differs only in sign, and so we change the signs on the two factors:

$$(7x + 3)(2x - 5) = 14x^2 - 29x - 15. \qquad \text{Correct}$$

Finally, the factored form of $28x^5 - 58x^4 - 30x^3$ is

$$28x^5 - 58x^4 - 30x^3 = 2x^3(7x + 3)(2x - 5).$$

EXERCISES 4.3 *Complete the factoring.*

1. $2x^2 - x - 1 = (2x + 1)(\qquad)$
2. $3a^2 + 5a + 2 = (3a + 2)(\qquad)$
3. $5b^2 - 16b + 3 = (5b - 1)(\qquad)$
4. $2x^2 + 11x + 12 = (2x + 3)(\qquad)$
5. $4y^2 + 17y - 15 = (y + 5)(\qquad)$
6. $7z^2 + 10z - 8 = (z + 2)(\qquad)$
7. $15x^2 + 7x - 4 = (3x - 1)(\qquad)$
8. $12c^2 - 7c - 12 = (4c + 3)(\qquad)$
9. $2m^2 + 19m - 10 = (2m - 1)(\qquad)$
10. $6x^2 + x - 12 = (2x + 3)(\qquad)$
11. $6a^2 + 7ab - 20b^2 = (2a + 5b)(\qquad)$
12. $9m^2 - 3mn - 2n^2 = (3m - 2n)(\qquad)$

13. $4k^2 + 13km + 3m^2 = (4k + m)(\qquad)$

14. $6x^2 - 13xy - 5y^2 = (3x + y)(\qquad)$

15. $4x^3 - 10x^2 - 6x = 2x(\qquad) = 2x(2x + 1)(\qquad)$

16. $15r^3 - 39r^2 - 18r = 3r(\qquad) = 3r(5r + 2)(\qquad)$

17. $6m^6 + 7m^5 - 20m^4 = m^4(\qquad) = m^4(3m - 4)(\qquad)$

18. $16y^5 - 4y^4 - 6y^3 = 2y^3(\qquad) = 2y^3(4y - 3)(\qquad)$

Factor as completely as possible. Remember to look for a greatest common factor first.

19. $2x^2 + 7x + 3$

20. $3y^2 + 13y + 4$

21. $3a^2 + 10a + 7$

22. $7r^2 + 8r + 1$

23. $4r^2 + r - 3$

24. $3p^2 + 2p - 8$

25. $15m^2 + m - 2$

26. $6x^2 + x - 1$

27. $8m^2 - 10m - 3$

28. $2a^2 - 17a + 30$

29. $5a^2 - 7a - 6$

30. $12s^2 + 11s - 5$

31. $3r^2 + r - 10$

32. $20x^2 - 28x - 3$

33. $4y^2 + 69y + 17$

34. $21m^2 + 13m + 2$

35. $38x^2 + 23x + 2$

36. $20y^2 + 39y - 11$

37. $10x^2 + 11x - 6$

38. $6b^2 + 7b + 2$

39. $6w^2 + 19w + 10$

40. $20q^2 - 41q + 20$

41. $6q^2 + 23q + 21$

42. $8x^2 + 47x - 6$

43. $10m^2 - 23m + 12$

44. $4t^2 - 5t - 6$

45. $8k^2 + 2k - 15$

46. $15p^2 - p - 6$

47. $10m^2 - m - 24$

48. $16a^2 + 30a + 9$

49. $8x^2 - 14x + 3$

50. $24b^2 - 37b - 5$

51. $40m^2 + m - 6$

52. $15a^2 + 22a + 8$

53. $2m^3 + 2m^2 - 40m$

54. $15n^4 - 39n^3 + 18n^2$

55. $24a^4 + 10a^3 - 4a^2$

56. $18x^5 + 15x^4 - 75x^3$

57. $32z^2w^4 - 20zw^4 - 12w^4$

58. $15x^2y^2 - 7xy^2 - 4y^2$

59. $12p^2 + 7pq - 12q^2$

60. $6m^2 - 5mn - 6n^2$

61. $25a^2 + 25ab + 6b^2$

62. $6x^2 - 5xy - y^2$

63. $6a^2 - 7ab - 5b^2$

64. $25g^2 - 5gh - 2h^2$

65. $4k^4 - 2k^3w - 6k^2w^2$

66. $4a^4 - a^3b - 3a^2b^2$

67. $6m^6n + 7m^5n^2 + 2m^4n^3$

68. $12k^3q^4 - 4k^2q^5 - kq^6$

69. $18z^3y - 3z^2y^2 - 105zy^3$

70. $30g^5 - 58g^4f + 12g^3f^2$

4.4 Two Special Factorizations

- **Factor the difference of two squares.**
- **Factor a perfect square trinomial.**

Recall from Section 3.7 that

$$(x + y)(x - y) = x^2 - y^2.$$

Based on this product, a **difference of two squares** can be factored as

$$x^2 - y^2 = (x + y)(x - y).$$

For example,

$$m^2 - 16 = m^2 - 4^2,$$

so that

$$m^2 - 16 = (m + 4)(m - 4).$$

To check, multiply $m + 4$ and $m - 4$.

$$(m + 4)(m - 4) = m^2 - 4m + 4m - 16$$
$$= m^2 - 16.$$

The two middle terms add to 0 and disappear.

EXAMPLE 1 Factor each difference of two squares.

(a) $x^2 - 49 = (x + 7)(x - 7)$

(b) $z^2 - 4 = (z + 2)(z - 2)$

(c) $y^2 - m^2 = (y + m)(y - m)$

(d) $p^2 + 16$ cannot be factored

EXAMPLE 2 Factor $25m^2 - 16$.
This is the difference of two squares, since

$$25m^2 - 16 = (5m)^2 - 4^2.$$

Factor this as

$$(5m + 4)(5m - 4).$$

EXAMPLE 3 Factor as completely as possible.

(a) $49z^2 - 64 = (7z)^2 - 8^2$
$$= (7z + 8)(7z - 8)$$

(b) $9a^2 - 4b^2 = (3a)^2 - (2b)^2$
$$= (3a + 2b)(3a - 2b)$$

(c) $81y^2 - 36 = 9(9y^2 - 4)$
$$= 9(3y + 2)(3y - 2)$$

(d) $p^4 - 36 = (p^2)^2 - 6^2$
$$= (p^2 + 6)(p^2 - 6)$$

Neither $p^2 + 6$ nor $p^2 - 6$ can be further factored.

(e) $m^4 - 16 = (m^2)^2 - 4^2$
$$= (m^2 + 4)(m^2 - 4)$$

While $m^2 + 4$ cannot be further factored, $m^2 - 4$ can be factored as $(m + 2)$ $(m - 2)$.

$$m^4 - 16 = (m^2 + 4)(m + 2)(m - 2)$$

A quantity is a perfect square if it can be expressed as the square of another quantity. Thus, 144, $4x^2$, and $81m^6$ are all perfect squares, since

$$144 = 12^2, \qquad 4x^2 = (2x)^2, \qquad 81m^6 = (9m^3)^2.$$

A **perfect square trinomial** is a trinomial that is the square of a binomial. For example,

$$x^2 + 8x + 16 = (x + 4)^2.$$

For a trinomial to be a perfect square, two of its terms must be perfect squares. Thus $16x^2 + 4x + 8$ is not a perfect square trinomial since only the term $16x^2$ is a perfect square.

On the other hand, just because two of the terms are perfect squares, we cannot be sure that the trinomial is a perfect square trinomial. For example, $x^2 + 6x + 36$ has two perfect square terms, but it is not a perfect square trinomial. (Try to find a binomial that can be squared to give $x^2 + 6x + 36$.)

In general, the square of a binomial is of the form

$$(a + b)^2 = a^2 + 2ab + b^2.$$

The middle term of a perfect square trinomial is always twice the product of the two terms in the squared binomial. We can use this fact to check any attempt to factor a trinomial that appears to be a perfect square.

Factor $x^2 + 10x + 25$. The term x^2 is a perfect square, and so is 25. We can try to factor the trinomial as

$$x^2 + 10x + 25 = (x + 5)^2.$$

To check, take twice the product of the two terms in the squared binomial.

$$2 \cdot x \cdot 5 = 10x$$

Since $10x$ is the middle term of the trinomial, the trinomial is a perfect square, and can be factored as $(x + 5)^2$.

EXAMPLE 4 Factor each perfect square trinomial.

(a) $x^2 - 22x + 121$

The first and last terms are perfect squares ($121 = 11^2$). We need to check and see if the middle term of $x^2 - 22x + 121$ is twice the product of the first and last terms of the binomial $(x - 11)$.

$$2 \cdot x \cdot 11 = 22x$$
$$\text{first} \underline{} \uparrow \; \uparrow \underline{} \text{last}$$

Since twice the product of the first and last terms of the binomial is the middle term, $x^2 - 22x + 121$ is a perfect square trinomial, and

$$x^2 - 22x + 121 = (x - 11)^2.$$

The middle sign in the binomial, a minus sign in this case, is always the same as the middle sign in the trinomial.

(b) $9m^2 - 24m + 16 = (3m - 4)^2$

(c) $16r^2 + 8r + 1 = (4r + 1)^2$

(d) $25y^2 + 20y + 16$

The first and last terms are perfect squares.

$$25y^2 = (5y)^2 \quad \text{and} \quad 16 = 4^2$$

Twice the product of the first and last terms of the binomial is

$$2 \cdot 5y \cdot 4 = 40y,$$

which is not the middle term of $25y^2 + 20y + 16$. This polynomial is not a perfect square.

EXERCISES 4.4 *Factor each binomial completely. The table of squares and square roots in the back of the book may be helpful. See Examples 1–3.*

1. $x^2 - 16$

2. $m^2 - 25$

3. $p^2 - 4$

4. $r^2 - 9$

5. $m^2 - n^2$

6. $p^2 - q^2$

7. $a^2 - b^2$

8. $r^2 - t^2$

9. $9m^2 - 1$

10. $16y^2 - 9$

11. $25m^2 - 16$

12. $144y^2 - 25$

13. $36t^2 - 16$

14. $9 - 36a^2$

15. $25a^2 - 16r^2$

16. $100k^2 - 49m^2$

17. $x^2 + 16$

18. $m^2 + 100$

19. $p^4 - 36$ **20.** $r^4 - 9$

21. $a^4 - 1$ **22.** $x^4 - 16$

23. $m^4 - 81$ **24.** $p^4 - 256$

Factor any expressions that are perfect square trinomials. See Example 4.

25. $a^2 + 4a + 4$ **26.** $p^2 + 2p + 1$

27. $x^2 - 10x + 25$ **28.** $y^2 - 8y + 16$

29. $a^2 + 14a + 49$ **30.** $m^2 - 20m + 100$

31. $k^2 + 22k + 121$ **32.** $r^2 + 24r + 144$

33. $y^2 - 10y + 100$ **34.** $z^2 + 7z + 49$

35. $9y^2 + 14y + 25$ **36.** $16m^2 + 42m + 49$

37. $16a^2 - 40ab + 25b^2$ **38.** $36y^2 - 60yp + 25p^2$

39. $100m^2 + 100m + 25$ **40.** $100a^2 - 140ab + 49b^2$

41. $49x^2 + 28xy + 4y^2$ **42.** $64y^2 - 48ya + 9a^2$

43. $4c^2 + 12cd + 9d^2$ **44.** $16t^2 - 40tr + 25r^2$

45. $25h^2 - 20hy + 4y^2$ **46.** $9x^2 + 24xy + 16y^2$

47. $9a^4 - 12a^3b + 4a^2b^2$ **48.** $4m^4 - 4m^3n + m^2n^2$

49. $x^3y + 6x^2y^2 + 9xy^3$ **50.** $4k^3w + 20k^2w^2 + 25kw^3$

Miscellaneous Factoring Exercises

To Factor a Polynomial

Step 1   Factor out any greatest common factor.

Step 2   If you have a binomial (2 terms), check to see if it is a difference of two squares.

Step 3   If you have a trinomial, check to see if it is a perfect square trinomial.

Step 4   If not, check to see if the coefficient of the squared term is 1. If so, use the method of Section 4.2.

Step 5   If the coefficient of the squared term of the trinomial is not 1, use the "general factoring" of Section 4.3.

Factor as completely as possible.

1. $16x + 20$

2. $15y + 5$

3. $8m - 16m^2$

4. $20y^5 - 30y^4$

5. $6a + 12b + 18c$

6. $50z^2 - 100$

7. $32m^9 + 16m^5 + 24m^3$

8. $100n^2r^2 + 30nr^3 - 50n^2r$

9. $45a^3b^5 - 60a^4b^2 + 75a^6b^4$

10. $72y^3z^2 + 12y^2 - 24y^4z^2$

11. $a^2 - 4a - 12$

12. $m^2 + 2m - 15$

13. $y^2 - y - 56$

14. $k^2 + 8k - 48$

15. $z^2 - 12z + 36$

16. $a^2 + 17a + 72$

17. $p^2 - 17p + 66$

18. $k^2 - 11k + 30$

19. $6y^2 - 6y - 12$

20. $2m^2 - 10m - 48$

21. $3k^3 - 12k^2 - 15k$

22. $5z^3 - 45z^2 + 70z$

23. $8a^5 - 8a^4 - 48a^3$

24. $7y^6 + 14y^5 - 168y^4$

25. $z^2 - 3za - 10a^2$

26. $m^2 - 3mn - 4n^2$

27. $y^2 - 4yk - 12k^2$

28. $a^2 - 3ab - 28b^2$

29. $2m^2 + 5m - 3$

30. $3k^2 + 4k - 4$

31. $5z^2 + 24z - 5$

32. $2a^2 - 7a - 30$

33. $6y^2 - 5y - 4$

34. $8k^2 - 10k - 3$

35. $6z^2 + 31z + 5$

36. $8p^2 + 23p - 3$

37. $6n^2 - 19n + 10$

38. $8m^2 - 2m - 3$

39. $10z^2 - 7z - 6$

40. $9y^2 + 12y - 5$

41. $6a^2 + 10a - 4$

42. $10m^2 + 25m - 60$

43. $14k^3 + 7k^2 - 70k$

44. $32z^3 + 56z^2 - 16z$

45. $36y^6 - 42y^5 - 120y^4$

46. $27p^{10} - 45p^9 - 252p^8$

47. $2m^2 + 7mn - 15n^2$

48. $8k^2 - 2kh - 3h^2$

49. $12p^2 + pq - 6q^2$

50. $10y^2 - 7yz - 6z^2$

51. $8a^2 + 23ab - 3b^2$

52. $15h^2 + 11hg - 14g^2$

53. $k^2 - 16$

54. $m^2 - 81$

55. $4y^2 - 25$

56. $9m^2 - 64$

57. $49z^2 - 16y^2$

58. $100a^2 - 81y^2$

59. $54m^2 - 24z^2$

60. $64p^2 - 100m^2$

61. $y^4 - 16$

62. $a^4 - 625$

63. $k^2 + 9$

64. $9z^2 + 64$

65. $a^2 + 8a + 16$

66. $m^2 - 4m + 4$

67. $4k^2 - 12k + 9$

68. $16z^2 - 8z + 1$

69. $16r^2 + 24rm + 9m^2$

70. $4k^2 - 20kz + 25z^2$

71. $5z^2 - 15zy + 9y^2$

72. $64m^2 - 40mn + 25n^2$

73. $16k^2 - 48k + 36$

74. $108m^2 - 36m + 3$

75. $125m^4 - 400m^3n + 195m^2n^2$

76. $24k^4p + 60k^3p^2 + 150k^2p^3$

4.5 Solving Quadratic Equations

- **Solve quadratic equations by factoring.**
- **Solve other equations by factoring.**

In this section we introduce **quadratic equations,** which are equations that contain a squared term, and no terms of higher degree. Quadratic equations have the form

$$ax^2 + bx + c = 0,$$

where a, b, and c are real numbers, with $a \neq 0$. Examples of quadratic equations include

$$x^2 + 5x + 6 = 0, \qquad 2a^2 - 5a = 3, \qquad \text{and} \qquad y^2 = 4.$$

Some quadratic equations can be solved by factoring. A more general method for those equations that cannot be solved by factoring is given in Chapter 9.

To solve a quadratic equation by factoring, we use the **zero-factor property:**

If a and b represent real numbers, and if $ab = 0$, then $a = 0$ or $b = 0$.

In other words, if the product of two numbers is zero, then at least one of the numbers must be zero.

EXAMPLE 1 Solve the equation $(x + 3)(2x - 1) = 0$.

Here we are told that the product $(x + 3)(2x - 1)$ is equal to zero. By the zero-factor property, the only way that the product of these two factors can be zero is if at least one of the factors is zero. Therefore, either $x + 3 = 0$ or $2x - 1 = 0$. Solve each of these two equations.

$$
\begin{array}{ll}
x + 3 = 0 & 2x - 1 = 0 \\
x = -3 & 2x = 1 \\
& x = \dfrac{1}{2}
\end{array}
$$

The given equation $(x + 3)(2x - 1) = 0$ has two solutions, $x = -3$ and $x = \frac{1}{2}$.
To check these answers, substitute -3 for x in the original equation. Then start over and substitute $\frac{1}{2}$ for x.

In Example 1 the equation that we were to solve was presented in factored form. If the equation is not already factored, we must make sure that 0 is alone on one side of the equals sign, and then factor the polynomial ourselves.

EXAMPLE 2   Solve the equation $x^2 - 5x = -6$.
First, rewrite the equation so that 0 is alone on one side. In this case, add 6 to both sides.

$$x^2 - 5x + 6 = -6 + 6$$
$$x^2 - 5x + 6 = 0$$

Now factor $x^2 - 5x + 6$. We need two numbers whose product is 6 and whose sum is -5. These two numbers are -2 and -3. This gives

$$(x - 2)(x - 3) = 0$$

Proceed as in Example 1. Make each factor equal to 0.

$$x - 2 = 0 \quad \text{or} \quad x - 3 = 0$$

To solve the equation on the left, add 2 to both sides. On the right, add 3 to both sides. Doing this, we get the solutions

$$x = 2 \quad \text{or} \quad x = 3.$$

Check by substituting 2 and 3 for x in the original equation.

EXAMPLE 3   Solve the equation $y^2 = y + 20$.
We need 0 alone on one side of the equals sign. We can get 0 alone if we add $-y$ and -20 to both sides of the equals sign.

$$y^2 - y - 20 = 0$$

Factor $y^2 - y - 20$.

$$(y - 5)(y + 4) = 0$$

This product of two factors can equal 0 only if at least one of the factors is 0. This gives two equations,

$$y - 5 = 0 \quad \text{or} \quad y + 4 = 0.$$

Solve each of these two equations to get the final solutions.

$$y = 5 \quad \text{or} \quad y = -4$$

EXAMPLE 4 Solve the equation $2p^2 - 13p + 20 = 0$.

Factor $2p^2 - 13p + 20$ by the method of trial and error.

$$(2p - 5)(p - 4) = 0$$

Make each of these two factors equal to 0.

$$2p - 5 = 0 \quad \text{or} \quad p - 4 = 0$$

To solve the equation on the left, first add 5 to both sides of the equation. Then multiply both sides by $\frac{1}{2}$. To solve the equation on the right, add 4 to both sides.

$$2p = 5 \text{ or } p = 4$$

$$p = \frac{5}{2}$$

The solutions of $2p^2 - 13p + 20 = 0$ are $\frac{5}{2}$ and 4.

We can also use the zero-factor property to solve equations which have more than two factors, as shown in Example 5. (These equations are *not* quadratic equations—why not?)

EXAMPLE 5 Solve the equation $6z^3 - 6z = 0$.

First, factor out the greatest common factor in $6z^3 - 6z$.

$$6z^3 - 6z = 0$$
$$6z(z^2 - 1) = 0$$

Now factor $z^2 - 1$ as $(z + 1)(z - 1)$ to get

$$6z(z + 1)(z - 1) = 0.$$

This product can equal 0 only if at least one of the factors is 0. This means that we can now write three equations, one for each factor.

$$6z = 0 \quad \text{or} \quad z + 1 = 0 \quad \text{or} \quad z - 1 = 0 \;\cdot$$

After solving all three of these equations, we get the final solutions.

$$z = 0 \quad \text{or} \quad z = -1 \quad \text{or} \quad z = 1$$

EXAMPLE 6 Solve the equation $(2x - 1)(x^2 - 9x + 20) = 0$.

Factor $x^2 - 9x + 20$ as $(x - 5)(x - 4)$. Then we can rewrite the original equation as

$$(2x - 1)(x - 5)(x - 4) = 0.$$

Make each of these three factors equal to 0.

$$2x - 1 = 0 \quad \text{or} \quad x - 5 = 0 \quad \text{or} \quad x - 4 = 0$$

After solving all three of these equations, we end up with

$$x = \frac{1}{2} \quad \text{or} \quad x = 5 \quad \text{or} \quad x = 4$$

as the solutions of the original equation.

In general, to solve quadratic equations by factoring, go through the following steps.

To Solve a Quadratic Equation

Step 1   Get all terms on one side of the equals sign, with 0 on the other side.

Step 2   Factor completely.

Step 3   Set each factor containing a variable equal to 0, and solve the resulting equations.

Step 4   Check each solution in the original equation.

EXERCISES 4.5   *Solve each equation. See Example 1.*

1. $(x - 2)(x + 4) = 0$

2. $(y - 3)(y + 5) = 0$

3. $(3x + 5)(2x - 1) = 0$

4. $(2a + 3)(a - 2) = 0$

5. $(5p + 1)(2p - 1) = 0$

6. $(3k - 8)(k + 7) = 0$

7. $(2m + 9)(3m - 1) = 0$

8. $(9a - 2)(3a + 1) = 0$

9. $(x - 1)(3x + 5) = 0$

10. $(k - 3)(k + 5) = 0$

11. $(3r - 7)(2r + 8) = 0$

12. $(5a + 2)(3a - 1) = 0$

Solve each equation. See Examples 2 and 3.

13. $x^2 + 5x + 6 = 0$

14. $y^2 - 3y + 2 = 0$

15. $r^2 - 5r - 6 = 0$

16. $y^2 - y - 12 = 0$

17. $m^2 + 3m - 28 = 0$

18. $p^2 - p - 6 = 0$

19. $a^2 = 24 - 5a$

20. $r^2 = 2r + 15$

21. $x^2 = 3 + 2x$

22. $m^2 = 3m + 4$

23. $z^2 = -2 - 3z$

24. $p^2 = 2p + 3$

25. $m^2 + 8m + 16 = 0$

26. $b^2 - 6b + 9 = 0$

Solve each equation. See Example 4.

27. $3a^2 + 5a - 2 = 0$

28. $6r^2 - r - 2 = 0$

29. $2k^2 - k - 10 = 0$

30. $6x^2 - 7x - 5 = 0$

31. $6p^2 = 4 - 5p$

32. $6x^2 - 5x = 4$

33. $6a^2 = 5 - 13a$

34. $9s^2 + 12s = -4$

35. $2z^2 + 3z = 20$

36. $25p^2 + 20p + 4 = 0$

37. $3a^2 + 7a = 20$

38. $6z^2 + 11z + 3 = 0$

39. $15r^2 = r + 2$

40. $3m^2 = 5m + 28$

41. $2b^2 + 3b - 9 = 0$

42. $5b^2 = 8b + 4$

43. $16r^2 - 25 = 0$

44. $4k^2 - 9 = 0$

45. $9m^2 - 36 = 0$

46. $16x^2 - 64 = 0$

In each of the following exercises, first simplify and then solve.

47. $m(m - 7) = -10$

48. $z(2z + 7) = 4$

49. $2(x^2 - 66) = -13x$

50. $3(m^2 + 4) = 20m$

51. $3r(r + 1) = (2r + 3)(r + 1)$

52. $(3k + 1)(k + 1) = 2k(k + 3)$

53. $12k(k - 4) = 3(k - 4)$

54. $y^2 = 4(y - 1)$

Solve each equation. See Examples 5 and 6.

55. $(2r - 5)(3r^2 - 16r + 5) = 0$

56. $(3m - 4)(6m^2 + m - 2) = 0$

57. $(2x + 7)(x^2 - 2x - 3) = 0$

58. $(x - 1)(6x^2 + x - 12) = 0$

59. $x^3 - 25x = 0$

60. $m^3 - 4m = 0$

61. $9y^3 - 49y = 0$

62. $16r^3 - 9r = 0$

63. $r^3 - 2r^2 - 8r = 0$

64. $x^3 - x^2 - 6x = 0$

65. $a^3 + a^2 - 20a = 0$

66. $y^3 - 6y^2 + 8y = 0$

4.6 Applications of Quadratic Equations

- **Convert word problems to quadratic equations and solve them.**

In this section we look at problems whose solutions involve quadratic equations.

EXAMPLE 1 The width of a rectangle is 4 centimeters less than the length. The area is 96 square centimeters. Find the length and width.

We can use x to represent the length of the rectangle. Then, according to the statement of the problem, we can write the width as $x - 4$ (the width is less than the length). See Figure 4.1. The area of a rectangle is given by the formula

$$\text{area} = lw = \text{length} \times \text{width}.$$

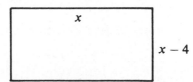

Figure 4.1

In our problem, the area is 96, the length is x, and the width is $x - 4$. We substitute these values into the formula.

$$96 = x(x - 4)$$
$$96 = x^2 - 4x$$

This is the quadratic equation

$$x^2 - 4x - 96 = 0.$$

Factor.

$$(x - 12)(x + 8) = 0$$

The solutions of the equations are $x = 12$ or $x = -8$.

However, the equation is only an algebraic representation of the area of a rectangle in the physical world. We must always be careful to check solutions against known physical facts. Since a rectangle cannot have a negative length, we discard the solution -8. Then 12 centimeters is the length of the rectangle, and $12 - 4 = 8$ centimeters is the width.

EXAMPLE 2   The length of a rectangle is 4 more than the width. The area of the rectangle is numerically 1 more than the perimeter. (See Figure 4.2.) Find the length and width of the rectangle.

$$\text{area} = x(x + 4)$$
$$\text{perimeter} = 2(x + 4) + 2x$$

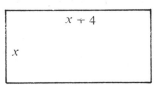

Figure 4.2

Let x be the width of the rectangle. Then the length is $x + 4$. The area is the product of the length and width or

$$\text{area} = x(x + 4).$$

The perimeter of a rectangle is given by the formula

$$P = 2l + 2w$$

In this problem, $l = x + 4$ and $w = x$, so that the perimeter is

$$P = 2(x + 4) + 2x.$$

According to the problem, the area is numerically 1 more than the perimeter.

The area	is	1	more than	the perimeter.
↓	↓	↓	↓	↓
$x(x + 4)$	=	1	+	$2(x + 4) + 2x$

Simplify and solve this equation.

$$x^2 + 4x = 1 + 2x + 8 + 2x$$
$$x^2 + 4x = 9 + 4x$$

$x^2 = 9$ Add $-4x$ to both sides

$x^2 - 9 = 0$ Add -9 to both sides

$(x + 3)(x - 3) = 0$ Factor

$x + 3 = 0$ or $x - 3 = 0$

$x = -3$ or $x = 3$

A rectangle cannot have a negative width, so we ignore $x = -3$. The answer is $x = 3$, so that

$$\text{width} = x = 3; \quad \text{length} = x + 4 = 3 + 4 = 7.$$

The rectangle is 3 by 7.

Quadratic equations often come up when we work problems about *consecutive integers*. Recall that these integers are in a row, such as 8 and 9, or 15 and 16. Consecutive *odd* integers are *odd* integers in a row, such as 5 and 7, or 19 and 21.

EXAMPLE 3   The product of two consecutive odd integers is one less than 5 times their sum. Find the integers.

Let's use s to represent the smaller of the two integers. Since the problem mentions consecutive *odd* integers, we use $s + 2$ for the larger of the two integers.

According to the problem, the product is 1 less than 5 times the sum.

The product	is	5 times sum	less one.
↓	↓	↓	↓
$s(s + 2)$	$=$	$5(s + s + 2)$	-1

Simplify this equation and solve it.

$$s^2 + 2s = 5s + 5s + 10 - 1$$
$$s^2 + 2s = 10s + 9$$
$$s^2 - 8s - 9 = 0$$
$$(s - 9)(s + 1) = 0$$

$s - 9 = 0$ or $s + 1 = 0$

$s = 9$ or $s = -1.$

We need to find two consecutive odd integers.

If $s = 9$ is the first, then $s + 2 = 11$ is the second.

If $s = -1$ is the first, then $s + 2 = 1$ is the second.

There are two pairs of integers satisfying our problem: 9 and 11 or -1 and 1.

EXERCISES 4.6   *Solve each problem. See Examples 1 and 2.*

1. The length of a rectangle is 5 centimeters more than the width. The area is 66 square centimeters. Find the length and width of the rectangle.

2. The length of a rectangle is 1 foot more than the width. The area is 56 square feet. Find the length and width of the rectangle.

3. The width of a rectangle is 3 meters less than its length. The area of the rectangle is 70 square meters. Find the dimensions of the rectangle.

4. The width of a rectangle is 7 meters less than its length. The area is 8 square meters. Find the dimensions of the rectangle.

5. The length of a rectangle is twice its width. If the width were increased by 2 inches, while the length remained the same, the resulting rectangle would have an area of 48 square inches. Find the dimensions of the original rectangle.

6. The length of a rectangle is 3 times its width. If the length were decreased by 1, while the width stayed the same, the area of the new figure would be 44 square centimeters. Find the length and width of the original rectangle.

7. The length of a rectangle is 3 more than the width. The area is numerically 4 less than the perimeter. Find the dimensions of the rectangle.

8. The width of a rectangle is 5 less than the length. The area is numerically 10 more than the perimeter. Find the dimensions of the rectangle.

Problems 9 and 10 require the formula for the area of a triangle.

$$\text{Area} = \frac{1}{2}bh$$

9. The area of a triangle is 25 square centimeters. The base is twice the height. Find the length of the base and the height of the triangle.

10. The height of a triangle is 3 inches more than the base. The area of the triangle is 27 square inches. Find the length of the base and the height of the triangle.

Problems 11 and 12 require the formula for the volume of a pyramid.

$$V = \frac{1}{3}Bh, \text{ where } B \text{ is the area of the base}$$

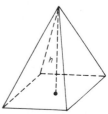

11. The volume of a pyramid is 32 cubic meters. Suppose the numerical value of the height is 10 meters less than the numerical value of the area of the base. Find the height and area of the base.

12. Suppose a pyramid has a rectangular base whose width is three centimeters less than the length. If the height is 8 and the volume is 144, find the dimensions of the base.

Work the following problems. See Example 2.

13. One square has sides one foot less than the length of the sides of a second square. If the difference of the areas of the two squares is 37 square feet, find the lengths of the sides of the two squares.

14. The sides of one square have a length 2 meters more than the sides of another square. If the area of the larger square is subtracted from three times the area of the smaller square, the answer is 12 square meters. Find the lengths of the sides of each square.

15. John wishes to build a box to hold his tools. The box is to be 4 feet high, and the width of the box is to be one foot less than the length. The volume of the box will be 120 cubic feet. Find the length and height of the box. (Hint: The formula for the volume of a box is given by $V = lwh$.)

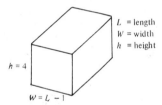

16. The volume of a box must be 315 cubic meters. The length of the box is to be 7 meters, and the height is to be 4 meters more than the length. Find the width and height of the box.

Work the following problems. See Example 3.

17. The product of two consecutive integers is two more than twice their sum. Find the integers.

18. The product of two consecutive even integers is 60 more than twice the larger. Find the integers.

19. Find three consecutive even integers such that four times the sum of all three equals the product of the smaller two.

20. One number is four more than another. The square of the smaller increased by three times the larger is 66. Find the numbers.

21. If the square of the sum of two consecutive integers is reduced by three times their product, the result is 31. Find the integers.

22. If the square of the larger of two numbers is reduced by six times the

smaller, the result is five times the larger. The larger is twice the smaller. Find the numbers.

23. The sum of three times the square of an integer and twice the integer is 8. Find the integer.

24. When four times an integer is subtracted from twice the square of the integer, the result is 16. Find the integer.

Work the following problems involving formulas.
If an object is dropped, the distance d it falls in t seconds (disregarding air resistance) is given by

$$d = \frac{1}{2}gt^2,$$

where g is approximately 32 feet per second per second. Find the distance an object would fall in

25. 4 seconds   26. 8 seconds

How long would it take an object to fall

27. 1600 feet   28. 2304 feet

If an object is projected straight up with an initial velocity of v_0 feet per second, its height h after t seconds is given by

$$h = v_0t - 16t^2.$$

Suppose an object is thrown upward with an initial velocity of 64 feet per second. Find its height after

29. 1 second   30. 2 seconds   31. 3 seconds

32. When will the object hit the ground? (Hint: It will hit the ground when $h = 0$.)

4.7 Solving Quadratic Inequalities (Optional)

- **Solve quadratic inequalities and graph the answer.**

A **quadratic inequality** is an inequality that involves a second degree polynomial. Examples of quadratic inequalities include

$$2x^2 + 3x - 5 < 0, \; x^2 \le 4, \text{ and } x^2 + 5x + 6 > 0.$$

Examples 1 and 2 show how to solve these inequalities.

EXAMPLE 1   Solve $x^2 - x - 6 > 0$.

Factor $x^2 - x - 6$:

$$x^2 - x - 6 > 0$$

becomes $(x - 3)(x + 2) > 0$.

The product $(x - 3)(x + 2)$ will be positive if both the factors are positive, or if both the factors are negative. The factor $x - 3$ will be positive if

$$x - 3 > 0$$

or

$$x > 3,$$

and will be negative if $x < 3$. The factor $x + 2$ will be positive if $x > -2$ and will be negative if $x < -2$. These results are shown on the **sign graph** of Figure 4.3.

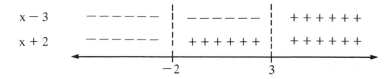

Figure 4.3

As shown on the sign graph, both factors are negative if $x < -2$, so that the product $(x - 3)(x + 2)$ will be positive.

Both factors are positive if $x > 3$, so that the product $(x - 3)(x + 2)$ is also positive. In summary, the solution of $x^2 - x - 6 > 0$ is

$$x < -2 \quad \text{or} \quad x > 3.$$

The solution is graphed in Figure 4.4.

Figure 4.4

A word of warning: there is no shortcut way to write the solution $x < -2$ or $x > 3$.

EXAMPLE 2 Solve $m^2 - 3m - 10 \le 0$.
Factor to get

$$(m - 5)(m + 2) \le 0$$

Make a sign graph. The factor $m - 5$ is negative if $m < 5$, and positive if $m > 5$. The factor $m + 2$ is negative if $m < -2$, and positive if $m > -2$. The sign graph for these factors is shown in Figure 4.5.

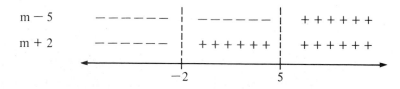

Figure 4.5

The product $(m - 5)(m + 2)$ will be negative only when the two factors $m - 5$ and $m + 2$ have different signs. As shown in Figure 4.5, this happens only when m is between -2 and 5. Because of the $\leq$ symbol (instead of just $<$), the endpoints -2 and 5 also belong to the solution. The final solution is written

$$-2 \leq m \leq 5.$$

The solution is graphed in Figure 4.6.

Figure 4.6

EXERCISES 4.7   *Solve each inequality and graph each solution. See Examples 1 and 2.*

1. $(m + 2)(m - 5) < 0$ **2.** $(k - 1)(k + 3) > 0$

3. $(t + 6)(t + 5) \geq 0$ **4.** $(g - 2)(g - 4) \leq 0$

5. $(a + 3)(a - 3) < 0$ **6.** $(b - 2)(b + 2) > 0$

7. $(a + 6)(a - 7) \geq 0$ **8.** $(z - 5)(z - 4) \leq 0$

9. $m^2 + 5m + 6 > 0$ **10.** $y^2 - 3y + 2 < 0$

11. $z^2 - 4z - 5 \leq 0$ **12.** $3p^2 - 5p - 2 \leq 0$

13. $5m^2 + 3m - 2 < 0$ **14.** $2k^2 + 7k - 4 > 0$

15. $6r^2 - 5r - 4 < 0$ **16.** $6r^2 + 7r - 3 > 0$

17. $a^2 - 16 < 0$ **18.** $9m^2 - 36 > 0$

19. $r^2 - 100 \geq 0$ **20.** $q^2 - 7q + 6 < 0$

21. $2k^2 - 7k - 15 \leq 0$ **22.** $6m^2 + m - 1 > 0$

23. $30r^2 + 3r - 6 \leq 0$ **24.** $12p^2 + 11p + 2 < 0$

25. $r^2 > 16$ **26.** $m^2 \geq 25$

The following inequalities are not quadratic inequalities, but they may be solved in a similar manner.

27. $(a + 2)(3a - 1)(a - 4) \geq 0$ **28.** $(2p - 7)(p - 1)(p + 3) \leq 0$

29. $(r - 2)(r^2 - 3r - 4) < 0$ **30.** $(m + 5)(m^2 - m - 6) > 0$

Chapter 4 Test

[**4.1–4.4**]   *Factor as completely as possible.*

1. $16m^2 - 24m$ **2.** $6xy + 12y^2$

3. $28pq + 14p + 56p^2$ **4.** $3m^2n + 9mn + 6mn^2$

5. $12p + 11r$ **6.** $x^2 + 11x + 30$

7. $p^2 + 6p - 7$ **8.** $2y^2 - 7y - 15$

9. $4m^2 + 4m - 3$

10. $3x^2 + 13x - 10$

11. $10z^2 + 7z + 1$

12. $10a^2 - 23a - 5$

13. $12r^2 + 19r + 5$

14. $m^2 + 11m + 14$

15. $a^2 + 3ab - 10b^2$

16. $6r^2 - rs - 2s^2$

17. $x^2 - 25$

18. $25m^2 - 49$

19. $4p^2 + 12p + 9$

20. $25z^2 - 10z + 1$

21. $4p^3 + 16p^2 + 16p$

22. $10m^4 + 55m^3 + 25m^2$

[**4.5**] *Solve each equation.*

23. $y^2 + 3y + 2 = 0$

24. $3x^2 + 5x = 2$

25. $2p^2 + 3p = 20$

26. $x^2 - 4 = 0$

27. $z^3 = 16z$

[**4.6**] *Write an equation for each problem and solve it.*

28. The length of a certain rectangle is one inch less than twice the width. The area is 15 square inches. Find the dimensions.

29. The length of a rectangle is 7 more than the width. The area is numerically 4 more than the perimeter. Find the length and width of the rectangle.

30. One number is nine larger than another. Their product is eleven more than five times their sum. Find the numbers.

[**4.7**] *Graph the solution of each quadratic inequality.*

31. $m^2 + 2m - 24 > 0$

32. $2p^2 + 5p - 3 \le 0$

33. $6r^2 + r - 2 \ge 0$

5

Rational Expressions

5.1 The Fundamental Property of Rational Expressions

- **Find the numerical value of a rational expression.**
- **Reduce a rational expression to lowest terms.**

The quotient of two integers (with denominator not 0) is called a rational number.* In the same way, the quotient of two polynomials is called a **rational expression.** Examples of rational expressions include

$$\frac{-6x}{x^3 + 8}, \qquad \frac{9x}{y + 3}, \qquad \frac{2m^3}{8}.$$

However, $\frac{8x}{0}$ is not a rational expression since division by zero is not possible. For that reason, be careful when substituting a number for the variable in the denominator of a rational expression. For example, in the rational expression

$$\frac{8x^2}{x - 3}$$

---

*A review of the arithmetic of fractions is given in Appendix A of this book. Also, see the Study Guide.

x can take on any numerical value except 3. When $x = 3$, the denominator of the rational expression becomes zero, making the expression meaningless.

EXAMPLE 1   Find any values for which the following rational expressions are meaningless.

(a) $\dfrac{p + 5}{p + 2}$

Since $p = -2$ will make the denominator equal to 0, the expression is meaningless for -2.

(b) $\dfrac{9m^2}{m^2 - 5m + 6}$

To find the numbers which will make the denominator 0, we must solve

$$m^2 - 5m + 6 = 0.$$

We can factor the polynomial and set each factor equal to 0.

$$(m - 2)(m - 3) = 0.$$

$$m - 2 = 0 \quad \text{or} \quad m - 3 = 0$$
$$m = 2 \quad \text{or} \quad m = 3$$

The expression is meaningless for 2 and for 3.

(c) $\dfrac{2r}{r^2 + 1}$

This denominator is never equal to 0, so that there are no values for which the rational expression is meaningless.

EXAMPLE 2   Find the numerical value of $\dfrac{3x + 6}{2x - 4}$ for each value of x.

(a) $x = 1$

We find the value of the rational expression by substitution.

$$\frac{3x + 6}{2x - 4} = \frac{3(1) + 6}{2(1) - 4}$$

$$= \frac{9}{-2}$$

$$= -\frac{9}{2}$$

(b) $x = 2$

If we substitute 2 for x, the denominator is zero. Thus there is no value for the rational expression when $x = 2$.

A rational expression represents a number for each value of the variable that does not make the denominator equal 0. Thus, the properties of rational numbers also apply to rational expressions. In order to reduce a rational expression to lowest terms, we use the **fundamental property of rational expressions:**

If $\dfrac{P}{Q}$ is a rational expression, and if K represents any rational expression, where $K \neq 0$, then

$$\frac{PK}{QK} = \frac{P}{Q}.$$

EXAMPLE 3 Reduce $\dfrac{14k^2}{2k^3}$ to lowest terms.

First factor the rational expression. Then use the fundamental property.

$$\frac{14k^2}{2k^3} = \frac{2 \cdot 7 \cdot k \cdot k}{2 \cdot k \cdot k \cdot k}$$

$$= \frac{7(2kk)}{k(2kk)}$$

$$= \frac{7}{k}$$

EXAMPLE 4 Reduce $\dfrac{3x - 12}{5x - 20}$ to lowest terms.

Begin by factoring both numerator and denominator. Then use the fundamental property.

$$\frac{3x - 12}{5x - 20} = \frac{3(x - 4)}{5(x - 4)}$$

$$= \frac{3}{5}$$

EXAMPLE 5 Reduce $\dfrac{m^2 + 2m - 8}{2m^2 - m - 6}$ to lowest terms.

Always begin by factoring both numerator and denominator, if possible. Then use the fundamental property.

$$\frac{m^2 + 2m - 8}{2m^2 - m - 6} = \frac{(m + 4)(m - 2)}{(2m + 3)(m - 2)} = \frac{m + 4}{2m + 3}$$

EXAMPLE 6 Reduce $\dfrac{x - y}{y - x}$ to lowest terms.

At first glance, there does not seem to be any way in which we can factor $x - y$ and $y - x$ to get a common factor. However,

$$y - x = -1(-y + x)$$

$$= -1(x - y).$$

With these factors, use the fundamental property to simplify the rational expression.

$$\frac{x - y}{y - x} = \frac{1(x - y)}{-1(x - y)}$$

$$= \frac{1}{-1}$$

$$= -1$$

EXERCISES 5.1 *Find any values for which the following are not defined. See Example 1.*

1. $\dfrac{3}{4x}$

2. $\dfrac{5}{2x}$

3. $\dfrac{8}{x - 4}$

4. $\dfrac{6}{x + 3}$

5. $\dfrac{x^2}{x + 5}$

6. $\dfrac{3x^2}{2x - 1}$

7. $\dfrac{a + 4}{a^2 - 8a + 15}$

8. $\dfrac{p + 6}{p^2 - p - 12}$

9. $\dfrac{8r + 2}{2r^2 - r - 3}$

10. $\dfrac{7k + 2}{3k^2 - k - 10}$

11. $\dfrac{9y}{y^2 + 16}$

12. $\dfrac{12z}{z^2 + 100}$

Find the numerical value of the expression when (a) $x = 2$ *and (b)* $x = -3$. *See Example 2.*

13. $\dfrac{x^3}{2x^2}$

14. $\dfrac{-5x + 1}{2x}$

15. $\dfrac{4x^2 - 2x}{3x}$

16. $\dfrac{x^2 - 1}{x}$

17. $\dfrac{(-8x)^2}{3x + 9}$

18. $\dfrac{2x^2 + 5}{3 + x}$

19. $\dfrac{x + 8}{x^2 - 4x + 2}$

20. $\dfrac{2x - 1}{x^2 - 7x + 3}$

21. $\dfrac{5x^2}{6 - 3x - x^2}$

22. $\dfrac{-2x^2}{8 + x - x^2}$

Reduce to lowest terms. If possible, factor the numerator and denominator first. See Examples 3–5.

23. $\dfrac{2y}{3y}$

24. $\dfrac{5m}{10}$

25. $\dfrac{12k^2}{6k}$

26. $\dfrac{9m^3}{3m}$

27. $\dfrac{-8y^6}{6y^3}$ **28.** $\dfrac{16x^4}{-8x^2}$

29. $\dfrac{12m^2p}{9mp^2}$ **30.** $\dfrac{6a^2b^3}{24a^3b^2}$

31. $\dfrac{6(y+2)}{8(y+2)}$ **32.** $\dfrac{9(m+2)}{5(m+2)}$

33. $\dfrac{(x+1)(x-1)}{(x+1)^2}$ **34.** $\dfrac{3(t+5)}{(t+5)(t-1)}$

35. $\dfrac{m^2-n^2}{m+n}$ **36.** $\dfrac{a^2-b^2}{a-b}$

37. $\dfrac{5m^2-5m}{10m-10}$ **38.** $\dfrac{3y^2-3y}{2(y-1)}$

39. $\dfrac{16r^2-4s^2}{4r-2s}$ **40.** $\dfrac{11s^2-22s^3}{6-12s}$

41. $\dfrac{m^2-4m+4}{m^2+m-6}$ **42.** $\dfrac{a^2-a-6}{a^2+a-12}$

43. $\dfrac{x^2+3x-4}{x^2-1}$ **44.** $\dfrac{8m^2+6m-9}{16m^2-9}$

Reduce to lowest terms. See Example 6.

45. $\dfrac{-a+b}{b-a}$ **46.** $\dfrac{b-a}{a-b}$

47. $\dfrac{x^2-1}{1-x}$ **48.** $\dfrac{p^2-q^2}{q-p}$

49. $\dfrac{m^2-4m}{4m-m^2}$ **50.** $\dfrac{s^2-r^2}{r^2-s^2}$

5.2 Multiplication and Division of Rational Expressions

- **Multiply rational expressions.**
- **Divide rational expressions.**

To multiply two fractions, we multiply the numerators and multiply the denominators. The same rule applies to multiplication of rational expressions.

The product of the rational expressions $\dfrac{P}{Q}$ and $\dfrac{R}{S}$ is

$$\frac{P}{Q} \cdot \frac{R}{S} = \frac{PR}{QS}.$$

EXAMPLE 1   Find the product of $\dfrac{6}{x}$ and $\dfrac{x^2}{12}$.

Using the definition of multiplication, we find the product of the numerators and the product of the denominators.

$$\frac{6}{x} \cdot \frac{x^2}{12} = \frac{6 \cdot x^2}{x \cdot 12}$$

$$= \frac{x}{2}$$

In the last step, use the fundamental property to reduce to lowest terms.

EXAMPLE 2   Find the product $\dfrac{x + y}{2x} \cdot \dfrac{x^2}{(x + y)^2}.$

Using the definition of multiplication,

$$\frac{x + y}{2x} \cdot \frac{x^2}{(x + y)^2} = \frac{(x + y)x^2}{2x(x + y)^2}$$

$$= \frac{(x + y)x \cdot x}{2x(x + y)(x + y)}$$

$$= \frac{x}{2(x + y)}.$$

In the last two steps, factor and use the fundamental property of rational expressions to reduce the answer to lowest terms.

EXAMPLE 3   Find the product.

$$\frac{x^2 + 3x}{x^2 - 3x - 4} \cdot \frac{x^2 - 5x + 4}{x^2 + 2x - 3}$$

Use the definition of multiplication. However, before multiplying, factor the numerators and denominators whenever possible. Then use the fundamental property to reduce to lowest terms.

$$\frac{x^2 + 3x}{x^2 - 3x - 4} \cdot \frac{x^2 - 5x + 4}{x^2 + 2x - 3} = \frac{x(x + 3)}{(x - 4)(x + 1)} \cdot \frac{(x - 4)(x - 1)}{(x + 3)(x - 1)}$$

$$= \frac{x(x + 3)(x - 4)(x - 1)}{(x - 4)(x + 1)(x + 3)(x - 1)}$$

$$= \frac{x}{x + 1}$$

Notice in the second step above that we do not multiply the factors together, since we want to look for common factors to reduce the product to lowest terms.

To *divide* the fraction $\dfrac{a}{b}$ by the nonzero fraction $\dfrac{c}{d}$, we multiply $\dfrac{a}{b}$ by the reciprocal of $\dfrac{c}{d}$, which is $\dfrac{d}{c}$. Division of rational expressions is defined in the same way.

If $\dfrac{P}{Q}$ and $\dfrac{R}{S}$ are any two rational expressions, with $\dfrac{R}{S} \neq 0$, then their quotient is

$$\frac{P}{Q} \div \frac{R}{S} = \frac{P}{Q} \cdot \frac{S}{R} = \frac{PS}{QR}.$$

EXAMPLE 4 Find the quotient.

$$\frac{y}{y+3} \div \frac{y}{y+5}$$

Multiply by the reciprocal of the second rational expression.

$$\frac{y}{y+3} \div \frac{y}{y+5} = \frac{y}{y+3} \cdot \frac{y+5}{y}$$

$$= \frac{y(y+5)}{(y+3)y}$$

$$= \frac{y+5}{y+3}$$

This result cannot be further reduced.

EXAMPLE 5 Find the quotient.

$$\frac{(3m)^2}{(2n)^3} \div \frac{6m^3}{16n^2} = \frac{9m^2}{8n^3} \div \frac{6m^3}{16n^2}$$

$$= \frac{9m^2}{8n^3} \cdot \frac{16n^2}{6m^3}$$

$$= \frac{9 \cdot 16m^2n^2}{8 \cdot 6n^3m^3}$$

$$= \frac{3}{mn}$$

EXAMPLE 6 Find the quotient.

$$\frac{x^2-4}{(x+3)(x-2)} \div \frac{(x+2)(x+3)}{2x}$$

First, use the definition of division.

$$\frac{x^2-4}{(x+3)(x-2)} \div \frac{(x+2)(x+3)}{2x} = \frac{x^2-4}{(x+3)(x-2)} \cdot \frac{2x}{(x+2)(x+3)}$$

Next, be sure all numerators and all denominators are factored. Here, we factor $x^2 - 4$. Recall that $x^2 - 4 = (x+2)(x-2)$.

$$\frac{x^2-4}{(x+3)(x-2)} \div \frac{(x+2)(x+3)}{2x} = \frac{(x+2)(x-2)}{(x+3)(x-2)} \cdot \frac{2x}{(x+2)(x+3)}$$

Now multiply the numerators and the denominators and simplify.

$$= \frac{(x + 2)(x - 2)(2x)}{(x + 3)(x - 2)(x + 2)(x + 3)}$$

$$= \frac{2x}{(x + 3)^2}.$$

EXAMPLE 7   Find the quotient.

$$\frac{m^2 - 4}{m^2 - 1} \div \frac{2m^2 + 4m}{1 - m}$$

Use the definition of division.

$$\frac{m^2 - 4}{m^2 - 1} \div \frac{2m^2 + 4m}{1 - m} = \frac{m^2 - 4}{m^2 - 1} \cdot \frac{1 - m}{2m^2 + 4m}$$

$$= \frac{(m + 2)(m - 2)}{(m + 1)(m - 1)} \cdot \frac{1 - m}{2m(m + 2)}$$

Since $\dfrac{1 - m}{m - 1} = -1$, we end up with

$$= \frac{-1(m - 2)}{2m(m + 1)}$$

$$= \frac{2 - m}{2m(m + 1)}.$$

EXERCISES 5.2   *Find each product or quotient. Write each answer in lowest terms. See Examples 1 and 5.*

1. $\dfrac{9m^2}{16} \cdot \dfrac{4}{3m}$

2. $\dfrac{21z^4}{8y} \cdot \dfrac{4y^3}{7z^5}$

3. $\dfrac{4p^2}{8p} \cdot \dfrac{3p^3}{16p^4}$

4. $\dfrac{6x^3}{9x} \cdot \dfrac{12x}{x^2}$

5. $\dfrac{8a^4}{12a^3} \cdot \dfrac{9a^5}{3a^2}$

6. $\dfrac{14p^5}{2p^2} \cdot \dfrac{8p^6}{28p^9}$

7. $\dfrac{3r^2}{9r^3} \div \dfrac{8r^4}{6r^5}$

8. $\dfrac{15m^{10}}{9m^5} \div \dfrac{6m^6}{10m^4}$

9. $\dfrac{3m^2}{(4m)^3} \div \dfrac{9m^3}{32m^4}$

10. $\dfrac{5x^3}{(4x)^2} \div \dfrac{15x^2}{8x^4}$

Find each product or quotient. Write each answer in lowest terms. See Examples 2, 3, 4, 6, and 7.

11. $\dfrac{a + b}{2} \cdot \dfrac{12}{(a + b)^2}$

12. $\dfrac{3(x - 1)}{y} \cdot \dfrac{2y}{5(x - 1)}$

13. $\dfrac{a - 3}{16} \div \dfrac{a - 3}{32}$

14. $\dfrac{9}{8 - 2y} \div \dfrac{3}{4 - y}$

15. $\dfrac{2k + 8}{6} \div \dfrac{3k + 12}{2}$

16. $\dfrac{5m + 25}{10} \cdot \dfrac{12}{6m + 30}$

17. $\dfrac{9y - 18}{6y + 12} \cdot \dfrac{3y + 6}{15y - 30}$

18. $\dfrac{12p + 24}{36p - 36} \div \dfrac{6p + 12}{8p - 8}$

19. $\dfrac{3r + 12}{8} \cdot \dfrac{16r}{9r + 36}$

20. $\dfrac{2r + 2p}{8z} \div \dfrac{r^2 + rp}{72}$

21. $\dfrac{y^2 - 16}{y + 3} \div \dfrac{y - 4}{y^2 - 9}$

22. $\dfrac{9(y - 4)^2}{8(z + 3)^2} \cdot \dfrac{16(z + 3)}{3(y - 4)}$

23. $\dfrac{6(m + 2)}{3(m - 1)^2} \div \dfrac{(m + 2)^2}{9(m - 1)}$

24. $\dfrac{4y + 12}{2y - 10} \div \dfrac{y^2 - 9}{y^2 - y - 20}$

25. $\dfrac{2 - y}{8} \cdot \dfrac{7}{y - 2}$

26. $\dfrac{9 - 2z}{3} \cdot \dfrac{9}{2z - 9}$

27. $\dfrac{8 - r}{8 + r} \div \dfrac{r - 8}{r + 8}$

28. $\dfrac{6r - 18}{3r^2 + 2r - 8} \cdot \dfrac{12r - 16}{4r - 12}$

29. $\dfrac{k^2 - k - 6}{k^2 + k - 12} \div \dfrac{k^2 + 2k - 3}{k^2 + 3k - 4}$

30. $\dfrac{m^2 + 3m + 2}{m^2 + 5m + 4} \cdot \dfrac{m^2 + 10m + 24}{m^2 + 5m + 6}$

31. $\dfrac{n^2 - n - 6}{n^2 - 2n - 8} \cdot \dfrac{n^2 + 7n + 12}{n^2 - 9}$

32. $\dfrac{6n^2 - 5n - 6}{6n^2 + 5n - 6} \cdot \dfrac{12n^2 - 17n + 6}{12n^2 - n - 6}$

33. $\dfrac{16 - r^2}{r^2 + 2r - 8} \div \dfrac{r^2 - 2r - 8}{4 - r^2}$

34. $\dfrac{y^2 + y - 2}{y^2 + 3y - 4} \div \dfrac{y + 2}{y + 3}$

35. $\dfrac{2m^2 - 5m - 12}{m^2 - 10m + 24} \div \dfrac{4m^2 - 9}{m^2 - 9m + 18}$

36. $\dfrac{9z^2 + 27zm}{9m^2 + 27zm} \div \dfrac{8zm + 24m^2}{16zm + 48z^2}$

37. $\dfrac{21p^2 - 20pq - q^2}{p^2 + pq - 2q^2} \div \dfrac{21p^2 + 22pq + q^2}{p^2 + pq - 2q^2}$

38. $\dfrac{2m^2 + 7m + 3}{m^2 - 9} \cdot \dfrac{m^2 - 3m}{2m^2 + 11m + 5}$

39. $\dfrac{(x + 1)^3(x + 4)}{x^2 + 5x + 4} \div \dfrac{x^2 + 2x + 1}{x^2 + 3x + 2}$

40. $\dfrac{m^2 - m - 6}{3m^2 + 10m + 8} \cdot \dfrac{6m^2 + 17m + 12}{4m^2 - 9}$

41. $\left(\dfrac{x^2 + 10x + 25}{x^2 + 10x} \cdot \dfrac{10x}{x^2 + 15x + 50}\right) \div \dfrac{x + 5}{x + 10}$

42. $\left(\dfrac{m^2 - 12m + 32}{8m} \cdot \dfrac{m^2 - 8m}{m^2 - 8m + 16}\right) \div \dfrac{m - 8}{m - 4}$

5.3 Least Common Denominators

- **Find least common denominators.**
- **Write rational expressions with given denominators.**

When we get to addition and subtraction of rational expressions in the next section, we will need to find least common denominators for many of the problems. A **least common denominator** is an expression that all denominators of a problem divide into without remainder. For example, the least common denominator for $\dfrac{2}{9}$ and $\dfrac{5}{12}$ is 36, since 36 is the smallest number that both 9 and 12 divide into.

Least common denominators are found with a procedure very similar to that used in Chapter 4 for finding the greatest common factor.

EXAMPLE 1   Find the least common denominator for the denominators $8x$ and $10x$.

Write each denominator in factored form, with numerical coefficients in prime factored form.

$$8x = 2 \cdot 2 \cdot 2 \cdot x \qquad 10x = 2 \cdot 5 \cdot x$$

The least common denominator is found by taking each factor the *most* number of times it appears. Here 2 appears three times in one product, and once in the other. The most number of times the 2 appears is 3. The most number of times the 5 appears is 1, and the most number of times x appears in either product is 1. Thus,

$$\text{least common denominator} = 2 \cdot 2 \cdot 2 \cdot 5 \cdot x$$
$$= 40x.$$

EXAMPLE 2   Find the least common denominator for $6r^2$ and $4r^3$.

Factor each denominator:

$$6r^2 = 2 \cdot 3 \cdot r^2 \qquad 4r^3 = 2 \cdot 2 \cdot r^3$$

The most number of times 2 appears is 2; the most number of times 3 appears is 1, and the most number of times r appears is 3, so that

$$\text{least common denominator} = 2 \cdot 2 \cdot 3 \cdot r^3$$
$$= 12r^3.$$

EXAMPLE 3   Find the least common denominator.

(a) $5m,\ m^2 - 3m$

Factor each denominator:

$$5m = 5 \cdot m \qquad m^2 - 3m = m(m - 3)$$

Take each factor the most number of times it appears:

$$\text{least common denominator} = 5 \cdot m \cdot (m - 3)$$
$$= 5m(m - 3)$$

(b) $r^2 - 4r - 5, r^2 - r - 20$

Factor each denominator:

$$r^2 - 4r - \ 5 = (r - 5)(r + 1)$$
$$r^2 - \ r - 20 = (r - 5)(r + 4)$$

The least common denominator is

$$(r - 5)(r + 1)(r + 4).$$

To find the least common denominator for a list of denominators:

Step 1 Factor all denominators.
Step 2 Take each factor the *most* number of times that it appears.

Once we find the least common denominator for a problem, we need to use the fundamental property to rewrite a rational expression so that it has this least common denominator. The next example shows how to do this.

EXAMPLE 4 Write each rational expression so that it has the indicated denominator.

(a) $\dfrac{9k}{25}$, denominator of $50k$

The given rational expression has a denominator of 25. To get $50k$ from 25, we must multiply by $2k$.

$$\frac{9k}{25} = \frac{9k(2k)}{25(2k)}$$
$$= \frac{18k^2}{50k}$$

(b) $\dfrac{6}{m - 1}$, denominator of $m^2 - m$

Since $m^2 - m = m(m - 1)$, multiply numerator and denominator of the given rational expression by m.

$$\frac{6}{m - 1} = \frac{6m}{(m - 1)m}$$

$$= \frac{6m}{m^2 - m}$$

(c) $\dfrac{12p}{p^2 + 8p}$, denominator of $p(p + 8)(p - 4)$

Factor $p^2 + 8p$ as $p(p + 8)$. This shows that we must multiply by $p - 4$.

$$\frac{12p}{p^2 + 8p} = \frac{12p}{p(p + 8)}$$

$$= \frac{12p(p - 4)}{p(p + 8)(p - 4)}$$

EXERCISES 5.3   *Find the least common denominator for the following lists of denominators. See Examples 1, 2, and 3.*

1. 12, 10

2. 4, 6

3. 15, 20, 24

4. 10, 25, 35

5. 100, 120, 180

6. 250, 300, 360

7. $5p, 6p$

8. $15k, 4k$

9. $25m, 30m$

10. $40a, 60a$

11. $15y^2, 36y^4$

12. $25m^3, 10m^4$

13. $50r^5, 60r^3$

14. $25a^5, 80a^6$

15. $6p, 4p - 8$

16. $8k, 12k - 24$

17. $32r^2, 16r - 32$

18. $18m^3, 9m - 36$

19. $6r - 12, 9r - 18$

20. $5p - 30, 6p - 36$

21. $12p + 60, p^2 + 5p$

22. $r^2 + 7r, 5r + 35$

23. $8y + 16, y^2 + 3y + 2$

24. $9m - 18, m^2 - 7m + 10$

25. $a^2 + 6a, a^2 + 3a - 18$

26. $y^2 - 5y, y^2 - 2y - 15$

27. $k^2 + 2k - 35, k^2 + 3k - 40$

28. $z^2 + 4z - 12, z^2 + z - 30$

29. $2y^2 + 7y - 4, 2y^2 - 7y + 3$

30. $5a^2 + 13a - 6, 5a^2 - 22a + 8$

31. $6r^2 - r - 15, 3r^2 - 8r + 5$

32. $2m^2 - 11m + 14, 2m^2 - m - 21$

Write each rational expression with the given denominator. See Example 4.

33. $\dfrac{7}{11}$,   66

34. $\dfrac{5}{8}$,   56

35. $\dfrac{9}{r}$, $6r$

36. $\dfrac{7}{k}$, $9k$

37. $\dfrac{-11}{m}$, $8m$

38. $\dfrac{-5}{z}$ $6z$

39. $\dfrac{12}{35y}$, $70y^3$

40. $\dfrac{17}{9r}$, $36r^2$

41. $\dfrac{15m^2}{8k}$, $32k^4$

42. $\dfrac{5t^2}{3y}$, $9y^2$

43. $\dfrac{19z}{2z-6}$, $6z-18$

44. $\dfrac{2r}{5r-5}$, $15r-15$

45. $\dfrac{-2a}{9a-18}$, $18a-36$

46. $\dfrac{-5y}{6y+18}$, $24y+72$

47. $\dfrac{6}{k^2-4k}$, $k(k-4)(k+1)$

48. $\dfrac{15}{m^2-9m}$, $m(m-9)(m+8)$

49. $\dfrac{36r}{r^2-r-6}$, $(r-3)(r+2)(r+1)$

50. $\dfrac{4m}{m^2-8m+15}$, $(m-5)(m-3)(m+2)$

5.4 Addition and Subtraction of Rational Expressions

- **Add rational expressions having the same denominator.**
- **Add rational expressions having different denominators.**
- **Subtract rational expressions.**

To find the sum of two rational expressions, we use a procedure similar to adding two fractions.

If P and Q are rational expressions, then

$$\frac{P}{Q} + \frac{R}{Q} = \frac{P+R}{Q}.$$

EXAMPLE 1 Add $\dfrac{3x}{x+1} + \dfrac{2x}{x+1}$.

Since the denominators are the same, the sum is found by adding the two numerators and keeping the same (common) denominator.

$$\frac{3x}{x+1} + \frac{2x}{x+1} = \frac{3x+2x}{x+1}$$

$$= \frac{5x}{x+1}$$

If the denominators of the two rational expressions to be added are different, the following steps are required. These are the same steps used to add fractions with different denominators.

To Add Rational Expressions

Step 1   Find the least common denominator.

Step 2   Rewrite each rational expression as a fraction with the least common denominator as the denominator.

Step 3   Add the numerators to get the numerator of the sum. The least common denominator is the denominator of the sum.

EXAMPLE 2   Add: $\dfrac{2}{3y} + \dfrac{1}{4y}$.

Using the methods of the last section, the least common denominator is found to be $12y$: the smallest expression that both $3y$ and $4y$ will divide into.

In the first term, $\dfrac{2}{3y}$, multiply both the numerator and denominator by 4 to get the least common denominator of $12y$ and still leave the value of the fraction unchanged.

Multiply the numerator and denominator of the second fraction, $\dfrac{1}{4y}$, by 3, to get $12y$ as the least common denominator. Doing all this gives

$$\frac{2}{3y} + \frac{1}{4y} = \frac{2(4)}{3y(4)} + \frac{1(3)}{4y(3)}$$

$$= \frac{8}{12y} + \frac{3}{12y}$$

$$= \frac{11}{12y}.$$

EXAMPLE 3   Add $\dfrac{x}{x^2-1} + \dfrac{x}{x+1}$.

To find the least common denominator, factor both denominators.

$$x^2 - 1 = (x+1)(x-1); \; x+1 \text{ cannot be factored.}$$

The expression is now written as

$$\frac{x}{(x + 1)(x - 1)} + \frac{x}{(x + 1)}.$$

Here only the second fraction must be changed. Multiply the numerator and denominator of the second fraction by $x - 1$.

$$\frac{x}{(x + 1)(x - 1)} + \frac{x(x - 1)}{(x + 1)(x - 1)}$$

With both denominators now the same, we add the numerators.

$$\frac{x + x(x - 1)}{(x + 1)(x - 1)} = \frac{x + x^2 - x}{(x + 1)(x - 1)}$$

$$= \frac{x^2}{(x + 1)(x - 1)}$$

EXAMPLE 4 Add $\dfrac{2x}{x^2 + 5x + 6} + \dfrac{x + 1}{x^2 + 2x - 3}$.

To begin, we factor the denominators completely.

$$\frac{2x}{(x + 2)(x + 3)} + \frac{x + 1}{(x + 3)(x - 1)}$$

The least common denominator is $(x + 2)(x + 3)(x - 1)$. By the fundamental property,

$$\frac{2x}{(x + 2)(x + 3)} + \frac{x + 1}{(x + 3)(x - 1)}$$

$$= \frac{2x(x - 1)}{(x + 2)(x + 3)(x - 1)} + \frac{(x + 1)(x + 2)}{(x + 3)(x - 1)(x + 2)}.$$

Since the two rational expressions above have the same denominator, add their numerators.

$$= \frac{2x(x - 1) + (x + 1)(x + 2)}{(x + 2)(x + 3)(x - 1)}$$

$$= \frac{2x^2 - 2x + x^2 + 3x + 2}{(x + 2)(x + 3)(x - 1)}$$

$$= \frac{3x^2 + x + 2}{(x + 2)(x + 3)(x - 1)}$$

In a problem of this type, it is often convenient to leave the denominator in factored form.

To *subtract* rational expressions, we use the following rule.

If $\dfrac{P}{Q}$ and $\dfrac{R}{S}$ are rational expressions, then

$$\frac{P}{Q} - \frac{R}{S} = \frac{P}{Q} + \left(\frac{-R}{S}\right).$$

EXAMPLE 5   Find $\dfrac{12}{x^2} - \dfrac{-8}{x^2}$.

$$\frac{12}{x^2} - \frac{-8}{x^2} = \frac{12}{x^2} + \left(-\frac{-8}{x^2}\right)$$

$$= \frac{12}{x^2} + \frac{8}{x^2}$$

$$= \frac{20}{x^2}$$

EXAMPLE 6   Find $\dfrac{9}{x-2} - \dfrac{3}{x}$.

By the definition of subtraction,

$$\frac{9}{x-2} - \frac{3}{x} = \frac{9}{x-2} + \frac{-3}{x}$$

The least common denominator is $x(x-2)$.

$$\frac{9}{x-2} - \frac{3}{x} = \frac{9x}{x(x-2)} + \frac{-3(x-2)}{x(x-2)}$$

$$= \frac{9x - 3(x-2)}{x(x-2)}$$

$$= \frac{9x - 3x + 6}{x(x-2)}$$

$$= \frac{6x + 6}{x(x-2)}$$

EXAMPLE 7   Find $\dfrac{6x}{(x-1)^2} - \dfrac{2}{x^2-1}$.

$$\frac{6x}{(x-1)^2} - \frac{2}{x^2-1} = \frac{6x}{(x-1)(x-1)} + \frac{-2}{(x-1)(x+1)}$$

We change subtraction to addition and change the numerator of the second fraction from 2 to -2. We also factor the two denominators, so we can identify a common denominator as $(x-1)(x-1)(x+1)$. We use the factor $x-1$ twice, since it appears twice in the first denominator.

$$= \frac{6x(x + 1)}{(x - 1)(x - 1)(x + 1)} + \frac{-2(x - 1)}{(x - 1)(x - 1)(x + 1)}$$

$$= \frac{6x(x + 1) + [-2(x - 1)]}{(x - 1)(x - 1)(x + 1)}$$

$$= \frac{6x^2 + 6x - 2x + 2}{(x - 1)(x - 1)(x + 1)}$$

$$= \frac{6x^2 + 4x + 2}{(x - 1)(x - 1)(x + 1)}$$

EXERCISES 5.4 *Find sums or differences. When possible, reduce the answers to lowest terms. See Examples 1 and 5.*

1. $\dfrac{2}{p} + \dfrac{5}{p}$

2. $\dfrac{3}{r} + \dfrac{6}{r}$

3. $\dfrac{9}{k} - \dfrac{12}{k}$

4. $\dfrac{15}{z} - \dfrac{25}{z}$

5. $\dfrac{y}{y + 1} + \dfrac{1}{y + 1}$

6. $\dfrac{3m}{m - 4} + \dfrac{-12}{m - 4}$

7. $\dfrac{m^2}{m - n} - \dfrac{n^2}{m - n}$

8. $\dfrac{a + b}{2} - \dfrac{a - b}{2}$

9. $\dfrac{m^2}{m + 6} + \dfrac{6m}{m + 6}$

10. $\dfrac{y^2}{y - 1} + \dfrac{-y}{y - 1}$

11. $\dfrac{2}{2r + 2} + \dfrac{2r}{2r + 2}$

12. $\dfrac{a^2}{a + b} + \dfrac{ab}{a + b}$

Find sums or differences. When possible, reduce the answers to lowest terms. See Examples 2, 3, 4, 6, and 7.

13. $\dfrac{3}{m} + \dfrac{1}{2}$

14. $\dfrac{6}{p} - \dfrac{2}{3}$

15. $\dfrac{9}{m} + \dfrac{3}{2}$

16. $\dfrac{9}{10} + \dfrac{r}{2}$

17. $\dfrac{3}{5} - \dfrac{1}{y}$

18. $\dfrac{9y}{7} - \dfrac{3y}{8}$

19. $\dfrac{5m}{6} - \left(\dfrac{2m}{3} - \dfrac{m}{6}\right)$

20. $\left(\dfrac{3}{x} + \dfrac{4}{2x}\right) - \dfrac{5}{4x}$

21. $\dfrac{4 + 2k}{5} + \dfrac{2 + k}{10}$

22. $\dfrac{5 - 4r}{8} - \dfrac{2 - 3r}{6}$

23. $\dfrac{6}{y^2} - \dfrac{2}{y}$

24. $\dfrac{3}{p} + \dfrac{5}{p^2}$

25. $\dfrac{9}{2p} + \dfrac{4}{p^2}$

26. $\dfrac{15}{4k^2} - \dfrac{3}{k}$

27. $\dfrac{3m + n}{3} + \dfrac{6m + n}{6}$

28. $\dfrac{5r + s}{3} - \dfrac{3r - 3s}{9}$

29. $\dfrac{-1}{x^2} + \dfrac{-3}{xy}$

30. $\dfrac{9}{p^2} + \dfrac{p}{x}$

31. $\dfrac{m + 2}{m} + \dfrac{m}{m + 2}$

32. $\dfrac{2x - 5}{x - 2} + \dfrac{x}{2x - 4}$

33. $\dfrac{8}{x - 2} - \dfrac{4}{x + 2}$

34. $\dfrac{6}{m - n} - \dfrac{2}{m + n}$

35. $\dfrac{4}{m + n} + \dfrac{4n}{m^2 - n^2}$

36. $\dfrac{1}{a - b} - \dfrac{2b}{a^2 - b^2}$

37. $\dfrac{1}{m^2 - 1} - \dfrac{1}{m^2 + 3m + 2}$

38. $\dfrac{2}{4y^2 - 16} + \dfrac{3}{4 + 2y}$

39. $\dfrac{12}{m^2 - 9} + \dfrac{2}{m + 3}$

40. $\dfrac{-6}{y^2 - 4} - \dfrac{3}{2y + 4}$

41. $\dfrac{4}{2 - m} + \dfrac{7}{m - 2}$

42. $\dfrac{9}{8 - y} + \dfrac{6}{y - 8}$

43. $\dfrac{-1}{3 - y} - \dfrac{2}{y - 3}$

44. $\dfrac{-8}{11 - p} - \dfrac{6}{p - 11}$

45. $\dfrac{5m}{m + 2n} - \dfrac{3m}{-m - 2n}$

46. $\dfrac{6k}{2k + 3m} - \dfrac{4k}{-2k - 3m}$

47. $\dfrac{x + 3y}{x^2 + 2xy + y^2} + \dfrac{x - y}{x^2 + 4xy + 3y^2}$

48. $\dfrac{m}{m^2 - 1} + \dfrac{m - 1}{m^2 + 2m + 1}$

5.5   Complex Fractions

- **Simplify complex fractions.**

A rational expression containing fractions in the numerator, denominator, or both, is called a **complex fraction.** Examples of complex fractions include

$$\dfrac{3 + \dfrac{4}{x}}{5}, \qquad \dfrac{\dfrac{3x^2 - 5x}{6x^2}}{2x - \dfrac{1}{x}}, \qquad \text{and} \qquad \dfrac{3 + x}{5 - \dfrac{2}{x}}.$$

One method of simplifying is to rewrite the numerator and denominator as single fractions, and then perform the indicated division.

EXAMPLE 1   Simplify the complex fraction

$$\frac{6 + \dfrac{3}{x}}{\dfrac{2x + 1}{8}}.$$

First write the numerator as a single fraction by adding 6 and $\dfrac{3}{x}$.

$$6 + \frac{3}{x} = \frac{6}{1} + \frac{3}{x}$$

$$= \frac{6x}{x} + \frac{3}{x}$$

$$= \frac{6x + 3}{x}$$

The complex fraction can now be written as

$$\frac{\dfrac{6x + 3}{x}}{\dfrac{2x + 1}{8}}.$$

Now use the rule for division and the fundamental property.

$$\frac{6x + 3}{x} \div \frac{2x + 1}{8} = \frac{6x + 3}{x} \cdot \frac{8}{2x + 1}$$

$$= \frac{3(2x + 1)}{x} \cdot \frac{8}{2x + 1}$$

$$= \frac{24}{x}$$

EXAMPLE 2 Simplify the complex fraction

$$\frac{\dfrac{xp}{q^3}}{\dfrac{p^2}{qx^2}}.$$

Here, the numerator and denominator are already single fractions, so we use the division rule and then the fundamental property.

$$\frac{xp}{q^3} \div \frac{p^2}{qx^2} = \frac{xp}{q^3} \cdot \frac{qx^2}{p^2}$$

$$= \frac{x^3}{q^2 p}$$

EXAMPLE 3 Simplify the complex fraction

$$\frac{\dfrac{x}{x + y}}{\dfrac{1}{x} + \dfrac{1}{y}}.$$

First simplify the denominator by adding $\frac{1}{x}$ and $\frac{1}{y}$.

$$\frac{1}{x} + \frac{1}{y} = \frac{y}{xy} + \frac{x}{xy}$$

$$= \frac{x + y}{xy}$$

Now use the division rule and the fundamental property.

$$\frac{x}{x + y} \div \frac{x + y}{xy} = \frac{x}{x + y} \cdot \frac{xy}{x + y}$$

$$= \frac{x^2y}{(x + y)^2}$$

Alternatively, complex fractions may be simplified by multiplying by the least common denominator of all the denominators.

EXAMPLE 4 Simplify: $\dfrac{6 + \dfrac{3}{x}}{\dfrac{2x + 1}{8}}$.

The least common denominator of all the denominators is $8x$, so multiply numerator and denominator by $8x$.

$$\frac{8x\left(6 + \dfrac{3}{x}\right)}{8x\left(\dfrac{2x + 1}{8}\right)} = \frac{8x(6) + 8x\left(\dfrac{3}{x}\right)}{x(2x + 1)}$$

$$= \frac{48x + 24}{x(2x + 1)}$$

$$= \frac{24(2x + 1)}{x(2x + 1)}$$

$$= \frac{24}{x}$$

This is the same answer that we got by the other method in Example 1 above.

EXERCISES 5.5 *Simplify each complex fraction. See Examples 1–3.*

1. $\dfrac{\dfrac{p}{q^2}}{\dfrac{p^2}{q}}$

2. $\dfrac{\dfrac{ab}{x}}{\dfrac{a^2}{2x}}$

3. $\dfrac{\dfrac{x}{y}}{\dfrac{x^2}{y}}$

4. $\dfrac{\dfrac{pq}{r}}{\dfrac{p^2q}{r^2}}$

5. $\dfrac{\dfrac{y+1}{y}}{\dfrac{y+1}{x}}$

6. $\dfrac{\dfrac{m-n}{m}}{\dfrac{m-n}{n}}$

7. $\dfrac{\dfrac{a}{b+1}}{\dfrac{a^2}{b}} \cdot$

8. $\dfrac{\dfrac{1}{x}}{\dfrac{1+x}{1-x}}$

9. $\dfrac{\dfrac{2x+3}{y}}{\dfrac{x-1}{2y}}$

10. $\dfrac{\dfrac{k}{k+1}}{\dfrac{5}{2(k+1)}}$

11. $\dfrac{\dfrac{3}{y}+1}{\dfrac{3+y}{2}}$

12. $\dfrac{y+\dfrac{2}{y}}{\dfrac{y^2+2}{3}}$

13. $\dfrac{\dfrac{1}{x}+\dfrac{1}{y}}{\dfrac{1}{x+y}}$

14. $\dfrac{m+\dfrac{1}{m}}{\dfrac{3}{m}-m}$

15. $\dfrac{x+\dfrac{1}{y}}{\dfrac{1}{x}+y}$

16. $\dfrac{y-\dfrac{1}{y}}{y+\dfrac{1}{y}}$

17. $\dfrac{\dfrac{p+q}{p}}{\dfrac{1}{p}+\dfrac{1}{q}}$

18. $\dfrac{r+\dfrac{1}{r}}{\dfrac{1}{r}-r}$

19. $\dfrac{\dfrac{1}{m+n}}{\dfrac{4}{m^2-n^2}}$

20. $\dfrac{\dfrac{a}{a+1}}{\dfrac{2}{a^2-1}}$

21. $\dfrac{\dfrac{1}{m+1}-1}{\dfrac{1}{m-1}+1}$

22. $\dfrac{\dfrac{2}{x-1}+2}{\dfrac{2}{x+1}-2}$

23. $\dfrac{\dfrac{y+1}{y-1}}{\dfrac{1}{y+1}}$

24. $\dfrac{\dfrac{a-b}{a+b}}{\dfrac{a}{a-b}}$

The following exercises are real "head scratchers." (Hint: work from the lower right up.)

25. $1 - \dfrac{1}{1 + \dfrac{1}{1 + 1}}$

26. $3 - \dfrac{2}{4 + \dfrac{2}{4 - 2}}$

27. $8 + \dfrac{1}{4 - \dfrac{2}{6 + 2}}$

28. $\dfrac{15}{7} - \dfrac{2}{6 + \dfrac{8}{4 + 4}}$

29. $1 - \dfrac{1}{1 + \dfrac{1}{1 - \dfrac{1}{1 + 1}}}$

30. $3 - \dfrac{2}{1 + \dfrac{1}{2 + \dfrac{1}{2}}}$

5.6 Equations Involving Rational Expressions

- **Solve equations involving rational expressions.**

To solve equations with fractions, we first simplify the equation by using the multiplication property of equality. The goal is to replace the equation having fractions with another equation which does not have fractions. To do this, we choose as a multiplier the least common denominator of all denominators in the fractions of the equation.

EXAMPLE 1   Solve $\dfrac{x}{3} + \dfrac{x}{4} = 10 + x$.

The least common denominator of the two fractions is 12. Therefore, we begin by multiplying both sides of the equation by 12.

$$12\left(\frac{x}{3} + \frac{x}{4}\right) = 12(10 + x)$$

$$12\left(\frac{x}{3}\right) + 12\left(\frac{x}{4}\right) = 12(10) + 12x$$

$$\frac{12x}{3} + \frac{12x}{4} = 120 + 12x$$

$$4x + 3x = 120 + 12x$$

$$7x = 120 + 12x$$

$$-5x = 120$$

$$x = -24$$

Check the solution $x = -24$ by substituting -24 for x in the original equation.

$$\frac{x}{3} + \frac{x}{4} = 10 + x$$

$$\frac{-24}{3} + \frac{-24}{4} = 10 + (-24)$$

$$-8 + -6 = -14$$

This true statement shows that -24 is the solution.

EXAMPLE 2 Solve $\frac{p}{2} - \frac{p-1}{3} = 1$.

Multiply both sides by the common denominator of 6.

$$6\left(\frac{p}{2} - \frac{p-1}{3}\right) = 6 \cdot 1$$

$$6\left(\frac{p}{2}\right) - 6\left(\frac{p-1}{3}\right) = 6$$

$$3p - 2(p - 1) = 6$$

Be very careful to put parentheses around $p - 1$; otherwise an incorrect solution may be found. Continue simplifying.

$$3p - 2p + 2 = 6$$

$$p + 2 = 6$$

$$p = 4$$

Check that 4 is correct by replacing p with 4 in the original equation.

When solving equations which have a variable in the denominator, we must remember that the number 0 cannot be used as a denominator. Therefore, the solution cannot be a number which will make the denominator equal to 0.

EXAMPLE 3 Solve $\frac{x}{x-2} = \frac{2}{x-2} + 2$.

The common denominator is $x - 2$. Multiply both sides of the equation by $x - 2$.

$$(x-2)\left(\frac{x}{x-2}\right) = (x-2)\left(\frac{2}{x-2}\right) + (x-2)(2)$$

$$x = 2 + 2x - 4$$

$$x = -2 + 2x$$

$$0 = -2 + x$$

$$2 = x.$$

The proposed solution is 2. However, we cannot have a solution of 2 in this equation because this x-value makes both denominators zero, so the equation is meaningless. Therefore, this equation has no solution.

EXAMPLE 4   Solve $\dfrac{2m}{m^2 - 4} + \dfrac{1}{m - 2} = \dfrac{2}{m + 2}$.

Since $m^2 - 4 = (m + 2)(m - 2)$, use $(m + 2)(m - 2)$ as the common denominator.

$$(m + 2)(m - 2)\left(\dfrac{2m}{m^2 - 4} + \dfrac{1}{m - 2}\right) = (m + 2)(m - 2)\dfrac{2}{m + 2}$$

$$(m + 2)(m - 2)\dfrac{2m}{m^2 - 4} + (m + 2)(m - 2)\dfrac{1}{m - 2} = (m + 2)(m - 2)\dfrac{2}{m + 2}$$

$$2m + m + 2 = 2(m - 2)$$

$$3m + 2 = 2m - 4$$

$$m = -6$$

Check that -6 is indeed a valid solution for the given equation.

EXAMPLE 5   Solve $\dfrac{2}{x^2 - x} = \dfrac{1}{x^2 - 1}$.

To solve the equation, we begin by finding a common denominator. We see that $x^2 - x$ can be factored as $x(x - 1)$, while $x^2 - 1$ can be factored as $(x + 1)(x - 1)$. The least common denominator of the two rational expressions is $x(x + 1)(x - 1)$. We multiply both sides of the equation by $x(x + 1)(x - 1)$.

$$x(x + 1)(x - 1)\dfrac{2}{x(x - 1)} = x(x + 1)(x - 1)\dfrac{1}{(x + 1)(x - 1)}$$

$$2(x + 1) = x$$

$$2x + 2 = x$$

$$x + 2 = 0$$

$$x = -2.$$

To be sure that $x = -2$ is a solution, substitute -2 for x in the original equation.

Since -2 satisfies the equation, the solution is -2.

EXAMPLE 6   Solve $\dfrac{1}{x - 1} + \dfrac{1}{2} = \dfrac{2}{x^2 - 1}$.

The least common denominator is $2(x + 1)(x - 1)$. We multiply both sides of the equation by this common denominator.

$$2(x + 1)(x - 1) \left(\frac{1}{x - 1} + \frac{1}{2} \right)$$

$$= 2(x + 1)(x - 1) \frac{2}{(x + 1)(x - 1)}$$

$$2(x + 1)(x - 1) \frac{1}{x - 1} + 2(x + 1)(x - 1) \frac{1}{2}$$

$$= 2(x + 1)(x - 1) \frac{2}{(x + 1)(x - 1)}$$

$$2(x + 1) + (x + 1)(x - 1) = 4$$

$$2x + 2 + x^2 - 1 = 4$$

$$x^2 + 2x + 1 = 4$$

$$x^2 + 2x - 3 = 0$$

Factoring, we have

$$(x + 3)(x - 1) = 0.$$

Therefore, it seems $x = -3$ or $x = 1$. But 1 makes a denominator of the original equation equal 0, and so is not a solution. However, -3 is a solution, as you can show by substituting -3 for x in the original equation.

EXAMPLE 7 Solve $\dfrac{1}{k^2 + 4k + 3} + \dfrac{1}{2k + 2} = \dfrac{3}{4k + 12}.$

Factor the three denominators to get the common denominator, $4(k + 1)(k + 3)$. Multiply both sides by this product.

$$4(k + 1)(k + 3) \left(\frac{1}{(k + 1)(k + 3)} + \frac{1}{2(k + 1)} \right) = 4(k + 1)(k + 3) \frac{3}{4(k + 3)}$$

$$4(k + 1)(k + 3) \frac{1}{(k + 1)(k + 3)} + 4(k + 1)(k + 3) \frac{1}{2(k + 1)}$$

$$= 4(k + 1)(k + 3) \frac{3}{4(k + 3)}$$

$$4 + 2(k + 3) = 3(k + 1)$$

$$4 + 2k + 6 = 3k + 3$$

$$2k + 10 = 3k + 3$$

$$7 = k$$

Check that 7 is actually a solution for the given equation.

EXERCISES 5.6 *Solve each equation and check your answers. See Examples 1–3.*

1. $\dfrac{1}{4} = \dfrac{x}{2}$

2. $\dfrac{2}{m} = \dfrac{5}{12}$

3. $\dfrac{9}{k} = \dfrac{3}{4}$

4. $\dfrac{15}{f} = \dfrac{30}{8}$

5. $\dfrac{3}{4} - m = 2m$

6. $3r - \dfrac{1}{2} = \dfrac{11}{2}$

7. $\dfrac{6}{x} - \dfrac{4}{x} = 5$

8. $\dfrac{3}{x} + \dfrac{2}{x} = 5$

9. $\dfrac{x}{2} - \dfrac{x}{4} = 6$

10. $\dfrac{4}{y} + \dfrac{2}{3} = 1$

11. $\dfrac{9}{m} = 5 - \dfrac{1}{m}$

12. $\dfrac{3x}{5} + 2 = \dfrac{1}{4}$

13. $\dfrac{2t}{7} - 5 = t$

14. $\dfrac{1}{2} + \dfrac{2}{m} = 1$

15. $\dfrac{x + 1}{2} = \dfrac{x + 2}{3}$

16. $\dfrac{t - 4}{3} = t + 2$

17. $\dfrac{3m}{2} + m = 5$

18. $\dfrac{9}{x + 1} = 3$

19. $\dfrac{9}{x - 2} = 3$

20. $\dfrac{2y - 1}{y} + 2 = \dfrac{1}{2}$

21. $\dfrac{2k + 3}{k} = \dfrac{3}{2}$

22. $\dfrac{a}{2} - \dfrac{17 + a}{5} = 2a$

23. $\dfrac{5 - y}{y} + \dfrac{3}{4} = \dfrac{7}{y}$

24. $\dfrac{x}{x - 4} = \dfrac{2}{x - 4} + 5$

25. $\dfrac{a - 4}{4} = \dfrac{a + 8}{16}$

26. $\dfrac{m - 2}{5} = \dfrac{m + 8}{10}$

27. $\dfrac{2p + 8}{9} = \dfrac{10p + 4}{27}$

28. $\dfrac{5r - 3}{7} = \dfrac{15r - 2}{28}$

29. $\dfrac{p}{2} - \dfrac{p - 1}{4} = \dfrac{5}{4}$

30. $\dfrac{r}{6} - \dfrac{r - 2}{3} = \dfrac{-4}{3}$

31. $\dfrac{5y}{3} - \dfrac{2y - 1}{4} = \dfrac{1}{4}$

32. $\dfrac{8k}{5} - \dfrac{3k - 4}{2} = \dfrac{5}{2}$

33. $\dfrac{y - 1}{2} - \dfrac{y - 3}{4} = 1$

34. $\dfrac{r + 5}{3} - \dfrac{r - 1}{4} = \dfrac{7}{4}$

Solve each equation and check your answers. See Examples 4–7.

35. $\dfrac{8x - 1}{6x + 8} = \dfrac{3}{4}$

36. $\dfrac{6m + 9}{5m + 10} = \dfrac{3}{5}$

37. $\dfrac{2}{y} = \dfrac{y}{5y - 12}$

38. $\dfrac{8x + 3}{x} = 3x$

39. $\dfrac{m}{2m + 2} = \dfrac{-2m}{4m + 4} + \dfrac{2m - 3}{m + 1}$

40. $\dfrac{5p + 1}{3p + 3} = \dfrac{5p - 5}{5p + 5} + \dfrac{3p - 1}{p + 1}$

41. $\dfrac{x + 1}{x - 3} = \dfrac{4}{x - 3} + 6$

42. $\dfrac{p}{p - 2} + 4 = \dfrac{2}{p - 2}$

43. $\dfrac{1}{x^2 + 5x + 6} + \dfrac{1}{x^2 - 2x - 8} = \dfrac{-1}{12(x + 2)}$

44. $\dfrac{x + 4}{x^2 - 3x + 2} - \dfrac{5}{x^2 - 4x + 3} = \dfrac{x - 4}{x^2 - 5x + 6}$

45. $\dfrac{2}{k - 3} - \dfrac{3}{k + 3} = \dfrac{12}{k^2 - 9}$

46. $\dfrac{1}{r + 5} - \dfrac{3}{r - 5} = \dfrac{-10}{r^2 - 25}$

47. $\dfrac{3y}{y^2 + 5y + 6} = \dfrac{5y}{y^2 + 2y - 3} - \dfrac{2}{y^2 + y - 2}$

48. $\dfrac{3}{r^2 + r - 2} - \dfrac{1}{r^2 - 1} = \dfrac{7}{2(r^2 + 3r + 2)}$

49. $\dfrac{4}{p} - \dfrac{2}{p + 1} = 3$

50. $\dfrac{6}{r} + \dfrac{1}{r - 2} = 3$

51. $\dfrac{2}{m - 1} + \dfrac{1}{m + 1} = \dfrac{5}{4}$

52. $\dfrac{5}{z - 2} + \dfrac{10}{z + 2} = 7$

5.7 Applications of Rational Expressions

- Solve word problems involving rational expressions.
- Solve word problems involving distance.
- Solve word problems involving work.

We are now ready to discuss some applications which involve rational expressions.

EXAMPLE 1   If the same number is added to both the numerator and denominator of the fraction $\dfrac{3}{4}$, the result is $\dfrac{5}{6}$. Find the number.

If x represents the number that is added to numerator and denominator, we can write

$$\dfrac{3 + x}{4 + x}$$

to represent the result of adding the same number to both the numerator and denominator. Since this result is $\frac{5}{6}$,

$$\frac{3 + x}{4 + x} = \frac{5}{6}.$$

If we multiply both sides of the equation by the common denominator $6(4 + x)$, we have

$$6(4 + x)\frac{3 + x}{4 + x} = 6(4 + x)\frac{5}{6}$$
$$6(3 + x) = 5(4 + x)$$
$$18 + 6x = 20 + 5x$$
$$x = 2.$$

Check in the words of the problem that 2 is the correct number.

EXAMPLE 2   The Big Muddy River has a current of 3 miles per hour. A motorboat takes as long to go 12 miles downstream as to go 8 miles upstream. What is the speed of the boat in still water?

This problem requires the distance formula,

$$d = rt \text{ (distance = rate} \cdot \text{time).}$$

For our problem, let's use x to represent the speed of the boat in still water. Since the current pushes the boat when the boat is going downstream, the speed of the boat downstream will be the sum of the speed of the boat and the speed of the current, or $x + 3$ miles per hour. Similarly, the boat's speed going upstream is given by $x - 3$ miles per hour.

We can summarize the information in the problem in a chart.

	d	r	t
downstream	12	$x + 3$	
upstream	8	$x - 3$	

To fill in the last column, representing time, we solve the formula $d = rt$ for t.

$$d = rt$$
$$\frac{d}{r} = t$$

Then the time upstream is

$$\frac{d}{r} = \frac{8}{x - 3},$$

while the time downstream is

$$\frac{d}{r} = \frac{12}{x + 3}.$$

Now we can complete the chart.

	d	r	t
downstream	12	$x + 3$	$\dfrac{12}{x + 3}$
upstream	8	$x - 3$	$\dfrac{8}{x - 3}$

The problem states that the time upstream equals the time downstream. Thus the two times from the chart are equal.

$$\frac{12}{x + 3} = \frac{8}{x - 3}$$

To solve this equation, multiply both sides by $(x + 3)(x - 3)$.

$$(x + 3)(x - 3)\frac{12}{x + 3} = (x + 3)(x - 3)\frac{8}{x - 3}$$

$$12(x - 3) = 8(x + 3)$$

$$12x - 36 = 8x + 24$$

$$4x = 60$$

$$x = 15$$

The speed of the boat in still water is 15 miles per hour.

To check, note that the speed of the boat downstream is $15 + 3 = 18$ miles per hour, and traveling 12 miles takes

$$12 = 18t,$$

$$t = \frac{2}{3} \text{ hour.}$$

On the other hand, the speed of the boat upstream is $15 - 3 = 12$ miles per hour, and traveling 8 miles takes

$$8 = 12t,$$

$$t = \frac{2}{3} \text{ hour.}$$

The time upstream equals the time downstream, as required.

EXAMPLE 3   Working alone, John can cut his lawn in 8 hours. If John's pet sheep is released to eat the grass, the lawn can be cut in 14 hours. If both John and the sheep work on the lawn, how long will it take to cut it?

Let x be the number of hours that it takes John and the sheep to cut the lawn, working together. Certainly x will be less than 8, since John alone can cut the lawn in 8 hours. In one hour, John can do $\frac{1}{8}$ of the lawn, and in one hour the sheep can do $\frac{1}{14}$ of the lawn. Since it takes them x hours to cut the lawn when working together, in one hour together they can do $\frac{1}{x}$ of the lawn. The amount of the lawn cut by John in one hour plus the amount cut by the sheep in one hour must equal the amount they can do together in one hour. In symbols,

$$\frac{1}{8} + \frac{1}{14} = \frac{1}{x}.$$

The quantity $56x$ is the least common denominator for 8, 14, and x, so we multiply both sides of the equation by $56x$.

$$56x \left(\frac{1}{8} + \frac{1}{14} \right) = 56x \cdot \frac{1}{x}$$

$$56x \cdot \frac{1}{8} + 56x \cdot \frac{1}{14} = 56x \cdot \frac{1}{x}$$

$$7x + 4x = 56$$

$$11x = 56$$

$$x = \frac{56}{11}.$$

Working together, John and his sheep can cut the lawn in $\frac{56}{11}$ hours, or $5\frac{1}{11}$ hours, about 5 hours and 5 minutes.

EXERCISES 5.7   *Solve each problem See Example 1.*

1. One half of a number is three more than one-sixth of the same number. What is the number?

2. The numerator of the fraction $\frac{4}{7}$ is increased by an amount so that the value of the resulting fraction is $\frac{27}{21}$. By what amount was the numerator increased?

3. In a certain fraction, the denominator is 5 larger than the numerator. If 3 is added to both the numerator and the denominator, the result is $\frac{3}{4}$. Find the original fraction.

4. The denominator of a certain fraction is three times the numerator. If 1 is added to the numerator and subtracted from the denominator, the result equals $\frac{1}{2}$. Find the original fraction.

5. One number is three more than another. If the smaller is added to two thirds the larger, the result is four fifths the sum of the original numbers. Find the numbers.

6. The sum of a number and its reciprocal is $\frac{5}{2}$. Find the number.

7. If twice the reciprocal of a number is subtracted from the number, the result is $-\frac{7}{3}$. Find the number.

8. The sum of the reciprocals of two consecutive integers is $\frac{5}{6}$. Find the integers.

9. If three times a number is added to twice its reciprocal, the answer is 5. Find the number.

10. If twice a number is subtracted from 3 times its reciprocal, the result is 1. Find the number.

11. A man and his son worked four days at a job. The son's daily wage was $\frac{2}{5}$ that of the father. If together they earned $336, what were their daily wages?

12. The profits from a student show are to be given to two scholarships so that one scholarship receives $\frac{3}{2}$ as much money as the other. If the total amount given to the two scholarships is $390, find the amount that goes to the scholarship that receives the lesser amount.

13. A new instructor is paid $\frac{3}{5}$ the salary of an experienced professor. In a certain college, the total salary paid an instructor and a professor was $21,000. Find the salary paid the professor.

14. A child takes $\frac{5}{8}$ of the number of pills that an adult takes for the same illness. In total, the child and the adult use 26 pills. Find the number used by the adult.

Solve each problem. See Example 2.

15. Sam can row four miles per hour in still water. It takes as long rowing 8 miles upstream as 24 miles downstream. How fast is the current?

	d	r	t
upstream	8	$x - 4$	
downstream	24	$x + 4$	

16. Mary flew from Philadelphia to Des Moines at 180 miles per hour, and from Des Moines to Philadelphia at 150 miles per hour. The trip at the slower speed took one hour longer than the trip at the higher speed. Find the distance between the two cities. (Assume there was no wind in either direction.)

	d	r	t
P to D	x	180	
D to P	x	150	

17. On a business trip, Arlene traveled to her destination at an average speed of 60 m.p.h. Coming home, her average speed was 50 m.p.h. and the trip took $\frac{1}{2}$ hour longer. How far did she travel each way?

18. Rae flew her airplane 500 miles against the wind in the same time it took her to fly it 600 miles with the wind. If the speed of the wind was 10 m.p.h., what was the average speed of her plane?

19. The distance from Seattle, Washington, to Victoria, British Columbia, is about 148 miles by ferry. It takes about 4 hours less to travel by ferry from Victoria to Vancouver, British Columbia, a distance of about 74 miles. What is the average speed of the ferry?

20. Ron flew his plane 800 miles in 1.5 hours more than it took him to fly 500 miles. What was his average speed?

Solve each problem. See Example 3.

21. Paul can tune his Toyota in 2 hours. His friend Marco can do the job in 3 hours. How long would it take them if they worked together?

22. George can paint a room, working alone, in 8 hours. Jenny can paint the same room, working alone, in 6 hours. How long will it take them if they work together?

23. Machine A can do a certain job in 7 hours, while machine B takes 12 hours. How long will it take the two machines working together?

24. One pipe can fill a swimming pool in 6 hours, while another pipe can do it in 9 hours. How long will it take the two pipes working together to fill the pool $\frac{3}{4}$ full?

25. Dennis can do a job in 4 days. When Dennis and Sue work together, the job takes $2\frac{1}{3}$ days. How long would the job take Sue if she worked alone?

26. An inlet pipe can fill a swimming pool in 9 hours, while an outlet pipe can empty the pool in 12 hours. Through an error, both pipes are left open. How long will it take to fill the pool?

27. A cold water faucet can fill a sink in 12 minutes, and a hot water faucet in 15. The drain can empty the sink in 25 minutes. If both faucets are on and the drain is open, how long will it take to fill the sink?

28. Refer to Exercise 26. Assume the error was discovered after both pipes had been running for 3 hours, and the outlet pipe was then closed. How much more time would then be required to fill the pool? (Hint: How much of the job had been done when the error was discovered?)

29. An experienced employee can enter tax data into a computer twice as fast as a new employee. Working together, it takes the employees 2 hours. How long would it take the experienced employee working alone?

30. One painter can paint a house three times faster than another. Working together, they can paint a house in four days. How long would it take the faster painter working alone?

5.8 Ratios and Proportions

- **Write ratios.**
- **See if proportions are true.**
- **Solve proportions.**
- **Solve word problems using proportions.**

Ratios give a way of comparing two numbers or quantities. A **ratio** is a quotient of two quantities. The ratio of the number a to the number b is written as

$$a \text{ to } b, \qquad a{:}b, \qquad \text{or} \qquad \frac{a}{b}.$$

This last way of writing a ratio is most common in algebra.

EXAMPLE 1 Write a ratio for each word phrase.

(a) The ratio of 5 hours to 3 hours is

$$\frac{5}{3}.$$

(b) To find the ratio of 5 hours to 3 days, first convert 3 days to hours.

$$3 \text{ days} = 3 \cdot 24$$
$$= 72 \text{ hours.}$$

The ratio of 5 hours to 3 days is thus

$$\frac{5}{72}.$$

A ratio is used to compare two numbers or amounts. A **proportion** says that two ratios are equal. For example,

$$\frac{3}{4} = \frac{15}{20}$$

is a proportion that says that the ratios $\frac{3}{4}$ and $\frac{15}{20}$ are equal. In the proportion

$$\frac{a}{b} = \frac{c}{d},$$

a, b, c, and d are the **terms** of the proportion. The terms a and d are called the **extremes,** while b and c are the **means.** If we begin with the proportion

$$\frac{a}{b} = \frac{c}{d}$$

and multiply both sides by bd, we get

$$bd \cdot \frac{a}{b} = bd \cdot \frac{c}{d}$$
$$ad = bc$$

In words:

In a proportion, the product of the extremes equals the product of the means.

$$\frac{a}{b} \diagdown\!\!\!\diagup \frac{c}{d}$$

$$ad = bc$$

EXAMPLE 2   Decide if the following proportions are true.

(a) $\dfrac{3}{4} = \dfrac{15}{20}$

Check to see if the product of the means equals the product of the extremes.

$$\text{product of extremes} = 3 \cdot 20$$
$$= 60$$
$$\text{product of means} = 4 \cdot 15$$
$$= 60$$

Both products are equal, so that the proportion is true.

(b) $\dfrac{6}{7} = \dfrac{30}{32}$

The product of the extremes is $6 \cdot 32 = 192$, while the product of the means is $7 \cdot 30 = 210$. The products are different, so that the proportion is false.

Four numbers are used in a proportion. If we know any three of these numbers, we can find the fourth.

EXAMPLE 3   Find x in the proportion

$$\frac{3}{5} = \frac{x}{40}$$

The product of the extremes must equal the product of the means, or

$$3 \cdot 40 = 5 \cdot x$$
$$120 = 5x$$

Multiply both sides by $\dfrac{1}{5}$ to get

$$24 = x$$

EXAMPLE 4   Find k.

$$\frac{3}{10} = \frac{5}{k}$$

Find the two products:

$$3k = 10 \cdot 5$$
$$3k = 50$$
$$k = \frac{50}{3}$$

EXAMPLE 5   Find m.

$$\frac{m - 2}{m + 1} = \frac{5}{3}$$

Find the product of the extremes and the product of the means.

$$3(m - 2) = 5(m + 1)$$
$$3m - 6 = 5m + 5$$
$$3m = 5m + 11$$
$$-2m = 11$$
$$m = -\frac{11}{2}$$

Proportions occur in many practical applications, as the next example shows.

EXAMPLE 6   A hospital charges a patient $7.80 for 12 capsules. How much should it charge for 18 capsules?

Let x be the cost of 18 capsules. Set up a proportion; one ratio in the proportion can involve the number of capsules, while the other ratio can use the costs. Make sure that corresponding numbers appear in the numerator and the denominator.

$$\frac{12}{18} = \frac{7.80}{x}$$

Solve the proportion. Find the product of the extremes and the product of the means.

$$12x = 18(7.80)$$
$$12x = 140.40$$
$$x = 11.70$$

The 18 capsules should cost $11.70.

EXERCISES 5.8   *Write the following ratios. Reduce each ratio to lowest terms. See Example 1.*

1. 30 miles to 20 miles

2. 50 feet to 90 feet

3. 72 dollars to 110 dollars

4. 120 people to 80 people

5. 6 feet to 5 yards

6. 10 yards to 8 feet

7. 30 inches to 4 feet

8. 100 inches to 5 yards

9. 12 minutes to 2 hours

10. 8 quarts to 5 pints

11. 4 dollars to 10 quarters

12. 35 dimes to 6 dollars

13. 20 hours to 5 days

14. 6 days to 9 hours

15. 80¢ to $3

16. 150¢ to $5

Decide whether or not the following proportions are true. See Example 2.

17. $\dfrac{4}{7} = \dfrac{12}{21}$

18. $\dfrac{9}{10} = \dfrac{18}{20}$

19. $\dfrac{6}{8} = \dfrac{15}{20}$

20. $\dfrac{12}{18} = \dfrac{8}{12}$

21. $\dfrac{7}{10} = \dfrac{82}{120}$

22. $\dfrac{18}{20} = \dfrac{56}{60}$

23. $\dfrac{16}{40} = \dfrac{22}{55}$

24. $\dfrac{19}{30} = \dfrac{57}{90}$

25. $\dfrac{110}{18} = \dfrac{160}{27}$

26. $\dfrac{420}{600} = \dfrac{14}{20}$

Solve each of the following proportions. See Examples 3–5.

27. $\dfrac{x}{36} = \dfrac{7}{12}$

28. $\dfrac{5}{y} = \dfrac{20}{8}$

29. $\dfrac{10}{5} = \dfrac{z}{20}$

30. $\dfrac{4}{8} = \dfrac{m}{32}$

31. $\dfrac{a}{25} = \dfrac{4}{20}$

32. $\dfrac{6}{x} = \dfrac{4}{18}$

33. $\dfrac{z}{20} = \dfrac{80}{100}$

34. $\dfrac{25}{100} = \dfrac{8}{m}$

35. $\dfrac{1}{2} = \dfrac{r}{7}$

36. $\dfrac{2}{3} = \dfrac{5}{s}$

37. $\dfrac{2}{9} = \dfrac{p}{12}$

38. $\dfrac{5}{6} = \dfrac{k}{10}$

39. $\dfrac{3}{a} = \dfrac{8}{9}$

40. $\dfrac{2}{y} = \dfrac{9}{7}$

41. $\dfrac{m}{m-3} = \dfrac{5}{3}$

42. $\dfrac{r+1}{r} = \dfrac{1}{3}$

43. $\dfrac{3k-1}{k} = \dfrac{6}{7}$

44. $\dfrac{y}{6y-5} = \dfrac{5}{11}$

45. $\dfrac{p+7}{p-1} = \dfrac{3}{4}$

46. $\dfrac{r+8}{r-9} = \dfrac{7}{3}$

Solve the following applications involving proportions. See Example 6.

47. If 8 ounces of medicine must be mixed with 20 ounces of water, how many ounces of medicine must be mixed with 50 ounces of water?

48. A certain lawn mower uses 3 tanks of gas to cut 10 acres of lawn. How many tanks of gas would be needed for 30 acres?

49. A Hershey bar contains 200 calories. How many bars would you need to eat to get 500 calories?

50. José can assemble 12 car parts in 40 minutes. How many minutes would he need to assemble 15 car parts?

51. If 2 pounds of fertilizer will cover 50 square feet of garden, how many pounds would be needed for 225 square feet?

52. The tax on a $20 item is $1. Find the tax on a $110 item.

53. On a road map, 3 inches represents 8 miles. How many inches would represent a distance of 24 miles?

54. If 22 dresses cost $176, find the cost of 12 dresses.

55. Five pounds of grass seed cover 3500 square feet of ground. How many pounds would be needed for 4900 square feet?

56. The distance between two cities on a road map is 5 inches. The two cities are really 600 miles apart. The distance between two other cities is 9 inches. How far apart are these cities?

57. A garden service charges $30 to install 50 square feet of sod. Find the charge to install 125 square feet.

58. If 4 days at a motel cost $75, find the cost to stay 11 days.

59. John plants his seeds early in the year. To keep them from freezing, he covers the ground with black plastic. A piece with an area of 80 square meters costs $90. Find the cost of a piece with an area of 200 square meters.

60. Stan paid $162,500 for a 5-unit apartment house. Find the cost for a 12 unit apartment house.

61. Eight yards of material are needed for 5 dresses. How much material is needed for 12 dresses?

62. A taxi ride of 3 miles costs $5. Find the cost of a ride of 5 miles.

Chapter 5   Test

[5.1]   *Reduce to lowest terms.*

1. $\dfrac{8m^2n^2}{4m^3n^5}$

2. $\dfrac{5s^3 - 5s}{2s + 2}$

[5.2]   *Multiply or divide. Write all answers in lowest terms.*

3. $\dfrac{x^6y}{x^3} \cdot \dfrac{y^2}{x^2y^3}$

4. $\dfrac{8y - 16}{9} \div \dfrac{3y - 6}{5}$

5. $\dfrac{6m^2 - m - 2}{8m^2 + 10m + 3} \cdot \dfrac{4m^2 + 7m + 3}{3m^2 + 5m + 2}$

[5.3] *Write each rational expression with the given denominator.*

6. $\dfrac{11}{7r}$, $49r^2$

7. $\dfrac{5}{8m - 16}$, $24m - 48$

[5.4] *Add or subtract. Write all answers in lowest terms.*

8. $\dfrac{5}{x} - \dfrac{6}{x}$

9. $\dfrac{1}{a + 1} + \dfrac{5}{6a + 6}$

10. $\dfrac{3}{2k} + \dfrac{1}{k + 2}$

[5.5] *Simplify.*

11. $\dfrac{\dfrac{3}{x}}{\dfrac{1}{1 + x}}$

12. $\dfrac{\dfrac{1}{k} - 2}{\dfrac{1}{k} + 3}$

[5.6] *Solve each equation.*

13. $\dfrac{1}{8} = \dfrac{x}{12}$

14. $\dfrac{3}{t - 1} + \dfrac{1}{t + 1} = \dfrac{6}{5}$

[5.7] *For each problem, write an equation and solve it.*

15. If four times a number is added to the reciprocal of twice the number, the result is 3. Find the number.

16. If the numerator of $\dfrac{3}{x}$ is decreased by x, the result is $\dfrac{2}{3}$. Find x.

17. A man can paint his house, working alone, in five hours. His wife can do it in four hours. How long will it take them working together?

[5.8] *Solve each proportion.*

18. $\dfrac{z}{16} = \dfrac{3}{48}$

19. $\dfrac{y + 5}{y - 2} = \dfrac{1}{4}$

20. If 11 hamburgers cost $6.05, find the cost of 32 hamburgers.

6
Graphing Linear Equations

6.1 Linear Equations in Two Variables

- **Find the value of one variable in an equation, given the value of the other.**
- **Complete ordered pairs for a given equation.**
- **Decide whether a given ordered pair is a solution of a given equation.**

All the equations we have studied so far have contained only one variable, such as

$$3x + 15 = 12 \quad \text{or} \quad 2x^2 + x + 5 = 0.$$

In this chapter, we begin a study of equations in *two* variables, such as

$$y = 4x + 5 \quad \text{or} \quad 2x + 3y = 6.$$

Solutions for these equations are made up of *two* numbers, one for each variable. As the next example shows, if we are given a value for one variable, we can find the corresponding value for the other variable.

EXAMPLE 1 Suppose $y = 4x + 5$. Find y for the given values of x.

(a) $x = 3$

Substitute 3 for x.

$$y = 4x + 5$$
$$y = 4(3) + 5 \qquad \text{Let } x = 3$$
$$y = 12 + 5$$
$$y = 17$$

If $x = 3$, then $y = 17$.

(b) $x = -5$

$$y = 4(-5) + 5$$
$$y = -20 + 5$$
$$y = -15$$

If $x = -5$, then $y = -15$.

In part (a) of Example 1, when $x = 3$, then $y = 17$. This statement is usually abbreviated as just

$$(3, 17).$$

This abbreviation gives the x-value, 3, and the y-value, 17, as a pair of numbers, written inside parentheses. The x-value is always given first. A pair of numbers written in this order is called an **ordered pair.** Each ordered pair produced from an equation is a **solution** for the equation.

EXAMPLE 2   Complete the following solutions for the equation $y = 4x + 5$.

(a) (7,)

In this ordered pair, $x = 7$. To find the corresponding value of y, replace x with 7 in the equation $y = 4x + 5$.

$$y = 4(7) + 5$$
$$y = 28 + 5$$
$$y = 33$$

This gives the ordered pair (7, 33).

(b) (−9,)

To find the value of y, replace x with −9 in the equation.

$$y = 4(-9) + 5$$
$$y = -36 + 5$$
$$y = -31$$

This gives the ordered pair (−9, −31).

(c) (,13)

In this ordered pair, $y = 13$. To find the value of x, replace y with 13 in the equation, and then solve for x.

$$y = 4x + 5$$

$$13 = 4x + 5 \qquad \text{Let } y = 13$$

$$8 = 4x \qquad \text{Add } -5 \text{ to both sides}$$

$$2 = x \qquad \text{Multiply both sides by } \frac{1}{2}$$

This gives the ordered pair (2, 13).

EXAMPLE 3 Complete the ordered pairs for the equation $5x - y = 24$.

Equation	*Ordered pairs*
$5x - y = 24$	(5,) (−3,)(0,)

To find the y-value of the ordered pair (5,), replace x with 5 in the equation and solve the resulting equation for y.

$$5x - y = 24$$

$$5(5) - y = 24 \qquad \text{Let } x = 5$$

$$25 - y = 24$$

$$-y = -1 \qquad \text{Add } -25 \text{ to both sides}$$

$$y = 1$$

This gives the ordered pair (5, 1).

We complete the ordered pair (−3,) by letting $x = -3$ in the equation. Likewise we complete (0,) by letting $x = 0$.

	If	$x = -3,$		If	$x = 0,$
then		$5x - y = 24$	then		$5x - y = 24$
becomes		$5(-3) - y = 24$	becomes		$5(0) - y = 24$
		$-15 - y = 24$			$0 - y = 24$
		$-y = 39$			$-y = 24$
		$y = -39$			$y = -24$

The completed ordered pairs are as follows.

Equation	*Ordered pairs*
$5x - y = 24$	(5, 1) (−3, −39) (0, −24)

EXAMPLE 4 Complete the ordered pairs for the equation $x - 2y = 8$.

Equation	*Ordered pairs*
$x - 2y = 8$	(2,) (, 0)
	(10,) (, −2)

Complete the two ordered pairs on the left by letting $x = 2$ and $x = 10$, respectively.

If	$x = 2$,			If	$x = 10$,
then	$x - 2y = 8$			then	$x - 2y = 8$
becomes	$2 - 2y = 8$			becomes	$10 - 2y = 8$
	$-2y = 6$				$-2y = -2$
	$y = -3$				$y = 1$

Now complete the two ordered pairs on the right by letting $y = 0$ and $y = -2$, respectively.

If	$y = 0$,			If	$y = -2$,
then	$x - 2y = 8$			then	$x - 2y = 8$
becomes	$x - 2(0) = 8$			becomes	$x - 2(-2) = 8$
	$x - 0 = 8$				$x + 4 = 8$
	$x = 8$				$x = 4$

The completed ordered pairs are as follows.

Equation	Ordered pairs
$x - 2y = 8$	$(2, -3)$ $(8, 0)$
	$(10, 1)$ $(4, -2)$

EXAMPLE 5 Complete the ordered pairs for the equation $x = 5$.

Equation	Ordered pairs
$x = 5$	$(\ , -2)\ (\ , 6)\ (\ , 3)$

The equation we are given here is $x = 5$. Therefore, no matter which value of y we might choose, we always have the same value of x, 5. Therefore, each ordered pair can be completed by placing 5 in the first position.

Equation	Ordered pairs
$x = 5$	$(5, -2)\ (5, 6)\ (5, 3)$

When an equation such as $x = 5$ is discussed along with equations of two variables, it is customary to think of $x = 5$ as an equation in two variables by rewriting $x = 5$ as $x + 0 \cdot y = 5$. This last form shows that for any value of y, x always equals 5.

The next example shows how to decide if an ordered pair gives a solution of an equation.

EXAMPLE 6 Decide whether or not the given ordered pair is a solution of the given equation.

(a) $(3, 2)$; $2x + 3y = 12$

To see whether or not the ordered pair (3, 2) is a solution of the equation $2x + 3y = 12$, substitute 3 for x and 2 for y in the given equation.

$$2x + 3y = 12$$
$$2(3) + 3(2) = 12 \qquad \text{Let } x = 3; \text{ let } y = 2$$
$$6 + 6 = 12$$
$$12 = 12 \qquad \text{True}$$

This result is true, so (3, 2) is a solution of $2x + 3y = 12$.

(b) $(-2, -7)$; $2x + 3y = 12$

$$2(-2) + 3(-7) = 12 \qquad \text{Let } x = -2; \text{ let } y = -7$$
$$-4 + (-21) = 12$$
$$-25 = 12 \qquad \text{False}$$

This result is false, so $(-2, -7)$ is *not* a solution of $2x + 3y = 12$.

The equations we worked with in this section all fit the pattern

$$ax + by = c,$$

where a, b, and c are real numbers and a and b cannot both equal 0. Such an equation is called a **linear (or first-degree) equation in two variables.** Examples of linear equations in two variables include the following.

$$2x + 3y = 12 \qquad y = 3x - 5 \qquad x = 5$$

EXERCISES 6.1

Complete the given ordered pairs for the equation $y = 3x + 5$. *See Example 2.*

1. (2,)   **2.** (5,)   **3.** (8,)   **4.** (0,)
5. (−3,)   **6.** (−4,)   **7.** (, 14)   **8.** (, −10)

Complete the given ordered pairs for the equation $y = -4x + 8$. *See Example 2.*

9. (0,)   **10.** (2,)   **11.** (, 16)   **12.** (, 24)
13. (, −4)   **14.** (, −8)

Complete the ordered pairs using the given equations. See Examples 2–4.

Equation	Ordered pairs
15. $y = 2x + 1$	(3,) (0,) (−1,)
16. $y = 3x - 5$	(2,) (0,) (−3,)
17. $y = 8 - 3x$	(2,) (0,) (−3,)
18. $y = -2 - 5x$	(4,) (0,) (−4,)
19. $2x + y = 9$	(0,) (3,) (12,)

	Equation	*Ordered pairs*
20.	$-3x + y = 4$	$(1, \ )$ $(0, \ )$ $(-2, \ )$
21.	$2x + 3y = 6$	$(0, \ )$ $(\ , 0)$ $(\ , 4)$
22.	$4x + 3y = 12$	$(0, \ )$ $(\ , 0)$ $(\ , 8)$
23.	$3x - 5y = 15$	$(0, \ )$ $(\ , 0)$ $(\ , -6)$
24.	$4x - 9y = 36$	$(\ , 0)$ $(0, \ )$ $(\ , 4)$
25.	$4x + 5y = 10$	$(0, \ )$ $(\ , 0)$ $(\ , 3)$
26.	$2x - 3y = 4$	$(\ , 0)$ $(0, \ )$ $(\ , 3)$
27.	$6x - 4y = 5$	$(0, \ )$ $(\ , 0)$ $(2, \ )$
28.	$4x - 3y = 7$	$(\ , 0)$ $(2, \ )$ $(\ , -1)$

Complete the ordered pairs using the given equations. See Example 5.

	Equation	*Ordered pairs*
29.	$x = -4$	$(\ , 6)$ $(\ , 2)$ $(\ , -3)$
30.	$x = 8$	$(\ , 3)$ $(\ , 8)$ $(\ , 0)$
31.	$y = 3$	$(8, \ )$ $(4, \ )$ $(-2, \ )$
32.	$y = -8$	$(4, \ )$ $(0, \ )$ $(-4, \ )$
33.	$x + 9 = 0$	$(\ , 8)$ $(\ , 3)$ $(\ , 0)$
34.	$y + 4 = 0$	$(9, \ )$ $(2, \ )$ $(0, \ )$

Decide whether or not the given ordered pair is a solution of the given equation. See Example 6.

35. $x + y = 9$; $(2, 7)$ **36.** $3x + y = 8$; $(0, 8)$

37. $2x - y = 6$; $(2, -2)$ **38.** $2x + y = 5$; $(2, 1)$

39. $4x - 3y = 6$; $(1, 2)$ **40.** $5x - 3y = 1$; $(0, 1)$

41. $y = 3x$; $(1, 3)$ **42.** $x = -4y$; $(8, -2)$

43. $x = -6$; $(-6, 8)$ **44.** $y = 2$; $(9, 2)$

45. $x + 4 = 0$; $(-5, 1)$ **46.** $x - 6 = 0$; $(5, -1)$

6.2 Graphing Ordered Pairs

- **Graph ordered pairs.**
- **Complete ordered pairs and graph them.**

Earlier in this book we used a number line to graph the solution of an equation in one variable. Now we want to graph the solutions of an equation in *two* variables. Since the solutions of such an equation are ordered pairs of numbers in the form (x, y), we need two number lines to do this. (One is for x and one for y.) These two number lines are drawn as shown in Figure 6.1. The horizontal number line is called the *x*-**axis.** The vertical line is called the *y*-**axis.** Together the *x*-axis and the *y*-axis form the **coordinate system.**

A coordinate system is divided into four regions, called **quadrants.** These quadrants are numbered counterclockwise as shown in Figure 6.1. The point where the *x*-axis and *y*-axis meet is called the **origin.**

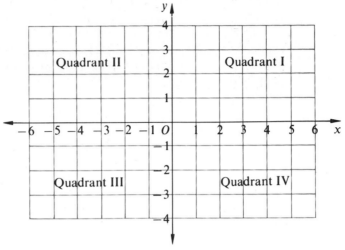

Figure 6.1

We can graph any ordered pair (*x*, *y*) on a coordinate system by using the *x*- and *y*- *coordinates* of the point. To graph the point (2, 3), start at the origin. Since the *x*-coordinate is 2, go 2 units to the right along the *x*-axis. Then since the *y*-coordinate is 3, turn and go up 3 units on a line parallel to the *y*-axis. This is called **plotting** the point (2, 3). See Figure 6.2.

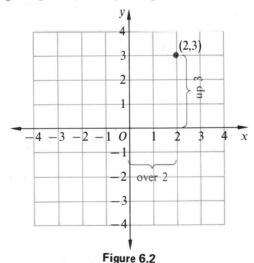

Figure 6.2

EXAMPLE 1   Plot the following ordered pairs on a coordinate system.

(a) (1, 5)

(b) $(-2, 3)$

(c) $(-1, -4)$

(d) $(7, -2)$

(e) $\left(\dfrac{3}{2}, 2\right)$.

To locate the point $(-1, -4)$, for example, go 1 unit to the left along the x-axis. Then turn and go 4 units down, parallel to the y-axis. To plot the point $(3/2, 2)$, go $3/2$ (or $1\frac{1}{2}$) units to the right along the x-axis. Then turn and go 2 units up parallel to the y-axis. Figure 6.3 shows the graph of the points in this example.

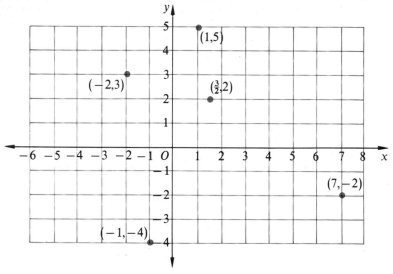

Figure 6.3

EXAMPLE 2 Complete the ordered pairs. Then plot the ordered pairs on a coordinate system.

Equation	*Ordered pairs*
$x + 2y = 7$	$(1,\ )\quad (-3,\ )\quad (3,\ )\quad (7,\ )$

To complete the ordered pairs, substitute the given x-values into the equation $x + 2y = 7$.

$x + 2y = 7$ Let $x = 1$		$x + 2y = 7$ Let $x = -3$
$1 + 2y = 7$		$-3 + 2y = 7$
$2y = 6$		$2y = 10$
$y = 3$		$y = 5$

This gives the ordered pairs $(1, 3)$ and $(-3, 5)$.

In the same way, if $x = 3$, then $y = 2$, giving $(3, 2)$. Finally, if $x = 7$, then $y = 0$, giving $(7, 0)$.

The completed ordered pairs are as follows.

Equation	*Ordered pairs*
$x + 2y = 7$	(1, 3) (−3, 5) (3, 2) (7, 0)

The graph of these ordered pairs is shown in Figure 6.4.

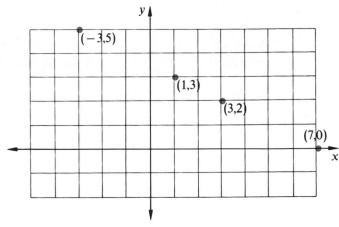

Figure 6.4

EXAMPLE 3 In a certain city, the cost of a taxi ride of x miles is given by the formula

$$y = 25x + 50,$$

where y represents the cost in cents. Complete the ordered pairs for this equation.

$$(1, \ ) (2, \ ) (3, \ )$$

To complete the ordered pair (1,), we let $x = 1$.

$$y = 25x + 50$$
$$y = 25(1) + 50 \qquad \text{Let } x = 1$$
$$y = 25 + 50$$
$$y = 75$$

This gives the ordered pair (1, 75), which tells us that a taxi ride of 1 mile costs 75¢.

We complete (2,) and (3,) as follows.

$y = 25x + 50$	$y = 25x + 50$
$y = 25(2) + 50 \qquad \text{Let } x = 2$	$y = 25(3) + 50 \qquad \text{Let } x = 3$
$y = 50 + 50$	$y = 75 + 50$
$y = 100$	$y = 125$

This gives the ordered pairs (2, 100) and (3, 125).

The ordered pairs obtained in Example 3 are plotted in Figure 6.5.

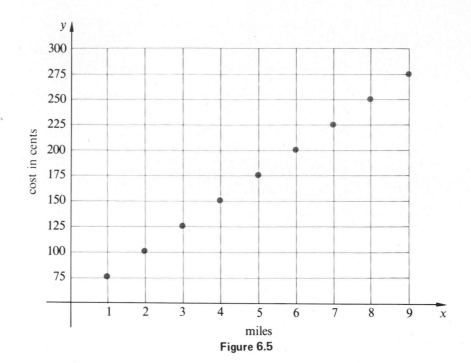

Figure 6.5

EXERCISES 6.2   *Write the x- and y- coordinates of the following points labeled in the figure.*

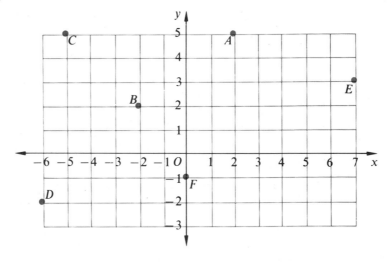

1. *A*   **2.** *B*   **3.** *C*   **4.** *D*   **5.** *E*   **6.** *F*

Plot the following ordered pairs on a coordinate system. See Example 1.

7. (6, 1)   **8.** (4, −2)   **9.** (3, 5)   **10.** (−4, −5)

11. (−2, 4)   **12.** (−5, −1)   **13.** (−3, 5)   **14.** (3, −5)

15. $(4, 0)$ **16.** $(1, 0)$ **17.** $(-2, 0)$ **18.** $(-5, 0)$

19. $(0, 3)$ **20.** $(0, 6)$ **21.** $(0, -5)$ **22.** $(0, 0)$

Without plotting the given point, state the quadrant in which each point lies.

23. $(2, 3)$ **24.** $(2, -3)$ **25.** $(-2, 3)$ **26.** $(-2, -3)$

27. $(-1, -1)$ **28.** $(4, 7)$ **29.** $(-3, 6)$ **30.** $(1, 5)$

31. $(5, -4)$ **32.** $(9, -1)$ **33.** $(0, 0)$ **34.** $(-2, 0)$

Complete the ordered pairs using the given equation. Then plot the ordered pairs. See Example 2.

Equation	*Ordered pairs*
35. $y = 2x + 6$	$(0,)$ $(2,)$ $(, 0)$ $(, 2)$
36. $y = 8 - 4x$	$(0,)$ $(3,)$ $(, 0)$ $(, 16)$
37. $3x + 5y = 15$	$(0,)$ $(10,)$ $(, 0)$ $(, 6)$
38. $2x - 5y = 10$	$(0,)$ $(10,)$ $(, 0)$ $(, -6)$
39. $y = 3x$	$(0,)$ $(-2,)$ $(4,)$ $(, -3)$
40. $x + 2y = 0$	$(0,)$ $(, 3)$ $(4,)$ $(, -1)$
41. $x = 3$	$(, 2)$ $(, 5)$ $(, 0)$ $(, -3)$
42. $y = -5$	$(2,)$ $(-3,)$ $(0,)$ $(-1,)$
43. $y + 2 = 0$	$(5,)$ $(0,)$ $(-3,)$ $(-2,)$
44. $x - 4 = 0$	$(, 7)$ $(, 0)$ $(, -4)$ $(, 4)$

6.3   Graphing Linear Equations

- **Graph linear equations by completing ordered pairs.**
- **Graph linear equations of the form y = a number.**
- **Graph linear equations of the form x = a number.**

An infinite number of ordered pairs can make an equation in two variables true. For example, we can find as many ordered pairs as we want that are solutions of $x + 2y = 7$. This is done by choosing as many values of x (or y) as we want.

For example, if we choose $x = 1$, then

$$x + 2y = 7$$
$$1 + 2y = 7$$
$$2y = 6$$
$$y = 3$$

This tells us the ordered pair (1, 3) is a solution of the equation $x + 2y = 7$.

Several ordered pairs that satisfy the equation $x + 2y = 7$ have been graphed in Figure 6.6.

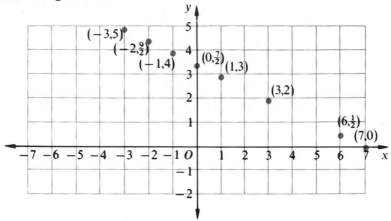

Figure 6.6

Notice that the points plotted in this figure all lie on a straight line. The line that goes through these points is shown in Figure 6.7. In fact, any point satisfying the equation $x + 2y = 7$ will lie on this straight line. (We only show a portion of this line here, but this line goes on forever in both directions.)

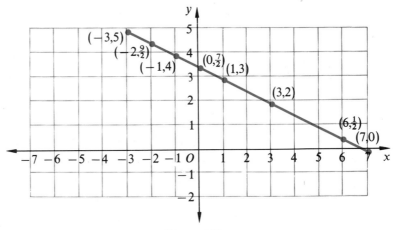

Figure 6.7

In general, the graph of any linear equation in two variables is a straight line. We can graph a straight line if we know any two points that lie on the graph. In many cases, we can graph a line by finding its **x-intercept** and **y-intercept**; the points (if any) where the line crosses the x-axis and y-axis respectively. In the line of Figure 6.7, the x-intercept is 7, since the line crosses the x-axis at (7, 0). The y-intercept is $\frac{7}{2}$.

In general,

to find the x-intercept, let $y = 0$ and
to find the y-intercept, let $x = 0$.

EXAMPLE 1   Graph $3x + 2y = 6$
Find the x-intercept and the y-intercept.

x-*intercept*		y-*intercept*	
$3x + 2y = 6$		$3x + 2y = 6$	
$3x + 2(0) = 6$	Let $y = 0$	$3(0) + 2y = 6$	Let $x = 0$
$3x + 0 = 6$		$0 + 2y = 6$	
$3x = 6$		$2y = 6$	
$x = 2$		$y = 3$	

The ordered pairs are $(2, 0)$ and $(0, 3)$.

As a check, we can get a third point on the line. To do this, let x or y equal some number other than 0. For example, let $x = -2$ (we could have used many other numbers instead).

$$3x + 2y = 6$$
$$3(-2) + 2y = 6 \qquad \text{Let } x = -2$$
$$-6 + 2y = 6$$
$$2y = 12$$
$$y = 6$$

The ordered pair is $(-2, 6)$.

Now plot the three ordered pairs we have found, $(0, 3)$, $(2, 0)$, and $(-2, 6)$, and draw a straight line through them. This straight line, shown in Figure 6.8, is the graph we want.

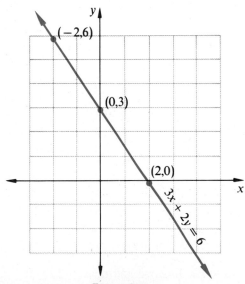

Figure 6.8

EXAMPLE 2 Graph $4x - 5y = 20$.

Begin by finding the intercepts.

	x-intercept			*y-intercept*	
	$4x - 5y = 20$			$4x - 5y = 20$	
	$4x - 5(0) = 20$	Let $y = 0$		$4(0) - 5y = 20$	Let $x = 0$
	$4x = 20$			$-5y = 20$	
	$x = 5$			$y = -4$	

The ordered pairs are $(5, 0)$ and $(0, -4)$.

To get a third ordered pair (as a check), choose some number other than zero for x or y. This time, let us choose $y = 2$.

$$4x - 5y = 20$$
$$4x - 5(2) = 20 \qquad \text{Let } y = 2$$
$$4x - 10 = 20$$
$$4x = 30$$
$$x = \frac{15}{2}$$

This gives the ordered pair $\left(\frac{15}{2}, 2\right)$.

Plot the three ordered pairs we have found, $(0, -4)$, $(5, 0)$, and $\left(\frac{15}{2}, 2\right)$, and draw a straight line through them. This straight line, shown in Figure 6.9, is the graph we want.

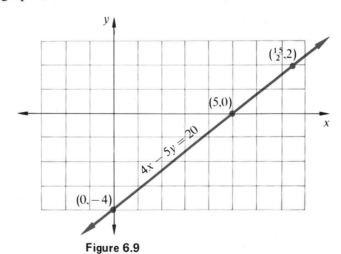

Figure 6.9

EXAMPLE 3 Graph the linear equation $x = 3y$.

If we let $x = 0$, we get $y = 0$, giving $(0, 0)$. If $y = 0$, we also get the same ordered pair, $(0, 0)$. This is the same point, so we want to find two more points satisfying $x = 3y$. If we choose $y = 2$, we get $x = 6$, giving the ordered pair (6, 2). Also, if we choose $x = -6$, we get $y = -2$, giving the ordered pair $(-6, -2)$. These three ordered pairs were used to get the graph shown in Figure 6.10.

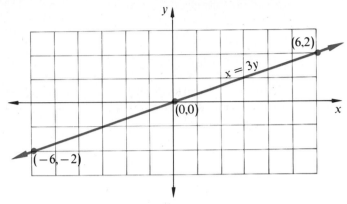

Figure 6.10

Some equations lead to vertical or horizontal straight lines, as the next two examples show.

EXAMPLE 4   Graph the linear equation $y = -4$.

We can rewrite the equation $y = -4$ as $y = 0 \cdot x - 4$. This form of the equation shows that for any value of x we might choose, y is always equal to -4. To get three ordered pairs which are solutions of this equation, we choose any three numbers for x, and always let $y = -4$. Three ordered pairs that we can use are $(-2, -4)$, $(0, -4)$, and $(3, -4)$. Drawing a line through these points gives us the horizontal line shown in Figure 6.11. This graph has a y-intercept, but no x-intercept.

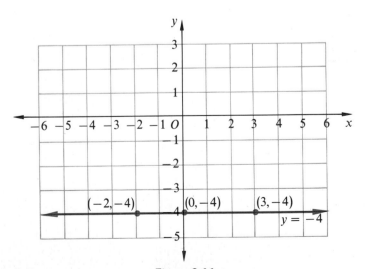

Figure 6.11

In general,

the graph of a linear equation $y = k$, where k is a real number, is a horizontal line going through the point $(0, k)$.

EXAMPLE 5 Graph the linear equation $x = 3$.

This equation tells us that all ordered pairs that are solutions of this equation have an x-value of 3. We can use any number for y. Three ordered pairs that work are (3, 3), (3, 0), and (3, −2). Drawing a line through these points gives us the vertical line shown in Figure 6.12. This graph has an x-intercept, but no y-intercept.

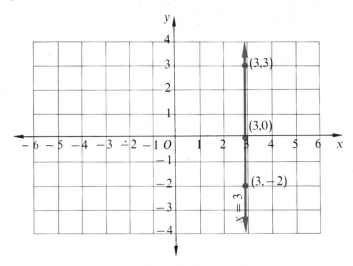

Figure 6.12

In general,

the graph of a linear equation $x = k$, where k is a real number, is a vertical line going through the point $(k, 0)$.

EXERCISES 6.3 *In Exercises 1–10, first complete the ordered pairs for each equation. Then graph the equation, using the ordered pairs to plot points.*

1. $x + y = 5$;   (0,   ) (,0) (2,   )

2. $y = x − 3$;   (0,   ) (,0) (5,   )

3. $y = x + 4$;   (0,   ) (,0) (−2,   )

4. $y + 5 = x$;   (0,   ) (,0) (6,   )

5. $y = 3x − 6$;   (0,   ) (,0) (3,   )

6. $y = 5x − 10$;   (0,   ) (,0) (3,   )

7. $2x + 5y = 20$;   (0,   ) (,0) (5,   )

8. $3x − 4y = 12$;   (0,   ) (,0) (8,   )

We now give a summary of the different forms of straight-line equations and how they are graphed.

Straight lines are graphed as follows:

1. If the equation is of the form $y = k$, the line will be horizontal, and go through $(0, k)$.
2. An equation of the form $x = k$ will have a vertical line as its graph and go through $(k, 0)$.
3. If the equation is of the form $x = ay$ or $y = ax$, its graph will go through the origin, $(0, 0)$. To get additional points that lie on the graph, choose any value of x, or y, except 0.
4. If the equation is none of the three types mentioned above, first let $x = 0$, and find the corresponding value of y. Then let $y = 0$, and find x. This gives two points the line goes through. As a check, get a third point by choosing a value of x or y that has not yet been used.

---

9. $x + 5 = 0$;   (,2) (,0) (, −3)

10. $y - 4 = 0$;   (3,   ) (0,   ) (−2,   )

In Exercises 11–36, graph each of the linear equations. See Examples 1–5.

11. $x - y = 2$ **12.** $x + y = 6$

13. $y = x + 2$ **14.** $y = x - 1$

15. $y = 2x - 4$ **16.** $y = 3x + 9$

17. $x = 3y - 12$ **18.** $x = 2y - 10$

19. $3x - 2y = 6$ **20.** $2x + 3y = 12$

21. $2x - 7y = 14$ **22.** $3x + 5y = 15$

23. $3x + 7y = 21$ **24.** $6x - 5y = 30$

25. $y = 2x$ **26.** $y = -3x$

27. $y + 6x = 0$ **28.** $y - 4x = 0$

29. $x + 2 = 0$ **30.** $y - 3 = 0$

31. $y = 6$ **32.** $x = 2$

33. $y = -1$ **34.** $x = 4$

35. $x = 0$ **36.** $y = 0.$

Translate each of the statements of Exercises 37–42 into an equation. Then graph the equation.

37. The x-value is 2 more than the y-value.

38. The y-value is 3 less than the x-value.

39. The y-value is 3 less than twice the x-value.

40. The x-value is 4 more than three times the y-value.

41. If 3 is added to the y-value, the result is 4 less than twice the x-value.

42. If 6 is subtracted from 4 times the y-value, the result is three times the x-value.

43. As a rough estimate, the weight of a man taller than about 60 inches is approximated by $y = 5.5x - 220$, where x is the height of the person in inches, and y is the weight in pounds. Estimate the weights of men whose heights are

(a) 62 inches
(b) 64 inches
(c) 68 inches
(d) 70 inches
(e) 72 inches
(f) Graph $y = 5.5x - 220$. Use only the numbers 62 through 76 on the x-axis.

6.4 Slope

- **Find slope given two points.**
- **Find slope from the equation of a line.**
- **Use slope to draw graphs.**
- **Find equations of lines.**

To graph a straight line, we need to find at least two different points that are on the line. We could also graph a line if we knew one point that the line goes through, and also know the "steepness" of the line.

The steepness of a line is measured by its **slope.** Slope is defined as

$$\text{slope} = \frac{\text{difference in } y\text{-values}}{\text{difference in } x\text{-values}}.$$

That is, if (x_1, y_1) (read "x-one, y-one") and (x_2, y_2) are any two different points on a line, the slope of the line is

$$m = \frac{y_2 - y_1}{x_2 - x_1}.$$

EXAMPLE 1   Find the slope of each of the following lines.

(a) the line through $(-4, 7)$ and $(1, -2)$

Use the definition given above.

$$\text{slope} = \frac{\text{difference in } y\text{-values}}{\text{difference in } x\text{-values}}$$

$$= \frac{7 - (-2)}{-4 - 1}$$

$$= \frac{9}{-5}$$

$$= -\frac{9}{5}$$

(b) the line through $(12, -5)$ and $(-9, -2)$

$$\text{slope} = \frac{-5 - (-2)}{12 - (-9)}$$

$$= \frac{-3}{21}$$

$$= -\frac{1}{7}$$

We would get the same slope if we subtracted in reverse order:

$$\frac{-2 - (-5)}{-9 - 12} = \frac{3}{-21}$$

$$= -\frac{1}{7}$$

The y-values and x-values may be subtracted in either order—just be sure to subtract consistently.

(c) the line shown in the graph of Figure 6.13.

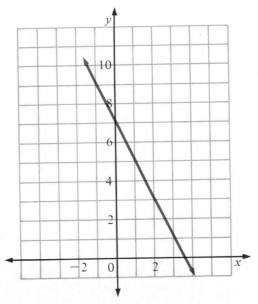

Figure 6.13

Inspect the graph to find two points that the line goes through. We use the two points $(-1, 9)$ and $(2, 3)$ to find the slope.

$$\text{slope} = \frac{9 - 3}{-1 - 2}$$

$$= \frac{6}{-3}$$

$$= -2$$

The next example shows how to find the slopes of horizontal and vertical lines.

EXAMPLE 2 Find the slope of each of the following lines.

(a) through $(-8, 4)$ and $(2, 4)$

$$\text{slope} = \frac{4 - 4}{-8 - 2}$$

$$= \frac{0}{-10}$$

$$= 0$$

As shown by a sketch of the graph through these two points, this line is horizontal. *All horizontal lines have a slope of 0.*

(b) through $(6, 2)$ and $(6, -9)$.

$$\text{slope} = \frac{2 - (-9)}{6 - 6}$$

$$= \frac{11}{0} \qquad \text{Meaningless}$$

Since division by zero is meaningless, this line has no slope. This line is vertical; *vertical lines have no slope.* In summary,

horizontal lines, having equations $y = k$, have a slope of 0 and vertical lines, having equation $x = k$, have no slope.

Slopes can also be found from the equation of a line. For example, let us find the slope of the line

$$y = -3x + 5.$$

To find the slope, we need two points on the line. To get these two points, we can choose two different values of x. Let us choose $x = -2$ and $x = 4$.

$x = -2$		$x = 4$	
$y = -3(-2) + 5$	Let $x = -2$	$y = -3(4) + 5$	Let $x = 4$
$y = 6 + 5$		$y = -12 + 5$	
$y = 11$		$y = -7$	

The ordered pairs are $(-2, 11)$ and $(4, -7)$.

Now we can find the slope.

$$\text{slope} = \frac{11 - (-7)}{-2 - 4}$$

$$= \frac{18}{-6}$$

$$= -3$$

This slope of -3 is the same number as the coefficient of x in the equation $y = -3x + 5$. It turns out that this always happens, as long as the equation is solved for y:

To find the slope of a line from its equation:

1. Solve the equation for y.
2. The slope is given by the coefficient of x.

EXAMPLE 3 Find the slope of each of the following lines.

(a) $2x - 5y = 4$

Solve the equation for y.

$$2x - 5y = 4$$
$$-5y = -2x + 4 \qquad \text{Add } -2x$$
$$y = \frac{2}{5}x - \frac{4}{5} \qquad \text{Multiply by } -\frac{1}{5}$$

The slope is given by the coefficient of x, or

$$\text{slope} = \frac{2}{5}.$$

(b) $8x + 4y = 1$

Solve for y; you should get

$$y = -2x + \frac{1}{4}.$$

The slope of this line is -2.

One application of slope is in drawing the graph of a straight line, as shown in the next example.

EXAMPLE 4 Graph each of the following straight lines.

(a) through $(-2, -1)$, with slope $\frac{5}{3}$

First locate the point $(-2, -1)$, as shown in the graph of Figure 6.14. To complete the graph, we need another point on the line. This second point is found from the slope. In this example, the slope is $\frac{5}{3}$. The number in the denominator, 3 here, gives the change in x, while the numerator of 5 gives the change in y. To find our second point, start at $(-2, -1)$, go 3 units to the right, and 5 units up. This locates a second point, with the desired line drawn through the two points.

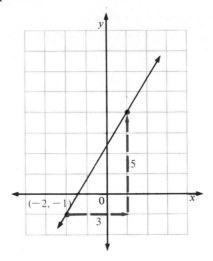

Figure 6.14

(b) through $(4, -3)$ with slope -2.

Write the slope as $-2 = \frac{-2}{1}$. Locate $(4, -3)$ on a graph. Then go 1 unit to the right and 2 units down. Complete the graph as shown in Figure 6.15.

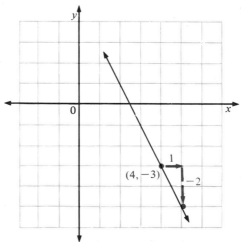

Figure 6.15

If we are given a point that a line goes through, and the slope of the line, we can find the equation of the line. To see how to do this, let m represent the slope of the line, and let (x_1, y_1) (read "x-one, y-one") represent the point on the line. The formula used to find the equation of the line is called the **point-slope form** of the equation of a line.

Point-slope form: the line with slope m going through (x_1, y_1) has equation

$$y - y_1 = m(x - x_1).$$

EXAMPLE 5 Find equations of each of the following lines.

(a) through $(-2, 4)$, with slope -3. Here $(x_1, y_1) = (-2, 4)$ so that $x_1 = -2$, and $y_1 = 4$. Also, $m = -3$. Substitute these values into the point-slope form.

$$y - y_1 = m(x - x_1)$$
$$y - 4 = -3[x - (-2)]$$
$$y - 4 = -3(x + 2)$$
$$y - 4 = -3x - 6$$
$$y = -3x - 2$$

(b) through $(4, 2)$, with slope $\dfrac{3}{5}$

Here $x_1 = 4$, $y_1 = 2$, and $m = \dfrac{3}{5}$.

$$y - y_1 = m(x - x_1)$$
$$y - 2 = \frac{3}{5}(x - 4)$$

Multiply both sides by 5 to clear of fractions.

$$5(y - 2) = 5 \cdot \frac{3}{5}(x - 4)$$
$$5(y - 2) = 3(x - 4)$$
$$5y - 10 = 3x - 12$$
$$5y = 3x - 2$$

EXAMPLE 6 Find the equation of the line through the points $(-2, 5)$ and $(3, 4)$.

First find the slope of the line, using the definition of slope.

$$\text{slope} = \frac{5 - 4}{-2 - 3}$$
$$= \frac{1}{-5}$$
$$= -\frac{1}{5}$$

Now use either $(-2, 5)$ or $(3, 4)$ and the point-slope form. If we use $(3, 4)$, we get

$$y - y_1 = m(x - x_1)$$

$$y - 4 = -\frac{1}{5}(x - 3)$$

$$5(y - 4) = -1(x - 3)$$

$$5y - 20 = -x + 3$$

$$5y = -x + 23$$

EXERCISES 6.4   *Find the slope of each of the following lines. See Example 1.*

1.

2.

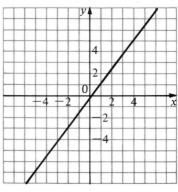

3.

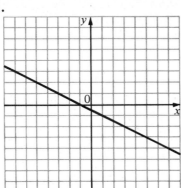

4.

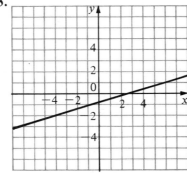

5.

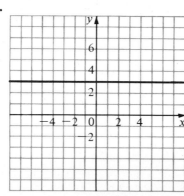

6.

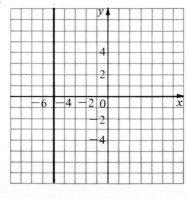

Find the slope of the lines going through each of the following pairs of points. See Examples 1 and 2.

7. $(-4, 1)$, $(2, 8)$

8. $(3, 7)$, $(5, 2)$

9. $(-1, 2)$, $(-3, -7)$

10. $(5, -4)$, $(-5, -9)$

11. $(8, 0)$, $(0, 5)$

12. $(0, -3)$, $(2, 0)$

13. $(-1, 6)$, $(4, 6)$

14. $(5, 3)$, $(5, -2)$

15. $(-9, 1)$, $(-9, 0)$

16. $(4, -11)$, $(-3, -11)$

Find the slope of each of the following lines. See Example 3.

17. $y = 2x - 1$

18. $y = 5x + 2$

19. $y = -x + 4$

20. $y = x + 1$

21. $y = 6 - 5x$

22. $y = 3 + 9x$

23. $2x + y = 5$

24. $4x - y = 8$

25. $-6x + 4y = 1$

26. $3x - 2y = 5$

27. $2x + 5y = 4$

28. $9x + 7y = 5$

Graph the line going through the given point and having the given slope. See Example 4. (In Exercises 39–42, recall the type of lines having zero slope and no slope.)

29. $(-1, 3)$, $m = \dfrac{4}{3}$

30. $(2, 5)$, $m = \dfrac{1}{2}$

31. $(-4, -3)$, $m = -\dfrac{2}{5}$

32. $(-1, -1)$, $m = -\dfrac{3}{8}$

33. $(0, 2)$, $m = \dfrac{7}{4}$

34. $(-3, 0)$, $m = \dfrac{5}{9}$

35. $(6, 4)$, $m = 2$

36. $(1, 8)$, $m = 1$

37. $(-4, 7)$, $m = -3$

38. $(2, 9)$, $m = -4$

39. $(1, 2)$, $m = 0$

40. $(-4, -8)$, $m = 0$

41. $(3, 5)$, no slope

42. $(2, 3)$, no slope

Write an equation for the line passing through the given point and having the given slope. See Example 5.

43. $(5, 3)$, $m = 2$

44. $(1, 4)$, $m = 3$

45. $(2, -8)$, $m = -2$

46. $(-1, 7)$, $m = -4$

47. $(3, 5)$, $m = \dfrac{2}{3}$

48. $(2, -4)$, $m = \dfrac{4}{5}$

49. $(-3, -2)$, $m = -\dfrac{3}{4}$

50. $(-8, -2)$, $m = -\dfrac{5}{9}$

51. $(6, 0)$, $m = -\dfrac{8}{11}$

52. $(0, -4)$, $m = -\dfrac{2}{5}$

Write equations of the lines passing through each of the following pairs of points. See Example 6.

53. (4, 2), (5, 3)

54. (7, 4), (8, 5)

55. (−2, 1), (3, 4)

56. (−8, −2), (−1, −7)

57. (3, −4), (−2, −1)

58. (−7, −1), (−9, −2)

59. (0, 2), (3, 0)

60. (4, 0) (0, −2)

Two lines with the same slope are **parallel.** *Two lines having slopes with a product of −1 are* **perpendicular.** *Find the slope of each line in the following pairs of lines and then decide if they are parallel, perpendicular, or neither.*

61. $x + y = 2$

$x + y = 7$

62. $y - x = 3$

$y - x = 5$

63. $x + y = 5$

$x - y = 1$

64. $y - x = 4$

$y + x = 3$

65. $2x - 5y = 4$

$4x - 10y = 1$

66. $3x - 2y = 4$

$2x + 3y = 1$

67. $3x - 5y = 2$

$5x + 3y = -1$

68. $4x - 3y = 4$

$8x - 6y = 0$

69. $x - 4y = 2$

$2x + 4y = 1$

70. $8x - 9y = 2$

$3x + 6y = 1$

6.5 Graphing Linear Inequalities

- **Graph linear inequalities.**

In the last two sections we discussed methods for graphing linear equations, such as $2x + 3y = 6$. In this section we extend this discussion to linear inequalities, such as

$$2x + 3y \leq 6.$$

(Recall that ≤ is read "less than or equal to.")

The points on the line $2x + 3y = 6$ are solutions of $2x + 3y \leq 6$ but are only part of the final graph. To complete the graph of the linear inequality $2x + 3y \leq 6$, go through the following steps.

Step 1 Graph the equation $2x + 3y = 6$. This graph is a line which divides the plane into three regions: one region below the line, one region above the line, and the points on the line itself.

Step 2 The graph of $2x + 3y \leq 6$ includes either all the points below the line or all the points above the line. To decide which, choose any point not on the line as a test point. The origin, (0, 0), is a good choice, and we will use it here. Substitute 0 for x and 0 for y in the original inequality $2x + 3y \leq 6$ to see if the resulting statement is true or false. We have

$$2x + 3y \leq 6 \qquad \text{Original inequality}$$
$$2(0) + 3(0) \leq 6 \qquad \text{Let } x = 0 \text{ and } y = 0$$
$$0 + 0 \leq 6$$
$$0 \leq 6 \qquad \text{True}$$

Step 3 Since this statement is true, the graph of the inequality includes the region containing (0, 0). Shade this region, as shown in Figure 6.16. The shaded region, along with the original line, is the graph we want.

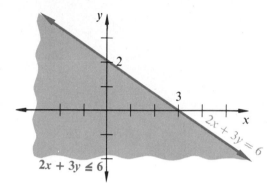

Figure 6.16

EXAMPLE 1 Graph the inequality $x - y > 5$.

This inequality is restricted to "greater than." Therefore, the points on the line $x - y = 5$ do not belong to the graph. However, the line does serve as a boundary for two regions, one of which satisfies the inequality. To graph the inequality, go through the following steps.

Step 1 Graph the equation $x - y = 5$. Use a dashed line to show that the points on the line are *not* solutions of the inequality $x - y > 5$.

Step 2 Choose a test point to see which side of the line satisfies the inequality. Let us choose (0, 0).

$$x - y > 5 \qquad \text{Original inequality}$$
$$0 - 0 > 5 \qquad \text{Let } x = 0 \text{ and } y = 0$$
$$0 > 5 \qquad \text{False}$$

Step 3 Since this statement is false, the graph of the inequality includes the region which does not contain (0, 0). Shade this region, as shown in Figure 6.17. This shaded region is the graph we want.

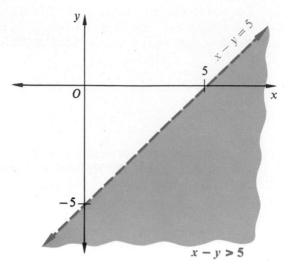

Figure 6.17

EXAMPLE 2 Graph the inequality $2x - 5y \geq 10$.

Step 1 Graph the equation $2x - 5y = 10$. Use a solid line to show that the points on the line are solutions of the inequality $2x - 5y \geq 10$.

Step 2 Choose any test point not on the line. Here we choose $(0, 0)$.

$$2x - 5y \geq 10 \qquad \text{Original inequality}$$
$$2(0) - 5(0) \geq 10 \qquad \text{Let } x = 0 \text{ and } y = 0$$
$$0 - 0 \geq 10$$
$$0 \geq 10 \qquad \text{False}$$

Step 3 Since this statement is false, shade the region *not* containing $(0, 0)$. See Figure 6.18.

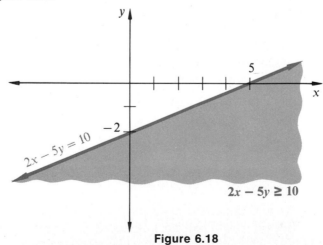

Figure 6.18

EXAMPLE 3   Graph the inequality $x \le 3$.

Step 1   Graph $x = 3$. This is a vertical line going through the point $(3, 0)$. Use a solid line. (Why?)

Step 2   Choose $(0, 0)$ as a test point.

$$x \le 3 \qquad \text{Original inequality}$$
$$0 \le 3 \qquad \text{Let } x = 0$$
$$0 \le 3 \qquad \text{True}$$

Step 3   Since this statement is true, shade the region containing $(0, 0)$. See Figure 6.19.

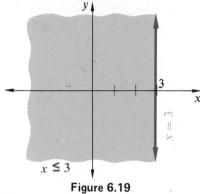

Figure 6.19

EXAMPLE 4   Graph the inequality $x \le 2y$.

Step 1   Graph $x = 2y$. Some ordered pairs you can use to graph this line include $(0, 0)$, $(6, 3)$, and $(4, 2)$. Use a solid line.

Step 2   We can't use $(0, 0)$ as a test point since $(0, 0)$ is on the line $x = 2y$. We must choose a different test point. Let's choose $(1, 3)$.

$$x \le 2y \qquad \text{Original inequality}$$
$$1 \le 2(3) \qquad \text{Let } x = 1 \text{ and } y = 3$$
$$1 \le 6 \qquad \text{True}$$

Step 3   Since this statement is true, shade the side of the graph containing $(1, 3)$. See Figure 6.20.

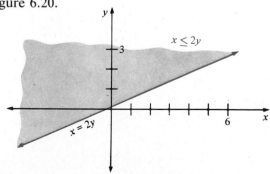

Figure 6.20

To graph a linear equality in two variables:

1. Graph the line which is the boundary of the region. Use the methods of the last two sections. Make the line solid if the inequality has ≤ or ≥; make the line dashed if the inequality has < or >.
2. If the boundary line *does not* go through the origin, use (0, 0) as a test point. Replace x with 0 and y with 0 in the original inequality. If a true statement results, shade the side containing (0, 0). If a false statement results, shade the other side.
3. If the boundary *does* go through the origin, use any point off the line as a test point.

EXERCISES 6.5 *In Exercises 1–12, the straight line for each inequality has been drawn. Complete each graph by shading the correct region. See Example 1, Steps 2 and 3.*

1. $x + y \leq 4$

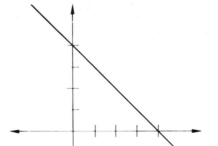

2. $x + y \geq 2$

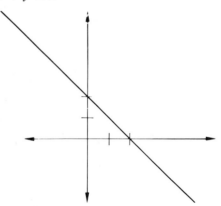

3. $x + 2y \leq 7$

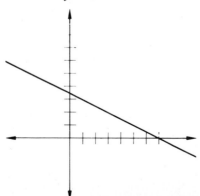

4. $2x + y \leq 5$

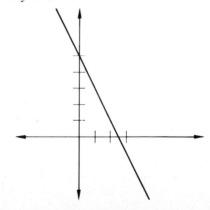

5. $-3x + 4y < 12$

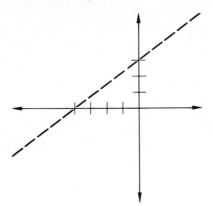

6. $4x - 5y > 20$

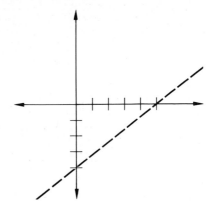

7. $5x + 3y > 15$

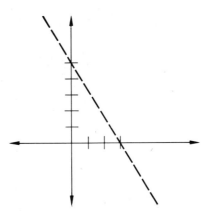

8. $6x - 5y < 30$

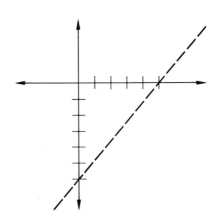

9. $x < 4$

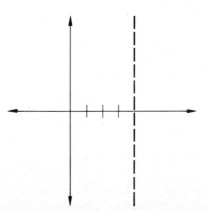

10. $y > -1$

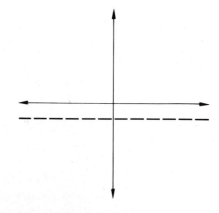

11. $x \le 4y$

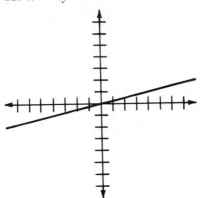

12. $-2x > y$

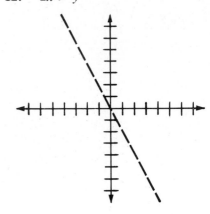

Graph each linear inequality. See Examples 1–4.

13. $x + y \le 8$ **14.** $x + y \ge 2$

15. $x - y \le -2$ **16.** $x - y \le 3$

17. $x + 2y \ge 4$ **18.** $x + 3y \le 6$

19. $2x + 3y > 6$ **20.** $3x + 4y > 12$

21. $3x - 4y < 12$ **22.** $2x - 3y < -6$

23. $3x + 7y \ge 21$ **24.** $2x + 5y \ge 10$

25. $4x - 5y \ge 20$ **26.** $3x + 5y \le 15$

27. $4x + 7y \le 14$ **28.** $x - y \le 2$

29. $x < 4$ **30.** $x < -2$

31. $y \le 2$ **32.** $y \le -3$

33. $x \ge -2$ **34.** $x \le 3y$

35. $x \le 5y$ **36.** $x \ge -2y$

37. $-4x \le y$ **38.** $2x + 3y \ge 0$

39. $3x + 4y \le 0$ **40.** $x + y < 0$

6.6 Functions (Optional)

- **Learn the definition of a function.**
- **Find domains and ranges.**
- **Learn the meaning of f(x).**
- **Use the vertical line test for a function.**

We have now studied equations in two variables, such as $4x + 5y = 8$, $2x - 6 = y$, and so on. A special type of equation in two variables comes up often enough that it deserves special study. This special type of equation in two variables is called a function:

A **function** is a rule or correspondence where each value of x gives exactly one value of y.

EXAMPLE 1   Decide whether or not the following equations are functions.

(a) $y = 2x - 9$

If we choose one value of x, then the corresponding value of y is found by multiplying x by 2 and then subtracting 9. This process leads to only one value of y for any given value of x that we might choose, so that $y = 2x - 9$ *is a* function.

(b) $y^2 = x$

Suppose we choose the x-value to be 36. If $x = 36$,

$$y^2 = x \qquad \text{becomes} \qquad y^2 = 36.$$

There are *two* solutions for $y^2 = 36$; $y = 6$ and $y = -6$. The *one* x-value, $x = 36$, leads to *two* y-values, so that $y^2 = x$ is *not* a function.

The set of all numbers that can be used as x-values in a function is called the **domain** of the function. The set of all possible y-values is called the **range** of the function.

EXAMPLE 2   Find the domain and range for the following functions.

(a) $y = 6x - 9$

Any number at all may be used for x, so that the domain is the set of all real numbers. Any number at all may be used for y, so that the range is also the set of all real numbers.

(b) $y = x^2$

We may square any number, so that the domain is the set of all real numbers. However, since the square of a real number cannot be negative, and since $y = x^2$, the y-value cannot be negative. The range is thus the set of all non-negative numbers. This range can be written as just $y \geq 0$.

It is common to use the letters f, g, and h to name functions. For example, the function $y = 3x + 5$ is often written

$$f(x) = 3x + 5,$$

where $f(x)$ is read "f of x." For this function $f(x) = 3x + 5$, if $x = 7$, then

$$f(7) = 3 \cdot 7 + 5$$
$$= 21 + 5$$

which is abbreviated

$$f(7) = 26.$$

("f of 7 equals 26.")

To find $f(-3)$, replace x with -3.

$$f(x) = 3x + 5$$
$$f(-3) = 3(-3) + 5$$
$$= -9 + 5$$
$$= -4$$

EXAMPLE 3   Use the function $f(x) = x^2 - 3$ and find the following.

(a) $f(2)$

Replace x with 2

$$f(x) = x^2 - 3$$
$$f(2) = 2^2 - 3$$
$$= 4 - 3$$
$$f(2) = 1$$

(b) $f(0) = 0^2 - 3$
$$= 0 - 3$$
$$= -3$$

(c) $f(-3) = (-3)^2 - 3$
$$= 9 - 3$$
$$= 6$$

EXAMPLE 4   Let $P(x) = 5x^2 - 4x + 3$. Find the following. (This function is named P instead of f or g to show that it is a polynomial.)

(a) $P(0)$

Replace x with 0.

$$P(x) = 5x^2 - 4x + 3$$
$$P(0) = 5 \cdot 0^2 - 4 \cdot 0 + 3$$
$$P(0) = 3$$

(b) $P(-2) = 5 \cdot (-2)^2 - 4 \cdot (-2) + 3$
$$= 20 + 8 + 3$$
$$P(-2) = 31$$

(c) $P(3) = 5 \cdot 3^2 - 4 \cdot 3 + 3$
$$= 36.$$

If we are given a graph, we can use the definition of a function to decide if the graph represents a function or not. By the definition of a function, for each value of x there must be exactly one value of y. As shown in Figure 6.21, there are two values of y for the indicated value of x, so that this graph is not the graph of a function. We can draw a vertical line that cuts the graph in more than one point.

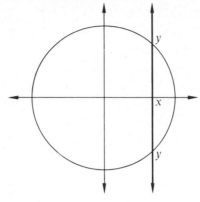

Figure 6.21

On the other hand, Figure 6.22, any vertical line will cut the graph in no more than one point. Thus, the graph in Figure 6.22 is the graph of a function.

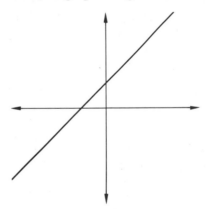

Figure 6.22

In summary, we have the **vertical line test** for a function.

If a vertical line cuts a graph in more than one point, the graph is not the graph of a function.

EXERCISES 6.6   *Decide which of the following are functions. See Example 1.*

1. $y = 5x - 1$

2. $y = 4x + 5$

3. $2x + 3y = 6$

4. $4x - 3y = 12$

5. $y = x^2 + 3$

6. $y = 5 - x^2$

7. $x = y^2 - 4$

8. $y = x^2 + 6$

9. $2x + y < 6$

10. $3x - 4y > 2$

Recall that $|x|$ represents the absolute value of x. For example, $|3| = 3$, $|-5| = 5$, and so on. Decide which of the following are functions.

11. $y = |x|$ 12. $x = |y|$

13. $x = |y| - 3$ 14. $y = |x| + 8$

15. $y = |x - 1|$ 16. $x = |y + 4|$

Find the domain and range of the following. See Example 2.

17. $y = 2x + 5$ 18. $y = 5x - 6$

19. $2x - y = 6$ 20. $2x + 3y = 12$

21. $y = x^2 - 3$ 22. $y = x^2 + 4$

23. $y = (x + 4)^2$ 24. $y = (x - 2)^2$

25. $y = -x^2 + 6$ 26. $y = -x^2 - 8$

27. $y = -(x - 3)^2$ 28. $y = -(x + 5)^2$

29. $y = |x| + 2$ 30. $y = |x| - 3$

31. $y = |x - 4|$ 32. $y = |x + 3|$

For the following, find (a) f(2), (b) f(0), and (c) f(−3). See Example 3.

33. $f(x) = 3x + 2$ 34. $f(x) = 4x - 1$

35. $f(x) = 4 - x$ 36. $f(x) = 2 - 3x$

37. $f(x) = -4 - 4x$ 38. $f(x) = -5 - 6x$

39. $f(x) = x^2 + 2$ 40. $f(x) = x^2 - 5$

41. $f(x) = (x - 3)^2$ 42. $f(x) = (x + 5)^2$

43. $f(x) = -(x + 2)^2$ 44. $f(x) = -(x - 4)^2$

45. $f(x) = -|x + 2|$ 46. $f(x) = -|x - 3|$

For the following, find (a) P(0), (b) P(−3), and (c) P(2). See Example 4.

47. $P(x) = x^2 + 2x$ 48. $P(x) = 2x^2 + 3x - 6$

49. $P(x) = -x^2 - 8x + 9$ 50. $P(x) = -3x^2 + 4x - 2$

51. $P(x) = x^3 - 4x^2 + 1$ 52. $P(x) = x^3 + 5x^2 - 11x + 2$

Decide which of the following are functions.

53.

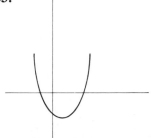

54.

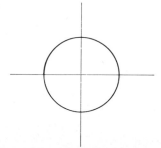

55.

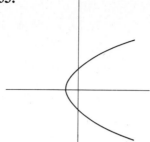

56.

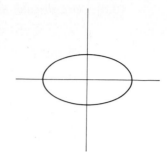

57.

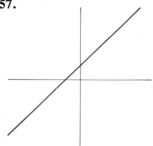

58.

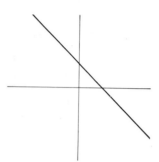

59.

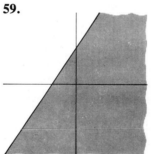

60.

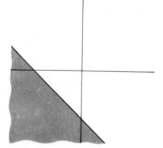

Chapter 6   Test

[6.1–6.2]   *Complete the ordered pairs using the given equations. Plot all the ordered pairs.*

Equation	Ordered pairs
1. $y = 5x - 6$	(0,) (−2,) (, 14)
2. $2x + 7y = 21$	(0,) (, 0) (3,) (, 2)
3. $x = 3y$	(0,) (, 2) (8,) (−12,)
4. $x + 4 = 0$	(, 2) (, 0) (, −3)
5. $y - 2 = 0$	(5,) (4,) (0,) (−3,)

[6.3] *Graph each linear equation.*

6. $x + y = 9$ 7. $2x + y = 6$

8. $4x + 5y = 10$ 9. $x = 4y$

10. $x + 5 = 0$ 11. $y = 2$

[6.4] *Find the slope of the lines through the following pairs of points.*

12. $(-1, 2)$, $(7, 4)$

13. $(-8, 9)$, $(2, 5)$

14. Graph the line through $(-4, 2)$ with slope $-\dfrac{5}{4}$.

Find the equation of each of the following lines.

15. through $(-2, 1)$, with slope 2

16. through $(-3, 4)$, with slope $-\dfrac{5}{2}$

[6.5] *Graph each linear inequality.*

17. $x + y \le 6$ 18. $3x - 4y > 12$

19. $x < 3y$ 20. $y \le -1$

[6.6] *Decide which of the following are functions.*

21. $y = 3x + 5$

22. $x^2 = y - 1$

23. $3x - 2y < 6$

Let $f(x) = 6x - 2$. *Find the following.*

24. $f(-3)$ 25. $f(5)$

7

Linear Systems

7.1 Solving Systems of Linear Equations by Graphing

- **Decide whether a given ordered pair is a simultaneous solution of a system.**
- **Solve linear systems by graphing.**

A **system of linear equations** is two or more linear equations which have the same variables. Some examples of systems of two linear equations are

System A	*System B*	*System C*
$2x + 3y = 4$	$x + 3y = 1$	$x - y = 1$
$3x - y = -5$	$-y = 4 - 2x$	$y = 3.$

In system C, you can think of $y = 3$ as an equation in two variables by writing it as

$$0x + y = 3.$$

The solutions of a system of two linear equations are all the ordered pairs that satisfy both equations at the same time. Such an ordered pair is called a **simultaneous solution** of the system.

EXAMPLE 1 Is $(4, -3)$ a simultaneous solution of the following systems?

(a) $x + 4y = -8$

$3x + 2y = 6$

To decide whether or not $(4, -3)$ is a simultaneous solution of the system, substitute 4 for x and -3 for y in each equation.

$$
\begin{array}{ll}
x + 4y = -8 & 3x + 2y = 6 \\
4 + 4(-3) = -8 & 3(4) + 2(-3) = 6 \\
4 + (-12) = -8 & 12 + (-6) = 6 \\
-8 = -8 \quad \text{True} & 6 = 6 \quad \text{True}
\end{array}
$$

Since $(4, -3)$ satisfies both equations, it is a simultaneous solution of the system.

(b) $2x + 5y = -7$

$3x + 4y = 2$

Again, substitute 4 for x and -3 for y in both equations.

$$
\begin{array}{ll}
2x + 5y = -7 & 3x + 4y = 2 \\
2(4) + 5(-3) = -7 & 3(4) + 4(-3) = 2 \\
8 + (-15) = -7 & 12 + (-12) = 2 \\
-7 = -7 \quad \text{True} & 0 = 2 \quad \text{False}
\end{array}
$$

Here, $(4, -3)$ is not a simultaneous solution since it does not satisfy the second equation.

One way to find the simultaneous solution of a system of two equations is **the graphical method** – graphing both equations on the same axes. The coordinates of any point where the lines cross give the simultaneous solution of the system. Since two different straight lines can cross at no more than one point, there can never be more than one solution for such a system.

EXAMPLE 2 Solve each system of equations by graphing both equations on the same axes.

(a) $2x + 3y = 4$

$3x - y = -5$

Figure 7.1 shows the graphs of $2x + 3y = 4$ and $3x - y = -5$ on the same axes. The graphs cross at the point $(-1, 2)$ which is the simultaneous solution of the system.

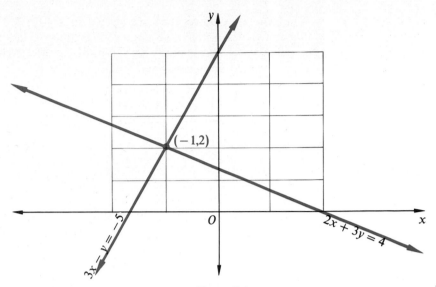

Figure 7.1

(b) $y = -2$

$x = 1$

To find the simultaneous solution of the system, graph the two lines on the same axes. The graph of $y = -2$ is a horizontal line. The graph of $x = 1$ is a vertical line. As shown in Figure 7.2, the simultaneous solution is $(1, -2)$, which is the point where the two graphs cross.

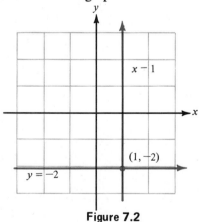

Figure 7.2

EXAMPLE 3 Solve each system by graphing.

(a) $2x + y = 2$

$2x + y = 8$

The graphs of these lines are shown in Figure 7.3. The two lines are parallel and therefore have no points in common. Thus there is no simultaneous solution for the system. A system of equations such as this, with no solution, is called an **inconsistent system.**

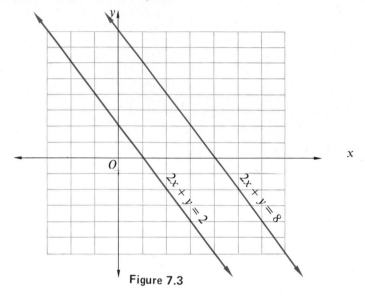

Figure 7.3

(b) $2x + 5y = 1$

$\quad 6x + 15y = 3$

The graphs of these two equations are the same line. See Figure 7.4. Note that the second equation can be obtained by multiplying both sides of the first equation by 3. In this case, every point on the line is a simultaneous solution of the system. Thus, the solution is made up of an infinite number of ordered pairs. This system, where both equations really are the same, is called a **dependent system.**

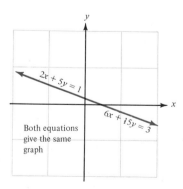

Figure 7.4

EXERCISES 7.1 *Decide whether or not the given ordered pair is the simultaneous solution of the given system. See Example 1.*

1. $(2, -5)$
$3x + y = 1$
$2x + 3y = -11$

2. $(-1, 6)$
$2x + y = 4$
$3x + 2y = 9$

3. $(4, -2)$
$x + y = 2$
$2x + 5y = 2$

4. $(-6, 3)$
$x + 2y = 0$
$3x + 5y = 3$

5. $(2, 0)$
$3x + 5y = 6$
$4x + 2y = 5$

6. $(0, -4)$
$2x - 5y = 20$
$3x + 6y = -20$

7. $(5, 2)$
$4x + 3y = 26$
$3x + 7y = 29$

8. $(9, 1)$
$2x + 5y = 23$
$3x + 2y = 29$

9. $(6, -8)$
$x + 2y + 10 = 0$
$2x - 3y + 30 = 0$

10. $(-5, 2)$
$3x - 5y + 20 = 0$
$2x + 3y + 4 = 0$

11. $(5, -2)$
$x - 5 = 0$
$y + 2 = 0$

12. $(-8, 3)$
$x = 8$
$y = 3$

Solve each system of equations by graphing both equations on the same axes. See Examples 2 and 3.

13. $x + y = 8$
$x - y = 2$

14. $x + y = -1$
$x - y = 3$

15. $x + y = 12$
$y - x = 4$

16. $y - x = -5$
$x + y = 1$

17. $2x + y = 6$
$x - 3y = 10$

18. $4x + y = 10$
$2x - y = 8$

19. $2x - 5y = 17$
$3x + y = 0$

20. $2x + 3y = 11$
$3x - y = 11$

21. $5x + 4y = 7$
$2x - 3y = 12$

22. $2x + 5y = 17$
$3x - 4y = -9$

23. $4x + 5y = 3$
$2x - 5y = 9$

24. $2x + y = 1$
$3x - 4y = 29$

25. $3x + 2y = -12$
$x - 2y = -20$

26. $4x + y = -14$
$3x - 2y = -5$

27. $3x - 4y = -8$
$5x + 2y = -22$

28. $x - 2y = -3$
$4x + 3y = -34$

29. $3x - 2y = 15$
$4x + 3y = 20$

30. $-4x + 3y = 16$
$2x - 3y = -8$

31. $3x - 4y = 8$
$4x + 5y = -10$

32. $3x + 2y = 10$
$4x - 3y = -15$

33. $2x + 5y = 20$
$x - 2y = 1$

34. $2x + 3y = 3$
$x + y = 3$

35. $x + 2y - 5 = 0$
$2x + y - 1 = 0$

36. $2x - y - 2 = 0$
$3x + y - 3 = 0$

37. $5x + y - 7 = 0$
$2x + 2y + 2 = 0$

38. $2x + 5y - 20 = 0$
$x + y - 10 = 0$

39. $x + y = 4$
$y = -2$

40. $2x + y = 1$
$y = 3$

41. $x = 2$
$3x - y = -1$

42. $x = 5$
$2x - y = 4$

43. $2x + 3y = 5$
$4x + 6y = 9$

44. $5x - 4y = 5$
$10x - 8y = 23$

45. $3x = y + 5$
$6x - 2y = 5$

46. $4y + 1 = x$
$2x - 3 = 8y$

47. $2x - y = 4$
$4x = 2y + 8$

48. $3x = 5 - y$
$6x + 2y = 10$

7.2 Solving Systems of Linear Equations by Addition

- **Solve linear systems by addition or elimination.**

Graphing to solve a system of equations has a serious drawback: it is difficult to estimate a solution such as $\left(\frac{1}{3}, -\frac{5}{6}\right)$ accurately from a graph.

An algebraic method can be used which depends on the addition property of equality. The additon property says that if two quantities are equal, then addition of the same quantity to each results in equal sums.

$$\text{If } A = B, \text{ then } A + C = B + C.$$

We now take this a step further. Addition of *equal* quantities, rather than the *same* quantity, also results in equal sums.

$$\text{If } A = B \text{ and } C = D, \text{ then } A + C = B + D.$$

EXAMPLE 1 Use the addition property of equality to find the simultaneous solution of the system

$$x + y = 5$$
$$x - y = 3.$$

Each equation of this system is a statement of equality, so, as discussed above, the sum of the right-hand sides equals the sum of the left-hand sides. Adding in this way, we have

$$(x + y) + (x - y) = 5 + 3.$$

Combining terms and simplifying gives

$$2x = 8$$
$$x = 4.$$

Thus, $x = 4$ gives the x-value of the simultaneous solution of the given system. To find the y-value of the solution, substitute 4 for x in either of the two equations of the system. Choose the first equation, $x + y = 5$.

$$x + y = 5$$
$$4 + y = 5 \qquad \text{Let } x = 4$$
$$y = 1$$

Then $y = 1$ gives the y-value of the simultaneous solution. The solution is given by the ordered pair (4, 1).

This can be checked by substituting the values we found into the other equation of the given system, $x - y = 3$.

$$x - y = 3$$
$$4 - 1 = 3 \qquad \text{Let } x = 4; \text{ let } y = 1$$
$$3 = 3 \qquad \text{True}$$

This result is true: the simultaneous solution of the given system is (4, 1).

EXAMPLE 2   Solve the system

$$-2x + y = -11$$
$$5x - y = 26.$$

We need to add left-hand sides and right-hand sides. The work is easier if we draw a line under the second equation and add vertically. To do this, the like terms must be lined up in columns.

$$-2x + y = -11$$
$$\underline{5x - y = 26}$$
$$3x = 15$$
$$x = 5$$

Substitute 5 for x in either of the original equations. We choose the first.

$$-2x + y = -11$$
$$-2(5) + y = -11 \qquad \text{Let } x = 5$$
$$-10 + y = -11$$
$$y = -1$$

The simultaneous solution is $(5, -1)$. The solution can be checked by substitution into both of the original equations.

Sometimes it is necessary to multiply one or both equations in a system by some number before we can use the addition method.

EXAMPLE 3   Solve the system

$$x + 3y = 7 \tag{1}$$
$$2x + 5y = 12. \tag{2}$$

If we add the two equations, we get $3x + 8y = 19$, which does not help us find the solution. However, if we multiply both sides of equation (1) by -2, the terms with the variable x would drop out when we add.

$$-2(x + 3y) = -2(7)$$
$$-2x - 6y = -14 \tag{3}$$

Now add equations (3) and (2).

$$-2x - 6y = -14 \tag{3}$$
$$\underline{2x + 5y = 12} \tag{2}$$
$$-y = -2$$

From this result, we get $y = 2$. Substituting back into equation (1) gives

$$x + 3y = 7$$
$$x + 3(2) = 7 \qquad \text{Let } y = 2$$
$$x + 6 = 7$$
$$x = 1.$$

The solution of this system is $(1, 2)$.

EXAMPLE 4   Solve the system

$$2x + 3y = -15 \tag{4}$$
$$5x + 2y = 1. \tag{5}$$

Here we use the multiplication property of equality with both equations instead of just one, as in Example 3. Multiply by numbers that will cause the coefficients of x (or of y) in the two equations to be negatives of each other. For example, multiply both sides of equation (4) by 5, and both sides of equation (5) by -2.

$$10x + 15y = -75$$
$$\underline{-10x - 4y = -2}$$
$$11y = -77$$

This gives $y = -7$. By substituting -7 for y in equation (4) or (5), we get $x = 3$. The solution of the system is $(3, -7)$.

We could have obtained the same result by multiplying equation (4) by 2 and equation (5) by -3. (Check this.)

EXAMPLE 5 Solve the system

$$6x - 6y = 7 \tag{6}$$
$$9x + 4y = 4. \tag{7}$$

Multiply equation (6) by 9 and equation (7) by -6.

$$
\begin{array}{r}
54x - 54y = 63 \\
-54x - 24y = -24 \\
\hline
-78y = 39.
\end{array}
$$

From the equation $-78y = 39$, we get $y = -\dfrac{39}{78} = -\dfrac{1}{2}$. Substitute $y = -\dfrac{1}{2}$ into equation (7) to find x.

$$9x + 4y = 4$$
$$9x + 4\left(-\frac{1}{2}\right) = 4 \qquad \text{Let } y = -\frac{1}{2}$$
$$9x - 2 = 4$$
$$9x = 6$$
$$x = \frac{2}{3}.$$

The solution of the system is $\left(\dfrac{2}{3}, -\dfrac{1}{2}\right)$.

The method of solving linear systems discussed in this section is called the **addition method** or **elimination method.** For most systems, this method is more efficient than graphing. The solution of a linear system of equations having exactly one solution can be found using the addition method summarized in Steps 1–7.

To Solve Linear Systems

Step 1 Write both equations of the system in the form $ax + by = c$.

Step 2 If necessary, multiply one or both equations by appropriate numbers so that the coefficients of x (or y) are negatives of each other.

Step 3 Add the two equations to get an equation with only one variable.

Step 4 Solve the equation from Step 3.

Step 5 Substitute the solution from Step 4 into either of the original equations.

Step 6 Solve the resulting equation from Step 5 for the remaining variable.

Step 7 Check the answer.

EXERCISES 7.2 *Solve each system by the addition method. See Examples 1 and 2.*

1. $x - y = 3$
   $x + y = -1$

2. $x + y = 7$
   $x - y = -3$

3. $x + y = 2$
   $2x - y = 4$

4. $3x - y = 8$
   $x + y = 4$

5. $2x + y = 14$
   $x - y = 4$

6. $2x + y = 2$
   $-x - y = 1$

7. $3x + 2y = 6$
   $-3x - y = 0$

8. $5x - y = 9$
   $-5x + 2y = -8$

9. $6x - y = 1$
   $-6x + 5y = 7$

10. $6x + y = -2$
    $-6x + 3y = -14$

11. $2x - y = 5$
    $4x + y = 4$

12. $x - 4y = 13$
    $-x + 6y = -18$

13. $5x - y = 15$
    $7x + y = 21$

14. $x - 4y = 12$
    $-x + 6y = -18$

Solve each system by the addition method. See Example 3.

15. $2x - y = 7$
    $3x + 2y = 0$

16. $x + y = 7$
    $-3x + 3y = -9$

17. $x + 3y = 16$
    $2x - y = 4$

18. $4x - 3y = 8$
    $2x + y = 14$

19. $x + 4y = -18$
    $3x + 5y = -19$

20. $2x + y = 3$
    $5x - 2y = -15$

21. $3x - 2y = -6$
    $-5x + 4y = 16$

22. $-4x + 3y = 0$
    $5x - 6y = 9$

23. $2x - y = -8$
    $5x + 2y = -20$

24. $5x + 3y = -9$
    $7x + y = -3$

25. $2x + y = 5$
    $5x + 3y = 11$

26. $2x + 7y = -53$
    $4x + 3y = -7$

Solve each system by the addition method. See Examples 4 and 5.

27. $5x - 4y = -1$
    $-7x + 5y = 8$

28. $3x + 2y = 12$
    $5x - 3y = 1$

29. $3x + 5y = 33$
    $4x - 3y = 15$

30. $2x + 5y = 3$
    $5x - 3y = 23$

31. $3x + 5y = -7$
    $5x + 4y = 10$

32. $2x + 3y = -11$
    $5x + 2y = 22$

33. $2x + 3y = -12$
    $5x - 7y = -30$

34. $2x + 9y = 16$
    $5x - 6y = 40$

35. $4x - 3y = 0$
    $6x + 6y = 7$

36. $8x + 3y = 9$
    $12x + 6y = 13$

37. $8x + 12y = 13$
$16x - 18y = -9$

38. $9x + 6y = -9$
$6x + 8y = -16$

39. $3x - 2y = 3$
$3x + 3y = 78$

40. $3x - 2y = 27$
$2x - 7y = -50$

41. $5x - 7y = 6$
$3x - 6y = 2$

42. $3x + 7y = -12$
$-4x + 3y = 16$

7.3 Solving Systems of Linear Equations by Substitution

- **Solve linear systems by substitution.**

We have looked at the graphical method and the addition method for solving systems of linear equations. A third method is the **substitution method,** which is useful for solving systems where one equation is solved for one of the variables.

EXAMPLE 1   Solve the system

$$3x + 5y = 26$$
$$y = 2x.$$

From the second of these two equations, we observe that $y = 2x$. Using this fact, we can substitute $2x$ for y in the first equation.

$$3x + 5y = 26$$
$$3x + 5(2x) = 26 \qquad \text{Let } y = 2x$$
$$3x + 10x = 26$$
$$13x = 26$$
$$x = 2$$

Since $y = 2x$, we have $y = 2(2) = 4$. The solution of the given system is $(2, 4)$. Check this by substituting 2 for x and 4 for y in both equations of the given system.

EXAMPLE 2   Use substitution to solve the system

$$2x + 5y = 7$$
$$x = -1 - y.$$

The second equation gives x in terms of y. Substitute $-1 - y$ for x in the first equation.

$$2x + 5y = 7$$
$$2(-1 - y) + 5y = 7 \qquad \text{Let } x = -1 - y$$
$$-2 - 2y + 5y = 7$$
$$-2 + 3y = 7$$
$$3y = 9$$
$$y = 3$$

Since $x = -1 - y$, we have $x = -1 - 3$, or $x = -4$. The solution of the given system is $(-4, 3)$.

EXAMPLE 3 Use substitution to solve the system

$$2x + 3y = 8$$
$$-4x - 2y = 0.$$

To use the substitution method, we need an equation giving x in terms of y (or y in terms of x). We can choose the first equation of the system, which is $2x + 3y = 8$, and solve the equation for x. This means that we need to have x alone on one side of the equation. To get this, we need to first add $-3y$ to both sides.

$$2x + 3y = 8$$
$$2x = 8 - 3y$$

Now divide both sides of this equation by 2.

$$x = \frac{8 - 3y}{2}$$

Finally, substitute this result for x in the second equation of the system.

$$-4x - 2y = 0$$
$$-4\left(\frac{8 - 3y}{2}\right) - 2y = 0 \qquad \text{Let } x = \frac{8 - 3y}{2}$$
$$-2(8 - 3y) - 2y = 0$$
$$-16 + 6y - 2y = 0$$
$$-16 + 4y = 0$$
$$4y = 16$$
$$y = 4$$

Let $y = 4$ in $x = \dfrac{8 - 3y}{2}$.

$$x = \frac{8 - 3 \cdot 4}{2}.$$

$$x = \frac{8 - 12}{2}$$

$$x = \frac{-4}{2}$$

$$x = -2$$

The solution of the given system is $(-2, 4)$.

EXAMPLE 4   Use substitution to solve the system

$$2x = 3 - 2y \tag{1}$$
$$6 + 3y + \quad x = 10 - x. \tag{2}$$

To begin, simplify the second equation by adding x and -6 to both sides. This gives the simplified system

$$2x = 3 - 2y \tag{1}$$
$$2x + 3y = 4. \tag{3}$$

We can use the substitution method if we solve one of the equations for either x or y. We can solve equation (1) for x if we multiply both sides by $\frac{1}{2}$. This gives

$$2x = 3 - 2y \tag{1}$$
$$\frac{1}{2}(2x) = \frac{1}{2}(3 - 2y)$$
$$x = \frac{3}{2} - y$$

Substitute $\frac{3}{2} - y$ for x in equation (3) from above.

$$2x + 3y = 4 \tag{3}$$
$$2\left(\frac{3}{2} - y\right) + 3y = 4$$
$$3 - 2y + 3y = 4$$
$$3 + y = 4$$
$$y = 1$$

Since $x = \frac{3}{2} - y$, and $y = 1$, we have

$$x = \frac{3}{2} - y$$

$$= \frac{3}{2} - 1$$

$$= \frac{1}{2},$$

so the solution is $\left(\frac{1}{2}, 1\right)$.

EXAMPLE 5   Solve the system

$$3x + \frac{1}{4}y = 2 \tag{4}$$

$$\frac{1}{2}x + \frac{3}{4}y = \frac{-5}{2} \tag{5}$$

by any method.

Begin by clearing both equations of fractions. To clear equation (4) of fractions, multiply both sides by 4.

$$4\left(3x + \frac{1}{4}y\right) = 4(2)$$

$$4(3x) + 4\left(\frac{1}{4}y\right) = 4(2)$$

$$12x + y = 8 \tag{6}$$

Now clear equation (5) of fractions by multiplying both sides by the common denominator 4.

$$4\left(\frac{1}{2}x + \frac{3}{4}y\right) = 4\left(\frac{-5}{2}\right)$$

$$4\left(\frac{1}{2}x\right) + 4\left(\frac{3}{4}y\right) = 4\left(\frac{-5}{2}\right)$$

$$2x + 3y = -10 \tag{7}$$

Now solve the system of equations (6) and (7).

$$12x + y = 8 \tag{6}$$

$$2x + 3y = -10 \tag{7}$$

If we choose the substitution method, we must solve one equation for either x or y. Let us solve equation (6) for y.

$$12x + y = 8$$

$$y = -12x + 8$$

Now substitute the result for y in equation (7).

$$2x + 3(-12x + 8) = -10$$
$$2x - 36x + 24 = -10$$
$$-34x = -34$$
$$x = 1$$

From $y = -12x + 8$ with $x = 1$, we get $y = -4$. The solution is $(1, -4)$. Check by substituting 1 for x and -4 for y in both of the original equations.

EXERCISES 7.3 *Solve each system by the substitution method. See Examples 1–3.*

1. $x + y = 6$
   $y = 2x$

2. $x + 3y = -11$
   $y = -4x$

3. $3x + 2y = 26$
   $x = y + 2$

4. $4x + 3y = -14$
   $x = y - 7$

5. $x + 5y = 3$
   $x = 2y + 10$

6. $5x + 2y = 14$
   $y = 2x - 11$

7. $5x + 7y = 40$
   $x = 2y - 9$

8. $4x + 9y = -7$
   $y = 2x - 13$

9. $3x - 2y = 14$
   $2x + y = 0$

10. $2x - 5 = -y$
   $x + 3y = 0$

11. $x + y = 6$
   $x - y = 4$

12. $3x - 2y = 13$
   $x + y = 6$

13. $3x + y = -1$
   $y = 3x + 5$

14. $5x - y = 14$
   $y = 4x - 18$

15. $6x - 8y = 4$
   $3x = 5y + 8$

16. $12x + 18y = 12$
   $2x = 2 + 3y$

17. $4x + 5y = 5$
   $2x + 3y = 1$

18. $3x + 4y = 10$
   $4x + 5y = 14$

19. $2x + 3y = 11$
   $y = 1$

20. $3x + 4y = -10$
   $x = -6$

21. $4x + y = 5$
   $x - 2 = 0$

22. $5x + 2y = -19$
   $y - 3 = 0$

Solve each system by either the addition method or the substitution method. First simplify any equations where necessary. See Example 4.

23. $x + 4y = 34$
   $y = 4x$

24. $3x - y = -14$
   $x = -2y$

25. $4 + 4x - 3y = 34 + x$
   $4x = -y - 2 + 3x$

26. $5x - 4y = 42 - 8y - 2$
   $2x + y = x + 1$

27. $4x - 2y + 8 = 3x + 4y - 1$
   $3x + y = x + 8$

28. $5x - 4y - 8x - 2 = 6x + 3y - 3$
$4x - y = -2y - 8$

29. $2x - 8y + 3y + 2 = 5y + 16$
$8x - 2y = 4x + 28$

30. $7x - 9 + 2y - 8 = -3y + 4x + 13$
$4y - 8x = -8 + 9x + 32$

31. $2x + 3y = 10 - 6x + 6$
$4x + 5y = 10 - x$

32. $10x + 21y = 0$
$5x + 11y = -5x$

33. $-2x + 3y = 12 + 2y$
$2x - 5y + 4 = -5y - 2$

34. $2x + 5y = 7 + 4y - x$
$5x + 3y + 8 = 18 + x + y$

35. $y + 9 = 3x - 2y + 6$
$5 - 3x + 24 = -2x + 4y + 3$

36. $5x - 2y = 16 + 4x - 10$
$4x + 3y = 60 + 2x + y$

Solve each system by either the addition method or the substitution method. First clear all fractions. See Example 5.

37. $x + \dfrac{1}{3}y = y - 2$

$\dfrac{1}{4}x - y = x - y$

38. $\dfrac{5}{3}x + 2y = \dfrac{1}{3} + y$

$2x - 3 + \dfrac{y}{3} = -2 + x$

39. $\dfrac{x}{6} + \dfrac{y}{6} = 1$

$-\dfrac{1}{2}x - \dfrac{1}{3}y = -5$

40. $\dfrac{x}{2} - \dfrac{y}{3} = \dfrac{5}{6}$

$\dfrac{x}{5} - \dfrac{y}{4} = \dfrac{1}{10}$

41. $\dfrac{x}{3} - \dfrac{3y}{4} = -\dfrac{1}{2}$

$\dfrac{2x}{3} + \dfrac{y}{2} = 3$

42. $\dfrac{x}{5} + 2y = \dfrac{8}{5}$

$\dfrac{3x}{5} + \dfrac{y}{2} = \dfrac{-7}{10}$

43. $\dfrac{x}{2} + \dfrac{y}{3} = \dfrac{7}{6}$

$\dfrac{x}{4} - \dfrac{3y}{2} = \dfrac{9}{4}$

44. $\dfrac{5x}{2} - \dfrac{y}{3} = \dfrac{5}{6}$

$\dfrac{4x}{3} + y = \dfrac{19}{3}$

7.4 Two Special Cases

- **Solve linear systems having parallel lines or the same line as their graphs.**

In Section 7.1 we saw that the graphs of a linear system are sometimes two parallel lines and sometimes the same line. In this section, we use the addition method to solve such systems.

EXAMPLE 1   Solve by the addition method.

$$2x + 4y = 5$$
$$4x + 8y = -9$$

If we multiply both sides of $2x + 4y = 5$ by -2, and then add $4x + 8y = -9$, we get

$$-4x - 8y = -10$$
$$\underline{4x + 8y = -9}$$
$$0 = -19. \quad \text{False}$$

The false statement, $0 = -19$, shows that the given system is self-contradictory. *It has no simultaneous solution.* This means that the graphs of the equations of this system are parallel lines, as shown in Figure 7.5.

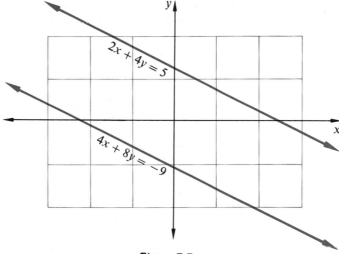

Figure 7.5

EXAMPLE 2   Solve by the addition method.

$$3x - y = 4$$
$$-9x + 3y = -12$$

If we multiply both sides of the first equation by 3 and add, we get

$$9x - 3y = 12$$
$$\underline{-9x + 3y = -12}$$
$$0 = 0. \quad \text{True}$$

This result, $0 = 0$, is true for any ordered pair (x, y) which satisfies either equation. Thus, any ordered pair which satisfies either equation is a simultaneous solution, and there are an infinite number of solutions. The solutions can be written as the solution set $\{(x, y) \mid 3x - y = 4\}$, or as the solution set

$\{(x, y)|-9x + 3y = -12\}$. However, in the answers at the back of this book, such a solution is indicated by the words "same line."

There are three possible outcomes to the use of the addition method of solving a linear system of equations.

1. The result of the addition step is a statement such ás $x = 2$ or $y = -3$. The solution will be exactly one ordered pair. The graphs of the equations of the system will cross at exactly one point.
2. The result of the addition step is a false statement, such as $0 = 4$. In this case, the graphs are parallel lines, and there is no simultaneous solution for the system. The system is inconsistent.
3. The result of the addition step is a true statement, such as $0 = 0$. The graphs of the equations of the system are the same line, and there is an infinite number of ordered pairs which are solutions. The system is dependent.

Inconsistent or dependent systems can also be solved by the substitution method, as the next example shows.

EXAMPLE 3 Solve the system

$$x = 5 - 2y$$
$$2x + 4y = 6.$$

Substitute $5 - 2y$ for x in the second equation.

$$2x + 4y = 6$$
$$2(5 - 2y) + 4y = 6 \qquad \text{Let } x = 5 - 2y$$
$$10 - 4y + 4y = 6$$
$$10 = 6 \qquad \text{False}$$

This false result means that the equations of the system have graphs that are parallel lines. The system is inconsistent and has no simultaneous solution. (In the same way, a *true* result means that the system is dependent.)

EXERCISES 7.4 *Use the addition method or the substitution method to solve each system. See Examples 1–3.*

1. $x + y = 4$
   $x + y = -2$

2. $2x - y = 1$
   $2x - y = 4$

3. $5x - 2y = 6$
   $10x - 4y = 10$

4. $3x - 5y = 2$
   $6x - 10y = 8$

5. $x + 3y = 5$
   $2x + 6y = 10$

6. $6x - 2y = 12$
   $-3x + y = -6$

7. $2x + 3y = 8$
   $4x + 6y = 12$

8. $4x + y = 6$
   $-8x - 2y = 21$

9. $5x = y + 4$
   $5x = y - 4$

10. $4y = 3x - 2$
    $4y = 3x + 5$

11. $6x + 3y = 0$
    $-12x - 6y = 0$

12. $3x - 5y = 0$
    $6x - 10y = 0$

13. $2x - 3y = 0$
    $4x + 5y = 0$

14. $3x - 5y = 0$
    $6x + 10y = 0$

15. $3x + 5y = 19$
    $4x - 3y = 6$

16. $2x + 5y = 17$
    $4x + 3y = -1$

17. $4x - 2y = 1$
    $8x - 4y = 1$

18. $-2x + 3y = 5$
    $4x - 6y = 5$

19. $3x - 2y = 8$
    $-3x + 2y = -8$

20. $4x + y = 4$
    $-8x - 2y = -8$

21. $4x - y = 3$
    $-2x + \dfrac{1}{2}y = -\dfrac{3}{2}$

22. $5x - 2y = 8$
    $-\dfrac{5}{2}x + y = -4$

23. $x - y = 6$
    $x = y + 1$

24. $y + x = 3$
    $y = 2 - x$

25. $8x - 4y = 0$
    $y = 2x$

26. $3x + 12y = 0$
    $x = -4y$

27. $3x + 4y = 0$
    $x = 3y$

28. $9x - 5y = 0$
    $x = 2y$

29. $6x - 3y + 2 = 0$
    $y = 2x$

30. $8x + 4y + 1 = 0$
    $y = -2x$

7.5 Applications of Linear Systems

- **Use linear systems to solve word problems.**

Many practical problems are more easily translated into equations if two variables are used. With two variables, we need two equations to find the desired solution. The examples in this section illustrate the method of solving word problems using two equations and two variables.

EXAMPLE 1   The sum of two numbers is 63. Their difference is 19. Find the two numbers.

Let x represent one number and y the other. From the information given in the problem, we set up a system of equations.

$$x + y = 63$$
$$x - y = 19$$

This system can be solved by the addition method. We have

$$x + y = 63$$
$$\underline{x - y = 19}$$
$$2x \quad\quad = 82.$$

From this last equation, $x = 41$. Substitute 41 for x in the first equation and check that $y = 22$. The numbers required in the problem are 41 and 22.

EXAMPLE 2 Admission prices at a football game were $1.25 for adults and $.50 for children. The total receipts from the game were $530.75. Tickets were sold to 454 people. How many adults and how many children attended the game?

Let a represent the number of adult tickets that were sold, and let c represent the number of child's tickets. The information given in the problem is summarized in the table.

Kind of ticket	Number sold	Cost of each (in dollars)	Receipts (in dollars)
Adult	a	1.25	$1.25a$
Child	c	.50	$.50c$

The total number of tickets sold was 454, so that

$$a + c = 454.$$

The receipts from the sale of a adult tickets at $1.25 each are $1.25a$, while the receipts from the sale of c children's tickets at $.50 each are $.50c$. Since the total receipts were $530.75,

$$1.25a + .50c = 530.75.$$

We have used the information in the problem to set up the system of equations

$$a + c = 454 \tag{1}$$
$$1.25a + .50c = 530.75. \tag{2}$$

Equation (2) can be simplified if we multiply both sides by 100 to clear the decimals.

$$100(1.25a + .50c) = 100(530.75)$$
$$125a + 50c = 53,075 \tag{3}$$

To solve the system of equations, multiply equation (1) on both sides by -50, then add to equation (3).

$$-50a - 50c = -50(454)$$
$$-50a - 50c = -22{,}700$$

Now we add.

$$-50a - 50c = -22{,}700$$
$$\underline{125a + 50c = 53{,}075}$$
$$75a = 30{,}375$$

From the equation $75a = 30375$, we get $a = 405$. We know that $a + c = 454$; therefore, $c = 49$. (Check this.) There were 405 adults and 49 children at the game.

EXAMPLE 3   A pharmacist needs 100 liters of 50% salt solution. She has on hand 30% salt solution and 80% salt solution, which she can mix. How many liters of each will be needed to make the 100 liters of 50% salt solution?

Let x represent the number of liters of 30% salt solution needed, and let y represent the number of liters of 80% salt solution. The information of the problem is summarized in the following table.

Liters of solution	Percent	Liters of pure salt
x	30	$.30x$
y	80	$.80y$
100	50	$.50(100)$

She will have $.30x$ liters of salt from the x liters of 30% solution, and $.80y$ liters of salt from the y liters of 80% solution. The total is $.30x + .80y$ liters of pure salt. In the mixture, she wants 100 liters of 50% solution. This 100 liters would contain $.50(100) = 50$ liters of pure salt. Since the amounts of pure salt must be equal,

$$.30x + .80y = 50.$$

We also know that the total number of liters is 100, or

$$x + y = 100.$$

These two equations give the system

$$.30x + .80y = 50$$
$$x + y = 100.$$

Let us solve this system by the substitution method. From the second equation of the system, we have $x = 100 - y$. If we substitute $100 - y$ for x in the first equation, we get

$$.30(100 - y) + .80y = 50 \qquad \text{Let } x = 100 - y$$
$$30 - .30y + .80y = 50$$
$$.50y = 20$$
$$y = 40.$$

Since $x + y = 100$, then $x = 60$. The pharmacist should use 60 liters of the 30% solution and 40 liters of the 80% solution.

EXAMPLE 4 Two cars start from positions 400 miles apart and travel toward each other. They meet after four hours. Find the average speed of each car if one car travels 20 miles per hour faster than the other.

We need the formula that relates distance, rate, and time. As we learned earlier, this formula is $d = rt$. Let x be the average speed of the first car, and y the average speed of the second car. This information is shown in the chart.

	r	t	d
First car	x	4	$4x$
Second car	y	4	$4y$

Since each car travels for four hours, t for each car is 4. The distance is found by using the formula $d = rt$ and the amounts already entered in the chart. Since the total distance traveled by both cars is 400 miles,

$$4x + 4y = 400.$$

One car traveled 20 miles per hour faster than the other. Assume that the first car was faster. Then

$$x = 20 + y.$$

We now have the system of equations.

$$4x + 4y = 400$$
$$x = 20 + y$$

This system can be solved by substitution. Replace x with $20 + y$ in the first equation of the system.

$$4(20 + y) + 4y = 400$$
$$80 + 4y + 4y = 400$$
$$80 + 8y = 400$$
$$8y = 320$$
$$y = 40.$$

Since $x = 20 + y$, we have $x = 60$. Thus, the speeds of the two cars were 40 miles per hour and 60 miles per hour.

EXERCISES 7.5   *Write a system of equations for each problem. Then solve the system. Formulas are in the back of the book. See Example 1.*

1. The sum of two numbers is 52, and their difference is 34. Find the numbers.

2. Find two numbers whose sum is 56 and whose difference is 18.

3. A certain number is three times as large as a second number. Their sum is 96. What are the two numbers?

4. One number is five times as large as another. The difference of the numbers is 48. Find the numbers.

5. A rectangle is twice as long as it is wide. Its perimeter is 60 inches. Find the dimensions of the rectangle.

6. The perimeter of a triangle is 21 inches. If two sides are of equal length, and the third side is 3 inches longer than one of the equal sides, find the length of the three sides.

Write a system of equations for each problem. Then solve the system. See Example 2.

7. The cashier at the Evergreen Ranch has some $10 bills and some $20 bills. The total value of the money is $1480. If there is a total of 85 bills, how many of each type are there?

8. A bank teller has 154 bills of $1 and $5 denominations. How many of each type of bill does he have if the total value of the money is $466?

9. A club secretary bought 8¢ and 10¢ pieces of candy to give to the members. She spent a total of $15.52. If she bought 170 pieces of candy, how many of each kind did she buy?

10. There were 311 tickets sold for a basketball game, some for students and some for non-students. Student tickets cost 25¢ each and non-student tickets cost 75¢ each. The total receipts were $108.75. How many of each type of ticket were sold?

11. A bank clerk has a total of 124 bills, both fives and tens. The total value of the money is $840. How many of each type of bill does he have?

12. A library buys a total of 54 books. Some cost $8 each and some cost $11 each. The total cost of the books is $492. How many of each type of book does the library buy?

13. An artist bought some large canvases, at $7 each, and some small ones at $4 each, paying $219 in total. Altogether, the artist bought 39 canvases. How many of each size were bought?

14. A hospital bought a total of 146 bottles of glucose solution. Small bottles cost $2 each, while large bottles are $3 each. The total cost was $336. How many of each size bottle were bought?

15. Ms. Sullivan has $10,000 to invest, part at 5% and part at 7%. She wants the income from simple interest on the two investments to total $550 yearly. How much should she invest at each rate?

16. Mr. Emerson has twice as much money invested at 7% as he has at 8%. If his yearly income from investments is $440, how much does he have invested at each rate?

Write a system of equations for each problem. Then solve the system. See Example 3.

17. A 90% antifreeze solution is to be mixed with a 75% solution to make 20 liters of a 78% solution. How many liters of 90% and 75% solutions should be used?

Liters of solution	Percent	Liters of pure antifreeze
x	90	$.90x$
y	75	$.75y$
20	78	

18. A 40% potassium iodide solution is to be mixed with a 70% solution to get 60 liters of a 50% solution. How many liters of the 40% and 70% solutions will be needed?

Liters of solution	Percent	Liters of pure potassium iodide
x	40	$.40x$
x	70	$.70y$
60	50	

19. How many liters of a 25% indicator solution should be mixed with a 55% solution to get 12 liters of a 45% solution?

20. A 60% solution of salt is to be mixed with an 80% solution to get 40 liters of a 65% solution. How many liters of the 60% and the 80% solutions will be needed?

21. A merchant wishes to mix coffee worth $6 per pound with coffee worth $3 per pound to get 90 pounds of a mixture worth $4 per pound. How many pounds of the $6 and the $3 coffee will be needed?

22. A grocer wishes to blend candy selling for 60¢ a pound with candy selling for 90¢ a pound to get a mixture which will be sold for 70¢ a pound. How many pounds of the 60¢ and the 90¢ candy should be used to get 30 pounds of the mixture?

23. How many barrels of olives worth $40 per barrel must be mixed with olives worth $60 per barrel to get 50 barrels of a mixture worth $48 per barrel.

24. A glue merchant wishes to mix some glue worth $70 per barrel with some glue worth $90 per barrel, to get 80 barrels of a mixture worth $77.50 per barrel. How many barrels of each type should be used?

Write a system of equations for each problem. Then solve the system. See Example 4.

25. A boat takes 3 hours to go 24 miles upstream, while it can go 36 miles downstream in the same time. Find the speed of the current and the speed of the boat in still water.

	d	r	t
downstream	36	$x + y$	3
upstream	24	$x - y$	3

26. It takes a boat $1\frac{1}{2}$ hours to go 12 miles downstream, and 6 hours to return. Find the speed of the boat in still water and the speed of the current.

	d	r	t
downstream	12	$x + y$	$\frac{3}{2}$
upstream	12	$x - y$	6

27. If a plane can travel 400 miles per hour into the wind and 540 miles per hour with the wind, find the speed of the wind and the speed of the plane in still air.

28. A small plane travels 100 miles per hour with the wind, and 60 miles per hour against it. Find the speed of the wind and the speed of the plane in still air.

29. At the beginning of a walk for charity, John and Harriet are 30 miles apart. If they leave at the same time and walk in the same direction, John overtakes Harriet in 60 hours. If they walk toward each other, they meet in 5 hours. What are their speeds?

30. Mr. Anderson left Farmersville in a plane at noon to travel to Exeter. Mr. Bentley left Exeter in his automobile at 2 P.M. to travel to Farmersville. It is 400 miles from Exeter to Farmersville. If the sum of their speeds is 120 miles per hour, and if they met at 4 P.M., find the speed of each.

The next problems are "brain-busters."

31. The Smith family is coming to visit, and no one knows how many children they have. Janet, one of the girls, says she has as many brothers as sisters; her brother Steve says he has twice as many sisters as brothers. How many boys and how many girls are in the family?

32. In the Lopez family, the number of boys is one more than half the number of girls. One of the Lopez boys, Rico, says that he has one more sister than brothers. How many boys and girls are in the family?

7.6 Solving Systems of Linear Inequalities

- **Solve systems of linear inequalities by graphing.**

In Section 6.5, we saw how to graph the solution of a linear inequality. Let us review the method. To graph the solution of $x + 3y > 12$, for example, first graph the line $x + 3y = 12$ by finding a few ordered pairs that satisfy the equation. Because the points on the line do not satisfy the inequality, make the line dashed. Choose a test point not on the line, say $(0, 0)$. Substitute 0 for x and 0 for y in the given inequality.

$$x + 3y > 12$$
$$0 + 0 > 12$$
$$0 > 12 \quad \text{False}$$

Since the test point does not satisfy the inequality, shade the region on the side of the line that does not include $(0, 0)$, as in Figure 7.6.

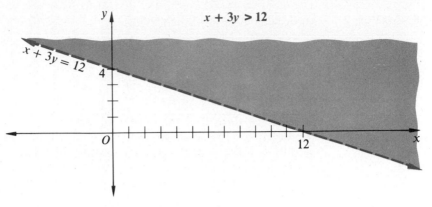

Figure 7.6

The same procedure is used to determine the solution of a **system of linear inequalities,** as shown in Examples 1–3.

EXAMPLE 1   Graph the solution of the system

$$3x + 2y \le 6$$
$$2x - 5y \ge 10.$$

First graph the inequality $3x + 2y \le 6$, using the steps described above. Then, on the same axes, graph the second inequality, $2x - 5y \ge 10$. The solution of the system is given by the overlap of the regions of the two graphs. This solution is the darkest shaded region in Figure 7.7 and includes portions of the two boundary lines.

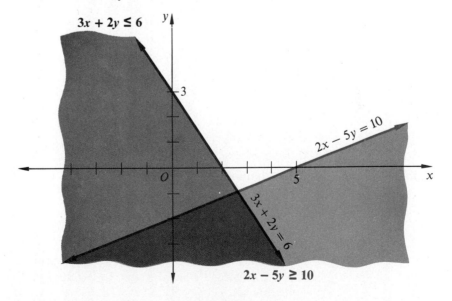

Figure 7.7

EXAMPLE 2 Graph the solution of the system

$$x - y > 5$$
$$2x + y < 2.$$

Figure 7.8 below shows the graphs of both $x - y > 5$ and $2x + y < 2$. Dashed lines show that the graphs of the inequalities do not include their boundary lines. The solution of the system is the darkest shaded region in the figure. The solution does not include either boundary line.

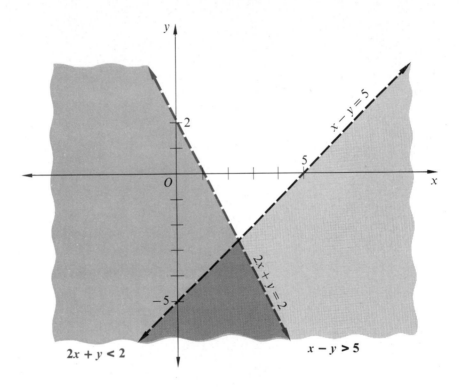

Figure 7.8

EXAMPLE 3 Graph the solution of the system

$$4x - 3y \leq 8$$
$$x \geq 2.$$

Recall that $x = 2$ is a vertical line through the point $(2, 0)$. The graph of the solution is the darkest shaded region in Figure 7.9.

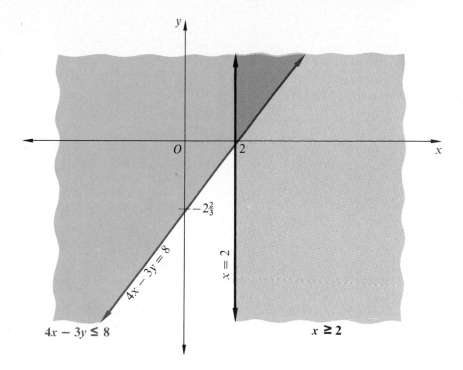

$4x - 3y \leq 8$
$-2\frac{2}{3}$
$4x - 3y = 8$
$x = 2$
$x \geq 2$

Figure 7.9

EXERCISES 7.6 *Graph the solution of each system of linear inequalities. See Examples 1–3.*

1. $x + y \leq 6$
    $x - y \leq 1$

2. $x + y \geq 2$
    $x - y \leq 3$

3. $2x - 3y \leq 6$
    $x + y + 1 \geq 0$

4. $4x + 5y \leq 20$
    $x - y \leq 3$

5. $x - 2y > 6$
    $2x + y > 4$

6. $3x + y < 4$
    $x + 2y > 2$

7. $x + 4y \leq 8$
    $2x - y \leq 4$

8. $3x + y \leq 6$
    $2x - y \leq 8$

9. $x - 4y \leq 3$
    $x \geq 2y$

10. $2x + 3y \leq 6$
    $x - y \geq 5$

11. $x + 2y \leq 4$
    $x + 1 \geq y$

12. $x < 2y + 3$
    $x + y > 0$

13. $y \leq 2x - 5$
    $x - 3y \leq 2$

14. $4x + 3y \leq 6$
    $x - 2y \geq 4$

15. $x - 3y \le 6$
$\qquad x \ge -1$

16. $2x + 5y \ge 20$
$\qquad x \le 4$

17. $3x - 2y \ge 9$
$\qquad y \le 3$

18. $4x + 5y < 8$
$\qquad y > -2$

19. $2x + 3y < 6$
$\quad 4x + 6y > 18$

20. $\quad 3x - y \le 4$
$\quad -6x + 2y \le -10$

21. $x \ge 2$
$\quad y \le 3$

22. $x \ge -1$
$\quad y \ge 4$

23. $x \le 0$
$\quad y \le 0$

24. $x > 0$
$\quad y > 0$

Chapter 7   Test

[7.1]   *Solve the following systems by the graphical method.*

1. $2x + y = 5$
$\quad 3x - y = 15$

2. $3x + 2y = 8$
$\quad 5x + 4y = 10$

3. $\quad x + 2y = 6$
$\quad 2x - y = 7$

[7.2]   *Solve the following systems by the addition method.*

4. $2x - 5y = -13$
$\quad 3x + 5y = 43$

5. $4x + 3y = 26$
$\quad 5x + 4y = 32$

6. $6x + 5y = -13$
$\quad 3x + 2y = -4$

7. $4x - 3y = 6$
$\quad x + 2y = -4$

8. $\quad 6x - 5y = 2$
$\quad -2x + 3y = 2$

9. $2x - y = 5$
$\quad 4x + 3y = 0$

[7.3]   *Solve the following systems by substitution.*

10. $2x + y = 1$
$\qquad x = 8 + y$

11. $4x + 3y = 0$
$\qquad x = 2 - y$

[7.4]   *Solve the following systems by any method.*

12. $\quad 4x + 5y = 8$
$\quad -8x - 10y = -6$

13. $8 + 3x - 4y = 14 - 3y$
$\quad 3x + y + 12 = 9x - y$

14. $\dfrac{x}{2} - \dfrac{y}{4} = -4$

$\quad \dfrac{2x}{3} + \dfrac{5y}{4} = 1$

[7.5] *Solve the following word problems.*

15. The sum of two numbers is 39. If one number is doubled, it equals three less than the other. Find the numbers.

16. The local record shop is having a sale. Some records cost $5 and some cost $7.50. Joe has exactly $40 to spend and wants to buy six records. How many can he buy at each price?

17. Two cars leave from the same place and travel in the same direction. The faster car travels 30 mph less than twice as fast as the other car. After three hours, they are 45 miles apart. What was the speed of each car?

18. A 40% solution of acid is to be mixed with a 60% solution to get 100 liters of a 45% solution. How many liters of the 40% solution and the 60% solution should be used?

[7.6] *Graph the solution of each system of inequalities.*

19. $2x + 7y \leq 14$
$x + y \geq 1$

20. $3x - 5y < 15$
$y < 2$

8

Roots and Radicals

8.1 Square Roots

- **Find square roots.**
- **Decide whether a given square root is rational or irrational.**
- **Find decimal approximations for irrational square roots.**

To square a number, we multiply it by itself.

$$\text{If } a = 7, \text{ then } a^2 = 7 \cdot 7 = 49.$$
$$\text{If } a = 10, \text{ then } a^2 = 10 \cdot 10 = 100.$$
$$\text{If } a = -5, \text{ then } a^2 = (-5)(-5) = 25.$$

In this chapter, we consider the opposite situation.

$$\text{If } a^2 = 49, \text{ then } a = ?$$
$$\text{If } a^2 = 100, \text{ then } a = ?$$
$$\text{If } a^2 = 25, \text{ then } a = ?$$

To answer these questions, we must find a number which, when multiplied by itself, will result in the given number. The number that we find is called the **square root** of the given number.

EXAMPLE 1 One square root of 49 is 7, since $7^2 = 49$. Another square root of 49 is -7, since $(-7)^2 = 49$. Therefore 49 has two square roots, 7 and -7. One of these is positive and one is negative.

All integers which have integer square roots are called **perfect squares.** The first one hundred perfect squares are listed on page 319.

The positive square root of a number is written with the symbol $\sqrt{}$. For example, the positive square root of 121 is 11, written

$$\sqrt{121} = 11.$$

The symbol $-\sqrt{}$ is used for the negative square root of a number. For example, the negative square root of 121 is -11, written

$$-\sqrt{121} = -11.$$

The symbol $\sqrt{}$ is called a **radical sign** and, used alone, always represents the positive square root (except that $\sqrt{0} = 0$). The number inside the radical sign is called the **radicand** and the entire expression, radical sign and radicand, is called a **radical.**

EXAMPLE 2 Find each square root.

(a) $\sqrt{144}$

The radical $\sqrt{144}$ represents the positive square root of 144, which is 12 (See the table of perfect squares on page 319). Thus,

$$\sqrt{144} = 12.$$

(b) $-\sqrt{1024}$

This symbol represents the negative square root of 1024, so

$$-\sqrt{1024} = -32.$$

(c) $\sqrt{256} = 16$

(d) $-\sqrt{900} = -30$

A real number which is not rational is called an **irrational number.** In general, it is difficult to prove that a given number is irrational. However, if a is a positive integer that is not a perfect square, then $\sqrt{a}$ is irrational.

Not every number has a square root, either rational or irrational. For example, there is no real number which we can square and get -36. (The square of a real number can never be negative.) Because of this $\sqrt{-36}$ is not a real number.

EXAMPLE 3 Tell whether each square root is rational or irrational.

(a) $\sqrt{17}$

Since 17 is not a perfect square (see the table), $\sqrt{17}$ is irrational.

(b) $\sqrt{64}$

The number 64 is a perfect square because $\sqrt{64} = 8$, a rational number.

(c) $\sqrt{85}$ is irrational.

(d) $\sqrt{81}$ is rational ($\sqrt{81} = 9$).

Not all irrational numbers are roots of integers. For example, π (approximately 3.14159) is an irrational number that is not a square root of any integer.

If a number is irrational, we can still find a decimal that approximately equals the number. This can be done with calculators. For square roots, we can use the square root table on page 319, as in Example 4.

EXAMPLE 4   Find decimal approximations for each square root.

(a) $\sqrt{11}$

Look in the square root table. Find 11 at the left. The approximate square root is given in the column having $\sqrt{n}$ at the top. You should find that

$$\sqrt{11} \approx 3.317,$$

where $\approx$ means "approximately equal to."

(b) $\sqrt{39} \approx 6.245$

(c) $\sqrt{740}$

There is no 740 in the "n" column of the square root table. However, $740 = 74 \times 10$, so that we can find $\sqrt{740}$ in the "$\sqrt{10n}$" column. You should find that

$$\sqrt{740} \approx 27.203.$$

(d) $\sqrt{180} \approx 13.416$

Look in the "n" column for 18; then read across to the "$\sqrt{10n}$" column.

(e) $\sqrt{810} \approx 28.460$

We know the following facts about square roots:

1. For any positive number a, the number $\sqrt{a}$ represents a positive number with the property that

$$\sqrt{a} \cdot \sqrt{a} = (\sqrt{a})^2 = a.$$

The number $\sqrt{a}$ is the positive square root of a, while $-\sqrt{a}$ is the negative square root of a.

2. If a is a positive perfect square integer, then $\sqrt{a}$ is an integer. Otherwise, $\sqrt{a}$ is an irrational number.

3. $\sqrt{0} = 0$.

4. If a is a negative number, then $\sqrt{a}$ is not a real number.

Finding the square root of a number is the inverse of squaring a number. In a similar way, there are inverses to finding the cube of a number, or finding the fourth or higher power of a number. These inverses are called finding the **cube root,** written $\sqrt[3]{a}$, the **fourth root,** written $\sqrt[4]{a}$, and so on. We could write $\sqrt[2]{a}$ instead of $\sqrt{a}$, but the simpler symbol $\sqrt{a}$ is customary since the square root is the most commonly used root.

EXAMPLE 5 Find $\sqrt[3]{8}$.

We need a number such that the cube of the number is 8. Since $2^3 = 8$, we find that $\sqrt[3]{8} = 2$.

EXAMPLE 6 Find $\sqrt[3]{-8}$.

Since $(-2)^3 = -8$, we have $\sqrt[3]{-8} = -2$. In general, the cube root of a positive number is positive, and the cube root of a negative number is negative. There is only one real number cube root for each real number.

EXAMPLE 7 (a) $\sqrt[4]{16} = 2$ and $-\sqrt[4]{16} = -2$.

(b) $\sqrt[3]{64} = 4$.

(c) $\sqrt[3]{-64} = -4$.

(d) $-\sqrt[5]{32} = -2$ (and $\sqrt[5]{32} = 2$).

EXERCISES 8.1 *Find all square roots of each number. See Example 1.*

1. 9	**2.** 16	**3.** 121	**4.** 196
5. 400	**6.** 900	**7.** 625	**8.** 961
9. 1521	**10.** 2209	**11.** 3969	**12.** 4624

Find each root that exists. See Example 2.

13. $\sqrt{4}$	**14.** $\sqrt{9}$	**15.** $\sqrt{25}$	**16.** $\sqrt{36}$
17. $-\sqrt{64}$	**18.** $-\sqrt{100}$	**19.** $\sqrt{169}$	**20.** $\sqrt{196}$
21. $\sqrt{900}$	**22.** $\sqrt{1600}$	**23.** $-\sqrt{1681}$	**24.** $-\sqrt{2116}$
25. $\sqrt{2601}$	**26.** $\sqrt{3025}$	**27.** $-\sqrt{4900}$	**28.** $-\sqrt{5625}$
29. $\sqrt{-9}$	**30.** $\sqrt{-25}$	**31.** $-\sqrt{-49}$	**32.** $-\sqrt{-81}$

Write "rational" or "irrational" for each root. If a root is rational, give its exact value. If a root is irrational, give a decimal approximation. See Examples 3 and 4.

33. $\sqrt{16}$	**34.** $\sqrt{81}$	**35.** $\sqrt{15}$	**36.** $\sqrt{31}$
37. $\sqrt{47}$	**38.** $\sqrt{53}$	**39.** $\sqrt{68}$	**40.** $\sqrt{72}$
41. $-\sqrt{121}$	**42.** $-\sqrt{144}$	**43.** $\sqrt{110}$	**44.** $\sqrt{170}$

45. $-\sqrt{200}$ **46.** $-\sqrt{260}$ **47.** $\sqrt{400}$ **48.** $\sqrt{900}$

49. $\sqrt{570}$ **50.** $\sqrt{690}$

Find each of the following roots that exist. See Examples 5, 6, and 7.

51. $\sqrt[3]{1000}$ **52.** $\sqrt[3]{1}$ **53.** $\sqrt[3]{-8}$ **54.** $\sqrt[3]{-27}$

55. $-\sqrt[3]{-64}$ **56.** $-\sqrt[3]{-216}$ **57.** $\sqrt[4]{81}$ **58.** $\sqrt[4]{1}$

59. $\sqrt[4]{-16}$ **60.** $\sqrt[4]{-625}$ **61.** $-\sqrt[4]{16}$ **62.** $-\sqrt[4]{81}$

63. $\sqrt[5]{-1}$ **64.** $\sqrt[5]{1}$ **65.** $\sqrt[5]{-32}$ **66.** $-\sqrt[5]{32}$

67. $\sqrt[6]{64}$ **68.** $\sqrt[7]{128}$ **69.** $\sqrt[8]{-256}$ **70.** $\sqrt[9]{-1}$

8.2   Products and Quotients of Radicals

- **Multiply and divide radicals.**
- **Simplify radicals.**

In this section, we develop rules for finding products and quotients of radicals. To get a rule for products, first look at these examples.

$$\sqrt{4} \cdot \sqrt{9} = 2 \cdot 3$$
$$= 6 \quad \text{and}$$
$$\sqrt{4 \cdot 9} = \sqrt{36}$$
$$= 6$$

We conclude that

$$\sqrt{4} \cdot \sqrt{9} = \sqrt{4 \cdot 9}.$$

This example generalizes as the **product rule for radicals:***

$$\sqrt{x} \cdot \sqrt{y} = \sqrt{x \cdot y},$$

as long as x and y are not negative. That is, the product of two radicals is the radical of the product.

EXAMPLE 1   Use the product rule for radicals to find each product

(a) $\sqrt{2} \cdot \sqrt{3} = \sqrt{2 \cdot 3}$
$= \sqrt{6}$

(b) $\sqrt{7} \cdot \sqrt{5} = \sqrt{35}$

(c) $\sqrt{11} \cdot \sqrt{a} = \sqrt{11a}$

---

*All the rules in this chapter are given only for square roots. However, rules are also valid for cube roots, fourth roots, etc.

One very important use of the product rule is in simplifying radicals. To **simplify a radical,** we write it so that there is no perfect square factor under the radical sign. Examples 2–5 show how this is done.

EXAMPLE 2 Simplify $\sqrt{20}$.

We can divide 20 by the perfect square 4. Therefore,

$$\sqrt{20} = \sqrt{4 \cdot 5} \qquad\qquad \text{4 is a perfect square}$$
$$= \sqrt{4} \cdot \sqrt{5} \qquad\qquad \text{Product rule}$$
$$= 2\sqrt{5} \qquad\qquad \sqrt{4} = 2$$

Thus, $\sqrt{20} = 2\sqrt{5}$. Since 5 is not divisible by a perfect square (other than 1), $2\sqrt{5}$ is called the **simplified form** of $\sqrt{20}$.

EXAMPLE 3 Simplify $\sqrt{72}$.

Look down the list of perfect squares. Find the largest of these numbers that divides into 72. The largest is 36, so that

$$\sqrt{72} = \sqrt{36 \cdot 2} \qquad\qquad \text{36 is a perfect square}$$
$$= \sqrt{36} \cdot \sqrt{2}$$
$$\sqrt{72} = 6\sqrt{2}.$$

EXAMPLE 4

$$\sqrt{300} = \sqrt{100 \cdot 3} \qquad\qquad \text{100 is a perfect square}$$
$$= \sqrt{100} \cdot \sqrt{3}$$
$$\sqrt{300} = 10\sqrt{3}$$

EXAMPLE 5 The number 15 is not divisible by any perfect square. Because of this, $\sqrt{15}$ cannot be further simplified.

Radicals can also be simplified by using prime factorization. Recall from Chapter 4 that a number is written in **prime factored form** when it is written as a product of primes. For example,

$$12 = 2^2 \cdot 3, \qquad 24 = 2^3 \cdot 3, \qquad 76 = 2^2 \cdot 19,$$

and so on. A list of the prime factored forms of the integers from 2 through 100 is given on page 318.

EXAMPLE 6 Use prime factored form to simplify each of the following.

(a) $\sqrt{12}$

Since $12 = 2^2 \cdot 3$,

$$\sqrt{12} = \sqrt{2^2 \cdot 3}$$
$$= \sqrt{2^2} \cdot \sqrt{3}$$
$$= 2\sqrt{3} \qquad\qquad \sqrt{2^2} = 2$$

(b) $\sqrt{54}$

From the table of prime factorizations, $54 = 2 \cdot 3^3$.

$$\sqrt{54} = \sqrt{2 \cdot 3^3}$$
$$= \sqrt{2 \cdot 3^2 \cdot 3}$$
$$= \sqrt{3^2} \cdot \sqrt{2 \cdot 3}$$
$$= 3\sqrt{6} \qquad\qquad \sqrt{3^2} = 3$$

Sometimes the product rule can be used to simplify an answer, as Examples 7 and 8 show.

EXAMPLE 7 $\quad \sqrt{9} \cdot \sqrt{75} = 3\sqrt{75} \qquad\qquad\qquad \sqrt{9} = 3$
$$= 3\sqrt{25 \cdot 3}$$
$$= 3 \cdot \sqrt{25} \cdot \sqrt{3}$$
$$= 3 \cdot 5 \cdot \sqrt{3}$$
$$= 15\sqrt{3}$$

EXAMPLE 8 $\quad \sqrt{8} \cdot \sqrt{12} = \sqrt{4 \cdot 2} \cdot \sqrt{4 \cdot 3}$
$$= 2\sqrt{2} \cdot 2\sqrt{3}$$
$$= 2 \cdot 2 \cdot \sqrt{2} \cdot \sqrt{3}$$
$$= 4\sqrt{6}$$

There is a **quotient rule for radicals** that is very similar to the product rule:

$$\sqrt{\frac{x}{y}} = \frac{\sqrt{x}}{\sqrt{y}}$$

as long as x and y are not negative, and y is not 0. That is, the radical of a quotient is the quotient of the radicals.

EXAMPLE 9 Use the quotient rule to simplify each radical.

(a) $\sqrt{\dfrac{25}{9}} = \dfrac{\sqrt{25}}{\sqrt{9}}$
$$= \frac{5}{3}$$

(b) $\sqrt{\dfrac{144}{49}} = \dfrac{\sqrt{144}}{\sqrt{49}}$
$$= \frac{12}{7}$$

(c) $\sqrt{\dfrac{3}{4}} = \dfrac{\sqrt{3}}{\sqrt{4}}$

$= \dfrac{\sqrt{3}}{2}$

(d) $\sqrt{.04} = \sqrt{\dfrac{4}{100}}$

$= \dfrac{\sqrt{4}}{\sqrt{100}}$

$= \dfrac{2}{10}$

$= .2$

EXAMPLE 10 $\dfrac{27\sqrt{15}}{9\sqrt{3}} = \dfrac{27}{9} \cdot \dfrac{\sqrt{15}}{\sqrt{3}}$

$= \dfrac{27}{9} \cdot \sqrt{\dfrac{15}{3}}$

$= 3\sqrt{5}$

Some problems require both the product and quotient rules, as Examples 11 and 12 show.

EXAMPLE 11   Simplify $\sqrt{\dfrac{3}{5}} \cdot \sqrt{10}$.

Use the product and quotient rules.

$$\sqrt{\dfrac{3}{5}} \cdot \sqrt{10} = \dfrac{\sqrt{3}}{\sqrt{5}} \cdot \dfrac{\sqrt{10}}{1}$$

$$= \dfrac{\sqrt{3} \cdot \sqrt{10}}{\sqrt{5}}$$

$$= \dfrac{\sqrt{30}}{\sqrt{5}}$$

$$= \sqrt{\dfrac{30}{5}}$$

$$= \sqrt{6}$$

Finally, the properties of this section are also valid when variables appear under the radical sign, as long as all the variables represent only positive numbers.

EXAMPLE 12   Simplify each radical.

(a) $\sqrt{25m^4} = \sqrt{25} \cdot \sqrt{m^4}$

$= 5m^2$

(b) $\sqrt{64p^{10}} = \sqrt{64} \cdot \sqrt{p^{10}}$

$= 8p^5$

(c) $\sqrt{r^9} = \sqrt{r^8 \cdot r}$

$= \sqrt{r^8} \cdot \sqrt{r}$

$= r^4 \sqrt{r}$

(d) $\sqrt{\dfrac{5}{x^2}} = \dfrac{\sqrt{5}}{\sqrt{x^2}}$

$= \dfrac{\sqrt{5}}{x}$

The product rule and quotient rule also work for cube roots, as the next example shows.

EXAMPLE 13   Simplify.

(a) $\sqrt[3]{16} = \sqrt[3]{8 \cdot 2}$

$= \sqrt[3]{8} \cdot \sqrt[3]{2}$

$= 2\sqrt[3]{2}$

(b) $\sqrt[3]{108} = \sqrt[3]{27 \cdot 4}$

$= \sqrt[3]{27} \cdot \sqrt[3]{4}$

$= 3\sqrt[3]{4}$

(c) $\sqrt[3]{\dfrac{8}{125}} = \dfrac{\sqrt[3]{8}}{\sqrt[3]{125}}$

$= \dfrac{2}{5}$

EXERCISES 8.2   *Use the product rule to simplify each expression. See Examples 1–8.*

1. $\sqrt{8} \cdot \sqrt{2}$ 2. $\sqrt{27} \cdot \sqrt{3}$

3. $\sqrt{6} \cdot \sqrt{6}$ 4. $\sqrt{11} \cdot \sqrt{11}$

5. $\sqrt{21} \cdot \sqrt{21}$ 6. $\sqrt{17} \cdot \sqrt{17}$

7. $\sqrt{3} \cdot \sqrt{7}$ 8. $\sqrt{2} \cdot \sqrt{5}$

9. $\sqrt{27}$ 10. $\sqrt{45}$

11. $\sqrt{28}$ 12. $\sqrt{40}$

13. $\sqrt{18}$ 14. $\sqrt{75}$

15. $\sqrt{48}$ 16. $\sqrt{80}$

17. $\sqrt{125}$ 18. $\sqrt{150}$

19. $\sqrt{700}$ 20. $\sqrt{1100}$

21. $\sqrt{100} \cdot \sqrt{27}$ 22. $\sqrt{16} \cdot \sqrt{8}$

23. $\sqrt{80} \cdot \sqrt{20}$ 24. $\sqrt{200} \cdot \sqrt{2}$

25. $\sqrt{27} \cdot \sqrt{48}$ 26. $\sqrt{75} \cdot \sqrt{27}$

27. $\sqrt{50} \cdot \sqrt{72}$ 28. $\sqrt{98} \cdot \sqrt{8}$

29. $\sqrt{7} \cdot \sqrt{21}$ 30. $\sqrt{12} \cdot \sqrt{48}$

31. $\sqrt{15} \cdot \sqrt{45}$ 32. $\sqrt{20} \cdot \sqrt{45}$

33. $\sqrt{80} \cdot \sqrt{15}$ 34. $\sqrt{60} \cdot \sqrt{12}$

35. $\sqrt{50} \cdot \sqrt{20}$ 36. $\sqrt{72} \cdot \sqrt{12}$

Use the quotient rule and product rule, as necessary, to simplify each expression. See Examples 9–11.

37. $\sqrt{\dfrac{100}{9}}$ 38. $\sqrt{\dfrac{225}{16}}$

39. $\sqrt{\dfrac{36}{49}}$ 40. $\sqrt{\dfrac{256}{9}}$

41. $\sqrt{\dfrac{5}{16}}$ 42. $\sqrt{\dfrac{11}{25}}$

43. $\sqrt{\dfrac{30}{49}}$ 44. $\sqrt{\dfrac{10}{121}}$

45. $\sqrt{\dfrac{1}{5}} \cdot \sqrt{\dfrac{4}{5}}$ 46. $\sqrt{\dfrac{2}{3}} \cdot \sqrt{\dfrac{2}{27}}$

47. $\sqrt{\dfrac{2}{5}} \cdot \sqrt{\dfrac{8}{125}}$ 48. $\sqrt{\dfrac{3}{8}} \cdot \sqrt{\dfrac{3}{2}}$

49. $\dfrac{\sqrt{75}}{\sqrt{3}}$ 50. $\dfrac{\sqrt{200}}{\sqrt{2}}$

51. $\dfrac{\sqrt{48}}{\sqrt{3}}$ 52. $\dfrac{\sqrt{72}}{\sqrt{8}}$

53. $\dfrac{15\sqrt{10}}{5\sqrt{2}}$ 54. $\dfrac{18\sqrt{20}}{2\sqrt{10}}$

55. $\dfrac{25\sqrt{50}}{5\sqrt{5}}$ 56. $\dfrac{26\sqrt{10}}{13\sqrt{5}}$

Find each of the following. See Example 9(d).

57. $\sqrt{.01}$ 58. $\sqrt{.09}$ 59. $\sqrt{.49}$ 60. $\sqrt{.81}$

61. $\sqrt{1.21}$ 62. $\sqrt{1.44}$ 63. $\sqrt{.0004}$ 64. $\sqrt{.0001}$

65. $\sqrt{.0016}$ 66. $\sqrt{.0081}$

Simplify each expression. Assume that all variables represent positive numbers. See Example 12.

67. $\sqrt{y} \cdot \sqrt{y}$ 68. $\sqrt{m} \cdot \sqrt{m}$

69. $\sqrt{x} \cdot \sqrt{z}$ 70. $\sqrt{p} \cdot \sqrt{q}$

71. $\sqrt{x^2}$ 72. $\sqrt{y^2}$

73. $\sqrt{x^4}$ **74.** $\sqrt{y^4}$

75. $\sqrt{x^2y^4}$ **76.** $\sqrt{x^4y^8}$

77. $\sqrt{x^3}$ **78.** $\sqrt{y^3}$

79. $\sqrt{\dfrac{16}{x^2}}$ **80.** $\sqrt{\dfrac{100}{m^4}}$

81. $\sqrt{\dfrac{11}{r^4}}$ **82.** $\sqrt{\dfrac{23}{y^6}}$

Simplify each of the following. See Example 13.

83. $\sqrt[3]{40}$ **84.** $\sqrt[3]{48}$ **85.** $\sqrt[3]{54}$ **86.** $\sqrt[3]{135}$

87. $\sqrt[3]{128}$ **88.** $\sqrt[3]{192}$ **89.** $\sqrt[3]{375}$ **90.** $\sqrt[3]{500}$

91. $\sqrt[3]{\dfrac{8}{27}}$ **92.** $\sqrt[3]{\dfrac{1}{64}}$ **93.** $\sqrt[3]{\dfrac{1000}{27}}$ **94.** $\sqrt[3]{\dfrac{216}{125}}$

8.3 Adding and Subtracting Radicals

● **Add and subtract radicals.**

We add or subtract radicals using the distributive property. For example,

$$8\sqrt{3} + 6\sqrt{3} = (8 + 6)\sqrt{3}$$
$$= 14\sqrt{3}.$$

Also, $2\sqrt{11} - 7\sqrt{11} = -5\sqrt{11}$. Only **like radicals** (those having the same radicands) can be added or subtracted.

EXAMPLE 1 Add or subtract, as indicated.

(a) $3\sqrt{6} + 5\sqrt{6} = (3 + 5)\sqrt{6}$
$$= 8\sqrt{6}$$

(b) $5\sqrt{10} - 7\sqrt{10} = (5 - 7)\sqrt{10}$
$$= -2\sqrt{10}$$

(c) $\sqrt{5} + \sqrt{5} = 1\sqrt{5} + 1\sqrt{5}$
$$= (1 + 1)\sqrt{5}$$
$$= 2\sqrt{5}$$

(d) $\sqrt{7} + 2\sqrt{7} = 1\sqrt{7} + 2\sqrt{7}$
$$= 3\sqrt{7}$$

(e) $\sqrt{3} + \sqrt{7}$ cannot be further simplified.

Sometimes it is necessary to first simplify each radical in a sum or difference. Then add or subtract, if possible.

EXAMPLE 2 $3\sqrt{2} + \sqrt{8} = 3\sqrt{2} + \sqrt{4 \cdot 2}$ Simplify $\sqrt{8}$
$$= 3\sqrt{2} + \sqrt{4} \cdot \sqrt{2}$$
$$= 3\sqrt{2} + 2\sqrt{2}$$
$$= 5\sqrt{2}$$

EXAMPLE 3 $\sqrt{18} - \sqrt{27} = \sqrt{9 \cdot 2} - \sqrt{9 \cdot 3}$
$$= \sqrt{9} \cdot \sqrt{2} - \sqrt{9} \cdot \sqrt{3}$$
$$= 3\sqrt{2} - 3\sqrt{3}$$

Since $\sqrt{2}$ and $\sqrt{3}$ are unlike radicals, this difference cannot be further simplified.

EXAMPLE 4 $2\sqrt{12} + 3\sqrt{75} = 2(\sqrt{4} \cdot \sqrt{3}) + 3(\sqrt{25} \cdot \sqrt{3})$
$$= 2(2\sqrt{3}) + 3(5\sqrt{3})$$
$$= 4\sqrt{3} + 15\sqrt{3}$$
$$= 19\sqrt{3}$$

EXAMPLE 5 $\sqrt{5} \cdot \sqrt{15} + 4\sqrt{3} = \sqrt{5 \cdot 15} + 4\sqrt{3}$
$$= \sqrt{75} + 4\sqrt{3}$$
$$= \sqrt{25 \cdot 3} + 4\sqrt{3}$$
$$= \sqrt{25} \cdot \sqrt{3} + 4\sqrt{3}$$
$$= 5\sqrt{3} + 4\sqrt{3}$$
$$= 9\sqrt{3}$$

EXAMPLE 6 $\sqrt{12k} + \sqrt{27k} = \sqrt{4 \cdot 3k} + \sqrt{9 \cdot 3k}$
$$= \sqrt{4} \cdot \sqrt{3k} + \sqrt{9} \cdot \sqrt{3k}$$
$$= 2\sqrt{3k} + 3\sqrt{3k}$$
$$= 5\sqrt{3k}$$

Here, we must assume that k is not negative.

We emphasize that a sum or difference of radicals can be simplified only if the radicals are like radicals.

EXERCISES 8.3   *Simplify and combine terms wherever possible. See Examples 1–5.*

1. $2\sqrt{3} + 5\sqrt{3}$ 2. $6\sqrt{5} + 8\sqrt{5}$

3. $4\sqrt{7} - 9\sqrt{7}$ 4. $6\sqrt{2} - 8\sqrt{2}$

5. $\sqrt{6} + \sqrt{6}$

6. $\sqrt{11} + \sqrt{11}$

7. $\sqrt{17} + 2\sqrt{17}$

8. $3\sqrt{19} + \sqrt{19}$

9. $5\sqrt{7} - \sqrt{7}$

10. $12\sqrt{14} - \sqrt{14}$

11. $5\sqrt{8} + \sqrt{8}$

12. $3\sqrt{27} - \sqrt{27}$

13. $\sqrt{45} + 2\sqrt{20}$

14. $\sqrt{24} + 5\sqrt{54}$

15. $3\sqrt{18} + \sqrt{8}$

16. $2\sqrt{27} - \sqrt{3}$

17. $-\sqrt{12} + \sqrt{75}$

18. $2\sqrt{27} - \sqrt{300}$

19. $5\sqrt{72} - 2\sqrt{50}$

20. $6\sqrt{18} - 4\sqrt{32}$

21. $-5\sqrt{32} + \sqrt{98}$

22. $4\sqrt{75} + 3\sqrt{12}$

23. $5\sqrt{7} - 2\sqrt{28} + 6\sqrt{63}$

24. $3\sqrt{11} + 5\sqrt{44} - 3\sqrt{99}$

25. $6\sqrt{5} + 3\sqrt{20} - 8\sqrt{45}$

26. $7\sqrt{3} + 2\sqrt{12} - 5\sqrt{27}$

27. $6\sqrt{2} + 5\sqrt{27} - 4\sqrt{12}$

28. $9\sqrt{24} - 2\sqrt{54} + 3\sqrt{20}$

29. $2\sqrt{8} - 5\sqrt{32} + 2\sqrt{48}$

30. $5\sqrt{72} - 3\sqrt{48} - 4\sqrt{128}$

31. $4\sqrt{50} + 3\sqrt{12} + 5\sqrt{45}$

32. $6\sqrt{18} + 2\sqrt{48} - 6\sqrt{28}$

33. $\frac{1}{4}\sqrt{288} - \frac{1}{6}\sqrt{72}$

34. $\frac{2}{3}\sqrt{27} - \frac{3}{4}\sqrt{48}$

35. $\frac{3}{5}\sqrt{75} - \frac{2}{3}\sqrt{45}$

36. $\frac{5}{8}\sqrt{128} - \frac{3}{4}\sqrt{160}$

37. $\sqrt{6} \cdot \sqrt{2} + 3\sqrt{3}$

38. $4\sqrt{15} \cdot \sqrt{3} - 2\sqrt{5}$

39. $\sqrt{3} \cdot \sqrt{7} + 2\sqrt{21} - \sqrt{7}$

40. $\sqrt{13} \cdot \sqrt{2} + 3\sqrt{26}$

Simplify each expression. Assume that all variables represent nonnegative real numbers. See Example 6.

41. $\sqrt{9x} + \sqrt{49x} - \sqrt{16x}$

42. $\sqrt{4a} - \sqrt{16a} + \sqrt{9a}$

43. $\sqrt{4a} + 6\sqrt{a} + \sqrt{25a}$

44. $\sqrt{6x^2} + x\sqrt{54}$

45. $\sqrt{75x^2} + x\sqrt{300}$

46. $\sqrt{20y^2} - 3y\sqrt{5}$

47. $3\sqrt{8x^2} - 4x\sqrt{2}$

48. $6r\sqrt{27r^2s} + 3r^2\sqrt{3s}$

49. $\sqrt{x^2y^3w} - xy\sqrt{yw}$

50. $2\sqrt{3m^2n} + 5m\sqrt{3n}$

8.4 Rationalizing the Denominator

- **Rationalize the denominator.**
- **Simplify expressions by rationalizing the denominator.**

We learned decimal approximation for radicals in the first section of this chapter. It is easier to find these decimals for more complicated radicals if the denominators do not contain any radicals. For example, to find a decimal for

$$\frac{\sqrt{3}}{\sqrt{2}},$$

we can look up $\sqrt{3}$ and $\sqrt{2}$ in the square root table, and get

$$\frac{\sqrt{3}}{\sqrt{2}} \approx \frac{1.732}{1.414}.$$

We would then need to divide 1.414 into 1.732, which would be very difficult. This calculation would be easier if there were no radical in the denominator.

To get rid of this radical, multiply numerator and denominator by a radical which will give a perfect square radicand in the denominator. The radical $\sqrt{2}$ does that here.

$$\frac{\sqrt{3}}{\sqrt{2}} = \frac{\sqrt{3} \cdot \sqrt{2}}{\sqrt{2} \cdot \sqrt{2}} \qquad \sqrt{2} \cdot \sqrt{2} = \sqrt{4}$$
$$= \frac{\sqrt{6}}{2} \qquad\qquad\qquad = 2$$

This process of changing the denominator from a radical (irrational number) to a rational number is called **rationalizing the denominator.** The value of the number is not changed; only the form of the number is changed.

EXAMPLE 1   Rationalize the denominator of $\dfrac{9}{\sqrt{6}}$.

Multiply both numerator and denominator by $\sqrt{6}$.

$$\frac{9}{\sqrt{6}} = \frac{9 \cdot \sqrt{6}}{\sqrt{6} \cdot \sqrt{6}}$$
$$= \frac{9\sqrt{6}}{6} \qquad \sqrt{6} \cdot \sqrt{6} = 6$$
$$= \frac{3\sqrt{6}}{2}$$

EXAMPLE 2   Rationalize the denominator of $\dfrac{12}{\sqrt{8}}$.

We could rationalize the denominator here by multiplying by $\sqrt{8}$. However, we can get the answer faster if we multiply by $\sqrt{2}$. This is because

$$\sqrt{8} \cdot \sqrt{2} = \sqrt{16} = 4, \text{ a rational number.}$$

$$\frac{12}{\sqrt{8}} = \frac{12 \cdot \sqrt{2}}{\sqrt{8} \cdot \sqrt{2}}$$
$$= \frac{12\sqrt{2}}{\sqrt{16}}$$
$$= \frac{12\sqrt{2}}{4}$$
$$= 3\sqrt{2}$$

In most cases, a radical is not considered simplified if it contains a radical in the denominator. Methods of simplifying such radicals are shown in the next few examples.

EXAMPLE 3   Simplify $\sqrt{\dfrac{27}{5}}$ by rationalizing the denominator.

First, use the quotient rule for radicals.

$$\sqrt{\frac{27}{5}} = \frac{\sqrt{27}}{\sqrt{5}}$$

Now multiply both numerator and denominator by $\sqrt{5}$.

$$\frac{\sqrt{27}}{\sqrt{5}} = \frac{\sqrt{27} \cdot \sqrt{5}}{\sqrt{5} \cdot \sqrt{5}}$$

$$= \frac{\sqrt{9 \cdot 3} \cdot \sqrt{5}}{5}$$

$$= \frac{\sqrt{9} \cdot \sqrt{3} \cdot \sqrt{5}}{5}$$

$$= \frac{3\sqrt{3} \cdot \sqrt{5}}{5}$$

$$= \frac{3\sqrt{15}}{5}$$

EXAMPLE 4   Simplify $\sqrt{\dfrac{5}{8}} \cdot \sqrt{\dfrac{1}{6}}$.

Use both the quotient rule and the product rule.

$$\sqrt{\frac{5}{8}} \cdot \sqrt{\frac{1}{6}} = \sqrt{\frac{5}{8} \cdot \frac{1}{6}}$$

$$= \sqrt{\frac{5}{48}}$$

$$= \frac{\sqrt{5}}{\sqrt{48}}$$

Now rationalize the denominator by multiplying by $\sqrt{3}$ (since $\sqrt{48} \cdot \sqrt{3} = \sqrt{48 \cdot 3} = \sqrt{144} = 12$.)

$$\frac{\sqrt{5}}{\sqrt{48}} = \frac{\sqrt{5} \cdot \sqrt{3}}{\sqrt{48} \cdot \sqrt{3}}$$

$$= \frac{\sqrt{15}}{\sqrt{144}}$$

$$= \frac{\sqrt{15}}{12}$$

EXAMPLE 5   Rationalize the denominator of $\dfrac{\sqrt{4x}}{\sqrt{y}}$. Assume that x and y are positive.

Multiply numerator and denominator by $\sqrt{y}$.

$$\frac{\sqrt{4x}}{\sqrt{y}} = \frac{\sqrt{4x} \cdot \sqrt{y}}{\sqrt{y} \cdot \sqrt{y}}$$

$$= \frac{\sqrt{4xy}}{y}$$

$$= \frac{2\sqrt{xy}}{y}$$

EXAMPLE 6   Rationalize the denominator in $\sqrt[3]{\dfrac{1}{9}}$.

By the quotient rule, we get

$$\sqrt[3]{\frac{1}{9}} = \frac{\sqrt[3]{1}}{\sqrt[3]{9}}$$

$$= \frac{1}{\sqrt[3]{9}}.$$

We can eliminate the radical sign in the denominator if we can replace the 9 by a number which is a perfect cube. The number 27 is a perfect cube ($3^3 = 27$). Since $9 \cdot 3 = 27$, we can rationalize the denominator by multiplying both numerator and denominator by $\sqrt[3]{3}$.

$$\frac{1}{\sqrt[3]{9}} = \frac{1 \cdot \sqrt[3]{3}}{\sqrt[3]{9} \cdot \sqrt[3]{3}}$$

$$= \frac{\sqrt[3]{3}}{\sqrt[3]{27}}$$

$$= \frac{\sqrt[3]{3}}{3}.$$

EXERCISES 8.4   *Perform the indicated operations. Write all answers in simplest form. Rationalize all denominators. See Examples 1–4.*

1. $\dfrac{6}{\sqrt{5}}$ 2. $\dfrac{4}{\sqrt{2}}$ 3. $\dfrac{5}{\sqrt{5}}$ 4. $\dfrac{15}{\sqrt{15}}$

5. $\dfrac{3}{\sqrt{7}}$ 6. $\dfrac{12}{\sqrt{10}}$ 7. $\dfrac{8\sqrt{3}}{\sqrt{5}}$ 8. $\dfrac{9\sqrt{6}}{\sqrt{5}}$

9. $\dfrac{12\sqrt{10}}{8\sqrt{3}}$ 10. $\dfrac{9\sqrt{15}}{6\sqrt{2}}$ 11. $\dfrac{8}{\sqrt{27}}$ 12. $\dfrac{12}{\sqrt{18}}$

13. $\dfrac{3}{\sqrt{50}}$ 14. $\dfrac{5}{\sqrt{75}}$ 15. $\dfrac{12}{\sqrt{72}}$ 16. $\dfrac{21}{\sqrt{45}}$

17. $\dfrac{9}{\sqrt{32}}$ 18. $\dfrac{50}{\sqrt{125}}$ 19. $\dfrac{\sqrt{8}}{\sqrt{2}}$ 20. $\dfrac{\sqrt{27}}{\sqrt{3}}$

21. $\dfrac{\sqrt{10}}{\sqrt{5}}$ 22. $\dfrac{\sqrt{6}}{\sqrt{3}}$ 23. $\dfrac{\sqrt{40}}{\sqrt{3}}$ 24. $\dfrac{\sqrt{5}}{\sqrt{8}}$

25. $\sqrt{\dfrac{1}{2}}$ 26. $\sqrt{\dfrac{1}{8}}$ 27. $\sqrt{\dfrac{10}{7}}$

28. $\sqrt{\dfrac{2}{3}}$ 29. $\sqrt{\dfrac{9}{5}}$ 30. $\sqrt{\dfrac{16}{7}}$

31. $\sqrt{\dfrac{7}{5}} \cdot \sqrt{10}$ 32. $\sqrt{\dfrac{1}{3}} \cdot \sqrt{3}$ 33. $\sqrt{\dfrac{3}{4}} \cdot \sqrt{\dfrac{1}{5}}$

34. $\sqrt{\dfrac{1}{10}} \cdot \sqrt{\dfrac{10}{3}}$ 35. $\sqrt{\dfrac{21}{7}} \cdot \sqrt{\dfrac{21}{8}}$ 36. $\sqrt{\dfrac{1}{11}} \cdot \sqrt{\dfrac{33}{16}}$

37. $\sqrt{\dfrac{2}{5}} \cdot \sqrt{\dfrac{3}{10}}$ 38. $\sqrt{\dfrac{9}{8}} \cdot \sqrt{\dfrac{7}{16}}$ 39. $\sqrt{\dfrac{16}{27}} \cdot \sqrt{\dfrac{1}{9}}$

Perform the indicated operations. Write all answers in simplest form. Rationalize all denominators. Assume that all variables represent positive real numbers. See Example 5.

40. $\sqrt{\dfrac{5}{x}}$ 41. $\sqrt{\dfrac{6}{p}}$ 42. $\sqrt{\dfrac{4r^3}{s}}$ 43. $\sqrt{\dfrac{6p^3}{3m}}$

44. $\sqrt{\dfrac{a^3b}{6}}$ 45. $\sqrt{\dfrac{x^2}{4y}}$ 46. $\sqrt{\dfrac{m^2n}{2}}$ 47. $\sqrt{\dfrac{9a^2r}{5}}$

48. $\sqrt{\dfrac{2x^2z^4}{3y}}$

Rationalize the denominator. See Example 6.

49. $\sqrt[3]{\dfrac{1}{2}}$ 50. $\sqrt[3]{\dfrac{1}{4}}$ 51. $\sqrt[3]{\dfrac{1}{32}}$ 52. $\sqrt[3]{\dfrac{1}{5}}$

53. $\sqrt[3]{\dfrac{1}{11}}$ 54. $\sqrt[3]{\dfrac{3}{2}}$ 55. $\sqrt[3]{\dfrac{2}{5}}$ 56. $\sqrt[3]{\dfrac{4}{9}}$

57. $\sqrt[3]{\dfrac{3}{4}}$ 58. $\sqrt[3]{\dfrac{3}{25}}$ 59. $\sqrt[3]{\dfrac{7}{36}}$ 60. $\sqrt[3]{\dfrac{11}{49}}$

8.5 Simplifying Radicals

- **Simplify products and quotients of radicals.**

What is the "simplest" form of a radical may not always be clear. In this book, a radical expression is simplified when the following five rules are satisfied.

1. If a radical represents a rational number, then that rational number should be used in place of the radical.

   For example, $\sqrt{49}$ is simplified by writing 7; $\sqrt{64}$ as 8; $\sqrt{169/9}$ as $\dfrac{13}{3}$.

2. If a radical expression contains products of radicals, the product rule for radicals, $\sqrt{x} \cdot \sqrt{y} = \sqrt{xy}$, should be used to get a single radical.

   For example, $\sqrt{3} \cdot \sqrt{2}$ is simplified to $\sqrt{6}$; $\sqrt{5} \cdot \sqrt{x}$ to $\sqrt{5x}$.

3. If a radicand has a factor that is a perfect square, the radical should be expressed as the product of the positive square root of the perfect square and the remaining radical factor.

   For example, $\sqrt{20}$ is simplified to $\sqrt{20} = \sqrt{4 \cdot 5} = \sqrt{4} \cdot \sqrt{5} = 2\sqrt{5}$; $\sqrt{75}$ as $5\sqrt{3}$.

4. If a radical expression contains sums or differences of radicals, the distributive property should be used to combine terms, if possible.

   For example, $3\sqrt{2} + 4\sqrt{2}$ is combined as $7\sqrt{2}$; but $3\sqrt{2} + 4\sqrt{3}$ cannot be further combined.

5. Any radicals in the denominator should be changed to rational numbers.

   For example, $\dfrac{5}{\sqrt{3}}$ is rationalized as

   $$\frac{5}{\sqrt{3}} = \frac{5 \cdot \sqrt{3}}{\sqrt{3} \cdot \sqrt{3}} = \frac{5\sqrt{3}}{3}$$

EXAMPLE 1   Simplify $\sqrt{16} + \sqrt{9}$.

$$\text{We have } \sqrt{16} + \sqrt{9} = 4 + 3$$
$$= 7.$$

EXAMPLE 2   Simplify $5\sqrt{2} + 2\sqrt{18}$.

First simplify $\sqrt{18}$.

$$5\sqrt{2} + 2\sqrt{18} = 5\sqrt{2} + 2(\sqrt{9} \cdot \sqrt{2})$$
$$= 5\sqrt{2} + 2(3\sqrt{2})$$
$$= 5\sqrt{2} + 6\sqrt{2}$$
$$= 11\sqrt{2}$$

EXAMPLE 3   Simplify $\sqrt{5}(\sqrt{8} - \sqrt{32})$.

Using the distributive property, we have

$$\sqrt{5}(\sqrt{8} - \sqrt{32}) = \sqrt{5} \cdot \sqrt{8} - \sqrt{5} \cdot \sqrt{32}$$
$$= \sqrt{40} - \sqrt{160}$$
$$= \sqrt{4} \cdot \sqrt{10} - \sqrt{16} \cdot \sqrt{10}$$
$$= 2\sqrt{10} - 4\sqrt{10}$$
$$= -2\sqrt{10}.$$

EXAMPLE 4   Simplify the product $(\sqrt{3} + 2\sqrt{5})(\sqrt{3} - 4\sqrt{5})$.

The product of these sums of radicals can be found in much the same way that we found the product of binomials in Chapter 3. The pattern of multiplication is the same.

$$(\sqrt{3} + 2\sqrt{5})(\sqrt{3} - 4\sqrt{5}) = \sqrt{3} \cdot \sqrt{3} + \sqrt{3}(-4\sqrt{5}) + 2\sqrt{5} \cdot \sqrt{3} + 2\sqrt{5}(-4\sqrt{5})$$
$$= 3 - 4\sqrt{15} + 2\sqrt{15} - 8 \cdot 5$$
$$= 3 - 2\sqrt{15} - 40$$
$$= -37 - 2\sqrt{15}$$

Just as we found certain special products of binomials in Chapter 3, there are special products of radicals.

The problems of Examples 5 and 6 use the difference of two squares,

$$(a + b)(a - b) = a^2 - b^2.$$

EXAMPLE 5   Simplify the product $(4 - \sqrt{3})(4 + \sqrt{3})$.

Follow the pattern for the difference of two squares.

$$(4 - \sqrt{3})(4 + \sqrt{3}) = 4 \cdot 4 - \sqrt{3} \cdot \sqrt{3}$$
$$= 16 - 3$$
$$= 13$$

EXAMPLE 6   Simplify $(\sqrt{12} - \sqrt{6})(\sqrt{12} + \sqrt{6})$.

$$(\sqrt{12} - \sqrt{6})(\sqrt{12} + \sqrt{6}) = \sqrt{12} \cdot \sqrt{12} - \sqrt{6} \cdot \sqrt{6}$$
$$= 12 - 6$$
$$= 6$$

We can use products of radicals similar to those in Examples 5 and 6 to rationalize the denominators in more complicated expressions, such as

$$\frac{2}{4 - \sqrt{3}}.$$

We saw in Example 5 that if we multiply this denominator, $4 - \sqrt{3}$, by the radical $4 + \sqrt{3}$, then the product $(4 - \sqrt{3})(4 + \sqrt{3})$ is the rational number 13. If we multiply numerator and denominator by $4 + \sqrt{3}$, we get

$$\frac{2}{4 - \sqrt{3}} = \frac{2(4 + \sqrt{3})}{(4 - \sqrt{3})(4 + \sqrt{3})}$$

$$= \frac{2(4 + \sqrt{3})}{13}.$$

The denominator has now been rationalized—it contains no radical signs.

EXAMPLE 7 Rationalize the denominator in the quotient

$$\frac{4}{3 + \sqrt{5}}.$$

To eliminate the radical in the denominator, multiply numerator and denominator by $3 - \sqrt{5}$.

$$\frac{4}{3 + \sqrt{5}} = \frac{4(3 - \sqrt{5})}{(3 + \sqrt{5})(3 - \sqrt{5})}$$

$$= \frac{4(3 - \sqrt{5})}{9 - 5}$$

$$= \frac{4(3 - \sqrt{5})}{4}$$

$$= 3 - \sqrt{5}$$

The expressions $3 + \sqrt{5}$ and $3 - \sqrt{5}$ are called **conjugates** of each other.

EXAMPLE 8 Simplify $\dfrac{6 + \sqrt{2}}{\sqrt{2} - 5}$.

Multiply numerator and denominator by $\sqrt{2} + 5$:

$$\frac{6 + \sqrt{2}}{\sqrt{2} - 5} = \frac{(6 + \sqrt{2})(\sqrt{2} + 5)}{(\sqrt{2} - 5)(\sqrt{2} + 5)}$$

$$= \frac{6\sqrt{2} + 30 + 2 + 5\sqrt{2}}{2 - 25}$$

$$= \frac{11\sqrt{2} + 32}{-23}$$

$$= -\frac{11\sqrt{2} + 32}{23}.$$

EXERCISES 8.5

Simplify each expression. Use the five rules given in the text. See Examples 1-6.

1. $3\sqrt{5} + 8\sqrt{45}$
2. $6\sqrt{2} + 4\sqrt{18}$
3. $9\sqrt{50} - 4\sqrt{72}$
4. $3\sqrt{80} - 5\sqrt{45}$
5. $\sqrt{2}(\sqrt{8} - \sqrt{32})$
6. $\sqrt{3}(\sqrt{27} - \sqrt{3})$
7. $\sqrt{5}(\sqrt{3} + \sqrt{7})$
8. $\sqrt{7}(\sqrt{10} - \sqrt{3})$
9. $2\sqrt{5}(\sqrt{2} + \sqrt{5})$
10. $3\sqrt{7}(2\sqrt{7} - 4\sqrt{5})$
11. $-\sqrt{14} \cdot \sqrt{2} - \sqrt{28}$
12. $\sqrt{6} \cdot \sqrt{3} - 2\sqrt{50}$
13. $(2\sqrt{6} + 3)(3\sqrt{6} - 5)$
14. $(4\sqrt{5} - 2)(2\sqrt{5} + 3)$
15. $(5\sqrt{7} - 2\sqrt{3})(3\sqrt{7} + 3\sqrt{3})$
16. $(2\sqrt{10} + 5\sqrt{2})(3\sqrt{10} - 4\sqrt{2})$
17. $(3\sqrt{2} + 4)(3\sqrt{2} + 4)$
18. $(4\sqrt{5} - 1)(4\sqrt{5} - 1)$
19. $(2\sqrt{7} - 3)^2$
20. $(3\sqrt{5} + 5)^2$
21. $(3 - \sqrt{2})(3 + \sqrt{2})$
22. $(7 - \sqrt{5})(7 + \sqrt{5})$
23. $(2 + \sqrt{8})(2 - \sqrt{8})$
24. $(3 + \sqrt{11})(3 - \sqrt{11})$
25. $(\sqrt{6} - \sqrt{5})(\sqrt{6} + \sqrt{5})$
26. $(\sqrt{11} + \sqrt{10})(\sqrt{11} - \sqrt{10})$
27. $(\sqrt{18} + \sqrt{2})(\sqrt{18} - \sqrt{2})$
28. $(\sqrt{21} - \sqrt{5})(\sqrt{21} + \sqrt{5})$
29. $(\sqrt{80} - \sqrt{60})(\sqrt{80} + \sqrt{60})$
30. $(\sqrt{92} + \sqrt{72})(\sqrt{92} - \sqrt{72})$
31. $(2\sqrt{5} + 3\sqrt{2})(2\sqrt{5} - 3\sqrt{2})$
32. $(5\sqrt{2} + 6\sqrt{3})(5\sqrt{2} - 6\sqrt{3})$

Rationalize the denominators. See Example 7.

33. $\dfrac{1}{3 + \sqrt{2}}$
34. $\dfrac{1}{4 - \sqrt{3}}$
35. $\dfrac{5}{2 + \sqrt{5}}$

36. $\dfrac{6}{3 + \sqrt{7}}$
37. $\dfrac{7}{2 - \sqrt{11}}$
38. $\dfrac{38}{5 - \sqrt{6}}$

39. $\dfrac{\sqrt{2}}{1 + \sqrt{2}}$
40. $\dfrac{\sqrt{7}}{2 + \sqrt{7}}$
41. $\dfrac{\sqrt{5}}{1 - \sqrt{5}}$

42. $\dfrac{\sqrt{3}}{2 + \sqrt{3}}$
43. $\dfrac{\sqrt{12}}{\sqrt{3} + 1}$
44. $\dfrac{\sqrt{18}}{\sqrt{2} - 1}$

45. $\dfrac{2\sqrt{3}}{\sqrt{3} + 5}$
46. $\dfrac{\sqrt{12}}{2 - \sqrt{2}}$

Simplify each expression. See Example 8.

47. $\dfrac{3 + \sqrt{5}}{\sqrt{2} + 1}$
48. $\dfrac{8 - \sqrt{2}}{\sqrt{3} + 1}$
49. $\dfrac{\sqrt{3} - 7}{\sqrt{3} + 4}$

50. $\dfrac{\sqrt{10} - 3}{\sqrt{10} + 5}$
51. $\dfrac{2\sqrt{6} + 1}{\sqrt{2} + 5}$
52. $\dfrac{3\sqrt{2} - 4}{\sqrt{3} + 2}$

53. $\dfrac{\sqrt{7} + \sqrt{2}}{\sqrt{3} - \sqrt{2}}$
54. $\dfrac{\sqrt{6} + \sqrt{5}}{\sqrt{3} + \sqrt{5}}$

8.6 Equations with Radicals

- **Solve equations with radicals.**

How can we solve an equation involving radicals, such as

$$\sqrt{x + 1} = 3?$$

The addition and multiplication properties of equality will not help us here; we need another property, a squaring property.

If $a = b$, then $a^2 = b^2$. For example, if $y = 4$, then we can square both sides of the equation to get

$$y^2 = 4^2 \quad \text{or} \quad y^2 = 16.$$

The last equation, $y^2 = 16$, has *two* solutions, $y = 4$ or $y = -4$, while the original equation, $y = 4$, has only *one* solution.

As shown by this example, squaring both sides of an equation can lead to a new equation with more solutions than the original equation. Because of this possibility, we need to check all proposed solutions in the *original* equation.

In summary, we have the **squaring property of equality.**

If both sides of a given equation are squared, all solutions of the original equation are also solutions of the squared equation.

EXAMPLE 1 Solve the equation $\sqrt{x + 1} = 3$.

Use the squaring property of equality to square both sides of the equation.

$$(\sqrt{x + 1})^2 = 3^2$$
$$x + 1 = 9$$
$$x = 8$$

Now check this answer in the original equation.

$$\sqrt{x + 1} = 3$$
$$\sqrt{8 + 1} = 3$$
$$\sqrt{9} = 3$$
$$3 = 3 \qquad \text{True}$$

Since this statement is true, the solution of $\sqrt{x + 1} = 3$ is the number 8.

EXAMPLE 2 Solve $3\sqrt{x} = \sqrt{x + 8}$.

Squaring both sides gives

$$(3\sqrt{x})^2 = (\sqrt{x + 8})^2$$
$$3^2(\sqrt{x})^2 = (\sqrt{x + 8})^2$$
$$9x = x + 8$$
$$8x = 8$$
$$x = 1.$$

Check this proposed solution.

$$3\sqrt{x} = \sqrt{x + 8}$$
$$3\sqrt{1} = \sqrt{1 + 8}$$
$$3(1) = \sqrt{9}$$
$$3 = 3 \qquad \text{True}$$

The solution of $3\sqrt{x} = \sqrt{x + 8}$ is the number 1.

Not all equations with radicals even have a solution as Example 3 shows.

EXAMPLE 3   Solve the equation $\sqrt{x} = -3$.
Square both sides.

$$(\sqrt{x})^2 = (-3)^2$$
$$x = 9$$

Check this proposed answer in the original equation.

$$\sqrt{x} = -3$$
$$\sqrt{9} = -3$$
$$3 = -3 \qquad \text{False}$$

Since the statement $3 = -3$ is false, the number 9 is not a solution of the given equation. Thus, $\sqrt{x} = -3$ has no real number solutions at all.

The next example uses the fact that

$$(a + b)^2 = a^2 + 2ab + b^2.$$

EXAMPLE 4   Solve the equation $\sqrt{2y - 3} = y - 3$.
To square both sides, we must square $y - 3$.

$$(y - 3)^2 = (y - 3)(y - 3)$$
$$= y^2 - 6y + 9$$

Now we can square both sides.

$$(\sqrt{2y - 3})^2 = (y - 3)^2$$
$$2y - 3 = y^2 - 6y + 9$$

This equation is quadratic, since it has a y^2 term. To solve the equation, we must get it equal to 0. To do this, add $-2y$ and 3 to both sides.

$$0 = y^2 - 8y + 12$$

This equation can be solved by factoring.

$$0 = (y - 6)(y - 2)$$

Make each factor equal to 0.

$$y - 6 = 0 \quad \text{or} \quad y - 2 = 0$$
$$y = 6 \quad \text{or} \quad y = 2$$

Check both of these proposed solutions in the original equation.

If $y = 6$,

$$\sqrt{2y - 3} = y - 3$$
$$\sqrt{2(6) - 3} = 6 - 3$$
$$\sqrt{12 - 3} = 3$$
$$\sqrt{9} = 3$$
$$3 = 3 \quad \text{True}$$

If $y = 2$,

$$\sqrt{2y - 3} = y - 3$$
$$\sqrt{2(2) - 3} = 2 - 3$$
$$\sqrt{4 - 3} = -1$$
$$\sqrt{1} = -1$$
$$1 = -1 \quad \text{False}$$

Only $y = 6$ is a valid solution of the equation.

EXAMPLE 5 Solve the equation $\sqrt{x} + 1 = 2x$.

Rewrite the equation so that the radical is alone on one side of the equals sign. To do this, add -1 to both sides.

$$\sqrt{x} = 2x - 1$$

Now square both sides.

$$(\sqrt{x})^2 = (2x - 1)^2$$
$$x = 4x^2 - 4x + 1$$

Add $-x$ to both sides.

$$0 = 4x^2 - 5x + 1$$

This equation is a quadratic equation, which can be solved by factoring.

$$0 = (4x - 1)(x - 1)$$
$$4x - 1 = 0 \quad \text{or} \quad x - 1 = 0$$
$$x = \frac{1}{4} \quad \text{or} \quad x = 1.$$

Both of these proposed solutions must be checked in the original equation. For $x = \frac{1}{4}$, we obtain a *false* statement, while $x = 1$ leads to a *true* statement. Therefore, the only solution to the original equation is the number 1.

EXERCISES 8.6 *Find all solutions for each equation. See Examples 1-3.*

1. $\sqrt{x} = 2$

2. $\sqrt{m} = 5$

3. $\sqrt{y + 3} = 2$

4. $\sqrt{z + 1} = 5$

5. $\sqrt{t - 3} = 2$

6. $\sqrt{r + 5} = 4$

7. $\sqrt{n + 8} = 1$

8. $\sqrt{k + 10} = 2$

9. $\sqrt{m + 5} = 0$

10. $\sqrt{y - 4} = 0$

11. $\sqrt{z + 5} = -2$

12. $\sqrt{t - 3} = -2$

13. $\sqrt{k} - 2 = 5$

14. $\sqrt{p} - 3 = 7$

15. $\sqrt{y} + 4 = 2$

16. $\sqrt{m} + 6 = 5$

17. $\sqrt{5t - 9} = 2\sqrt{t}$

18. $\sqrt{3n + 4} = 2\sqrt{n}$

19. $3\sqrt{r} = \sqrt{8r + 16}$

20. $2\sqrt{r} = \sqrt{3r + 9}$

21. $\sqrt{5y - 5} = \sqrt{4y + 1}$

22. $\sqrt{2x + 2} = \sqrt{3x - 5}$

23. $\sqrt{x + 2} = \sqrt{2x - 5}$

24. $\sqrt{3m + 3} = \sqrt{5m - 1}$

25. $\sqrt{2t + 9} = \sqrt{t + 5}$

26. $\sqrt{6z + 22} = \sqrt{2z + 10}$

27. $\sqrt{2x + 6} = \sqrt{4x - 4}$

28. $\sqrt{5x - 6} = \sqrt{4x - 3}$

Find all solutions for each equation. See Examples 4 and 5. Remember that $(a + b)^2 = a^2 + 2ab + b^2$ and $(\sqrt{a})^2 = a$.

29. $\sqrt{2x + 1} = x - 7$

30. $\sqrt{5x + 1} = x + 1$

31. $\sqrt{3x + 10} = 2x - 5$

32. $\sqrt{4x + 13} = 2x - 1$

33. $\sqrt{x + 1} - 1 = x$

34. $\sqrt{3x + 3} + 5 = x$

35. $\sqrt{4x + 5} - 2 = 2x - 7$

36. $\sqrt{6x + 7} - 1 = x + 1$

37. $3\sqrt{x + 13} = x + 9$

38. $2\sqrt{x + 7} = x - 1$

39. $\sqrt{4x} - x + 3 = 0$

40. $\sqrt{2x} - x + 4 = 0$

41. $\sqrt{3x} - 4 = x - 10$

42. $\sqrt{x} + 9 = x + 3$

In the following two exercises, it is necessary to square both sides twice.

43. $\sqrt{x} = \sqrt{x - 5} + 1$

44. $\sqrt{2x} = \sqrt{x + 7} - 1$

Solve each problem.

45. The square root of the sum of a number and 4 is 5. Find the number.

46. A certain number is the same as the square root of the product of 8 and the number. Find the number.

47. Three times the square root of two equals the square root of the sum of some number and ten. Find the number.

48. The negative square root of a number equals that number decreased by two. Find the number.

49. To estimate the speed at which a car was traveling at the time of an accident, police sometimes use the following procedure: A police officer drives the car involved in the accident under conditions similar to those when the accident took place and skids to a stop. If the car is driven at 30 miles per hour, then the speed at the time of the accident is given by

$$s = \sqrt{\frac{900a}{p}},$$

where a is the length of the skid marks left at the time of the accident, and p is the length of the skid marks in the police test. Find s if

(a) $a = 900$ feet and $p = 100$ feet.

(b) $a = 400$ feet and $p = 25$ feet.

(c) $a = 80$ feet and $p = 20$ feet.

(d) $a = 120$ feet and $p = 30$ feet.

Chapter 8   Test

[8.1]   *Find each root. Use the square root table if necessary.*

1. $\sqrt{100}$

2. $\sqrt{77}$

3. $\sqrt{190}$

4. $\sqrt{1521}$

5. $\sqrt[3]{-27}$

6. $\sqrt[4]{625}$

[8.2]   *Simplify each expression.*

7. $\sqrt{\dfrac{64}{169}}$

8. $\sqrt{8}$

9. $\sqrt{50}$

10. $\sqrt{27}$

11. $\sqrt[3]{32}$

12. $\sqrt{.0025}$

[8.3]   13. $\sqrt{20} - \sqrt{45}$

14. $\sqrt{8} + 2\sqrt{18}$

15. $3\sqrt{6} + \sqrt{14}$

16. $3\sqrt{28} + \sqrt{63}$

17. $3\sqrt{27x} - 4\sqrt{48x}$

18. $\sqrt{32x^2y^3}$

[8.4]   *Rationalize each denominator.*

19. $\dfrac{4}{\sqrt{3}}$

20. $\dfrac{6\sqrt{30}}{2\sqrt{5}}$

21. $\dfrac{3\sqrt{2}}{\sqrt{6}}$

22. $\sqrt[3]{\dfrac{5}{9}}$

[8.5]   *Simplify.*

23. $(6 - \sqrt{5})(6 + \sqrt{5})$

24. $(1 - \sqrt{3})^2$

25. $(\sqrt{5} + \sqrt{6})^2$

26. $(2 - \sqrt{7})(3\sqrt{2} + 1)$

Rationalize the denominator in the following.

27. $\dfrac{2}{1 - \sqrt{5}}$

28. $\dfrac{\sqrt{3} + 1}{2 - \sqrt{2}}$

[8.6] *Solve each equation.*

29. $\sqrt{x} = 4$

30. $\sqrt{m + 2} = 5$

31. $\sqrt{2k + 8} = 2\sqrt{k}$

32. $\sqrt{2z + 11} = \sqrt{z + 6}$

33. $\sqrt{r + 2} = 2 + r$

9

Quadratic Equations

9.1 Solving Quadratic Equations by the Square Root Method

- **Solve equations involving only a squared term.**
- **Solve equations of the form $(2x + 3)^2 = 25$.**

In Chapter 4 we solved quadratic equations (second-degree equations) by factoring. However, not all quadratic equations can be solved by factoring. To solve equations like

$$(x - 3)^2 = 16,$$

where the square of a binomial is equal to some number, we can use square roots.

If two positive numbers are equal, then they must have the same square roots or square roots which are additive inverses of each other. That is, if b is a positive number and

if $a^2 = b$, then $a = \sqrt{b}$ or $a = -\sqrt{b}$.

EXAMPLE 1 Solve the equations.

(a) $x^2 = 16$

By the statement above, if $x^2 = 16$, then

$$x = \sqrt{16} \qquad \text{or} \qquad x = -\sqrt{16}$$
$$= 4 \qquad\qquad\qquad = -4.$$

(b) $p^2 = 9$

Taking square roots on both sides gives

$$p = 3 \quad \text{or} \quad p = -3.$$

These two solutions are sometimes written as just ± 3 (read "plus or minus 3.")

(c) $z^2 = 5$

The solution is $z = \sqrt{5}$ or $z = -\sqrt{5}$.

(d) $m^2 = 8$

We have $m = \sqrt{8}$ or $m = -\sqrt{8}$. Since $\sqrt{8} = 2\sqrt{2}$, $m = 2\sqrt{2}$ or $m = -2\sqrt{2}$.

(e) $y^2 = -4$

Since -4 is a negative number, and since the square of a real number cannot be negative, there is no real number solution for this equation.

We can solve the equation $(x - 3)^2 = 16$ in the same way we solved the equations in Example 1:

$$\text{If } (x - 3)^2 = 16, \text{ then } x - 3 = 4 \text{ or } x - 3 = -4.$$

From the last two equations we get

$$x = 7 \quad \text{or} \quad x = -1.$$

Check both answers in the original equation.

$$(7 - 3)^2 = 16 \qquad (-1 - 3)^2 = 16$$
$$4^2 = 16 \qquad (-4)^2 = 16$$
$$16 = 16 \qquad 16 = 16$$

Both 7 and -1 are solutions.

EXAMPLE 2   Solve $(x - 1)^2 = 6$.

Take the square root on both sides.

$$x - 1 = \sqrt{6} \qquad \text{or} \qquad x - 1 = -\sqrt{6}$$
$$x = 1 + \sqrt{6} \qquad \text{or} \qquad x = 1 - \sqrt{6}$$

Check:

$$(1 + \sqrt{6} - 1)^2 = 6 \qquad (1 - \sqrt{6} - 1)^2 = 6$$
$$(\sqrt{6})^2 = 6 \qquad (-\sqrt{6})^2 = 6$$
$$6 = 6 \qquad 6 = 6$$

The solutions are $1 + \sqrt{6}$ and $1 - \sqrt{6}$.

EXAMPLE 3 Solve the equation $(3r - 2)^2 = 27$.

Taking square roots gives

$$3r - 2 = \sqrt{27} \quad \text{or} \quad 3r - 2 = -\sqrt{27}.$$

Now simplify the radical: $\sqrt{27} = \sqrt{9 \cdot 3} = \sqrt{9} \cdot \sqrt{3} = 3\sqrt{3}$, so

$$3r - 2 = 3\sqrt{3} \quad \text{or} \quad 3r - 2 = -3\sqrt{3}$$
$$3r = 2 + 3\sqrt{3} \quad \text{or} \quad 3r = 2 - 3\sqrt{3}$$
$$r = \frac{2 + 3\sqrt{3}}{3} \qquad\qquad r = \frac{2 - 3\sqrt{3}}{3}.$$

The solutions are

$$\frac{2 + 3\sqrt{3}}{3} \quad \text{and} \quad \frac{2 - 3\sqrt{3}}{3}.$$

EXAMPLE 4 Solve $(x + 3)^2 = -9$.

The square root of -9 is not a real number. Hence there is no real number solution.

EXERCISES 9.1 *Solve each equation by taking the square root of both sides. Express all radicals in simplest form. See Example 1.*

1. $x^2 = 25$ 2. $x^2 = 100$

3. $x^2 = 64$ 4. $x^2 = 81$

5. $x^2 = 13$ 6. $x^2 = 7$

7. $x^2 = 2$ 8. $x^2 = 6$

9. $x^2 = 24$ 10. $x^2 = 27$

Solve each equation by taking the square root of both sides. Express all square roots in simplest form. See Examples 2–4.

11. $(x - 2)^2 = 16$ 12. $(r + 4)^2 = 25$

13. $(a + 4)^2 = 10$ 14. $(r - 3)^2 = 15$

15. $(x - 1)^2 = 32$ 16. $(y + 5)^2 = 28$

17. $(2m - 1)^2 = 9$ 18. $(3y - 7)^2 = 4$

19. $(3z + 5)^2 = 9$ 20. $(2y - 7)^2 = 49$

21. $(6m - 2)^2 = 121$ 22. $(7m - 10)^2 = 144$

23. $(2a - 5)^2 = 30$ 24. $(2y + 3)^2 = 45$

25. $(3p - 1)^2 = 18$ 26. $(5r - 6)^2 = 75$

27. $(2k - 5)^2 = 98$ 28. $(4x - 1)^2 = 48$

29. $(3m + 4)^2 = 8$ 30. $(5y - 3)^2 = 50$

31. One expert at marksmanship can hold a silver dollar at forehead level, drop it, draw his gun, and shoot the coin as it passes waist level. The distance traveled by a falling object is given by $d = 16t^2$, where d is the distance the object falls in t seconds. If the coin falls about 4 feet, estimate the time that elapses between the dropping of the coin and the shot.

9.2 Solving Quadratic Equations by Completing the Square

● **Solve quadratic equations by completing the square.**

Consider the equation

$$x^2 + 6x + 7 = 0.$$

In the preceding section, we learned to solve equations of the type

$$(x + 3)^2 = 2.$$

If we can rewrite the equation

$$x^2 + 6x + 7 = 0$$

in a form like

$$(x + 3)^2 = 2,$$

we can solve it by taking square roots of both sides. We show how to do this in the following example.

EXAMPLE 1 Solve $x^2 + 6x + 7 = 0$.

To start, add -7 to both sides of the equation to get

$$x^2 + 6x = -7.$$

We want the quantity on the left-hand side of $x^2 + 6x = -7$ to be a perfect square trinomial. Note that $x^2 + 6x + 9$ is a perfect square, since

$$x^2 + 6x + 9 = (x + 3)^2.$$

Hence, if we add 9 to both sides, we will have an equation with a perfect square trinomial on the left-hand side, as desired.

$$x^2 + 6x + 9 = -7 + 9$$
$$(x + 3)^2 = 2$$

Now take the square root of both sides of the equation to complete the solution.

$$x + 3 = \sqrt{2} \qquad \text{or} \qquad x + 3 = -\sqrt{2}$$
$$x = -3 + \sqrt{2} \qquad \text{or} \qquad x = -3 - \sqrt{2}$$

The solutions of the original equation are $-3 + \sqrt{2}$ and $-3 - \sqrt{2}$. Verify this by substituting $-3 + \sqrt{2}$ and $-3 - \sqrt{2}$ for x in the equation.

The process of changing the form of the equation in Example 1 from

$$x^2 + 6x + 7 = 0 \quad \text{to} \quad (x + 3)^2 = 2$$

is called **completing the square.**

EXAMPLE 2   Find the solutions of the quadratic equation

$$m^2 - 5m = 2.$$

To find the number to be added to both sides, take *half* the coefficient of m. In this equation, the coefficient of m is -5, and half of -5 is $-\frac{5}{2}$. If we square $-\frac{5}{2}$ we get $\frac{25}{4}$, which is added to both sides.

$$m^2 - 5m + \frac{25}{4} = 2 + \frac{25}{4}$$

The trinomial $m^2 - 5m + \frac{25}{4}$ is a perfect square trinomial.

$$m^2 - 5m + \frac{25}{4} = \left(m - \frac{5}{2} \right)^2.$$

Thus,

$$\left(m - \frac{5}{2} \right)^2 = 2 + \frac{25}{4}$$

$$= \frac{33}{4}.$$

Now take square roots.

$$m - \frac{5}{2} = \sqrt{\frac{33}{4}} \qquad \text{or} \qquad m - \frac{5}{2} = -\sqrt{\frac{33}{4}}$$

$$m = \frac{5}{2} + \sqrt{\frac{33}{4}} \qquad\qquad m = \frac{5}{2} - \sqrt{\frac{33}{4}}$$

Simplify the radical: $\sqrt{\frac{33}{4}} = \frac{\sqrt{33}}{\sqrt{4}} = \frac{\sqrt{33}}{2}$.

The solutions are

$$\frac{5 + \sqrt{33}}{2} \qquad \text{and} \qquad \frac{5 - \sqrt{33}}{2}$$

EXAMPLE 3   Solve the equation $2x^2 - 7x = 9$.

To complete the square, we need a coefficient of 1 for the x^2 term. To get x^2 instead of $2x^2$, multiply both sides of the equation by $\frac{1}{2}$, giving

$$x^2 - \frac{7}{2}x = \frac{9}{2}.$$

Now take half the coefficient of x and square it. Half of $-\frac{7}{2}$ is $-\frac{7}{4}$, and $-\frac{7}{4}$ squared is $\frac{49}{16}$. Add $\frac{49}{16}$ to both sides of the equation, and write the left side as a perfect square.

$$x^2 - \frac{7}{2}x + \frac{49}{16} = \frac{9}{2} + \frac{49}{16}$$

$$\left(x - \frac{7}{4}\right)^2 = \frac{121}{16}$$

Take the square root of both sides.

$$x - \frac{7}{4} = \sqrt{\frac{121}{16}} \qquad \text{or} \qquad x - \frac{7}{4} = -\sqrt{\frac{121}{16}}$$

Since $\sqrt{\frac{121}{16}} = \frac{11}{4}$, the two solutions are

$$x - \frac{7}{4} = \frac{11}{4} \qquad \text{or} \qquad x - \frac{7}{4} = \frac{-11}{4}$$

$$x = \frac{18}{4} \qquad\qquad\qquad x = \frac{-4}{4}$$

$$= \frac{9}{2} \qquad\qquad\qquad = -1.$$

The solutions are $\frac{9}{2}$ and -1. Since the solutions are rational numbers, the original equation could have been factored as follows.

$$2x^2 - 7x - 9 = (2x - 9)(x + 1)$$

EXAMPLE 4   Use the method of completing the square to solve the equation

$$4p^2 + 8p + 5 = 0.$$

First multiply both sides by $\frac{1}{4}$ to get the coefficient 1 for the p^2 term. The result is

$$p^2 + 2p + \frac{5}{4} = 0.$$

Add $\frac{-5}{4}$ to both sides, which gives

$$p^2 + 2p = \frac{-5}{4}.$$

The coefficient of p is 2. Take half of 2, square the result, and add it to both sides. The left-hand side can then be written as a perfect square.

$$p^2 + 2p + 1 = \frac{-5}{4} + 1$$

$$(p + 1)^2 = \frac{-1}{4}$$

At this point, we should take the square root of both sides. However, the square root of $-\frac{1}{4}$ is not a real number. This equation has no real number solution.

In summary, use the following four steps to complete the square in a quadratic equation.

Completing the Square in a Quadratic Equation

Step 1   If the coefficient of the squared term is 1, proceed to step 2. If the coefficient of the squared term is not 1, but some other number a, multiply both sides of the equation by the reciprocal of a, $\frac{1}{a}$. This gives an equation which has 1 as coefficient of the squared term.

Step 2   Make sure all terms with variables are on one side of the equals sign, and all numbers are on the other side.

Step 3   Take half the coefficient of x and square it. Add the square to both sides of the equation. The side containing the variables should now be written as a perfect square.

Step 4   Take the square root of both sides. The solutions are determined by solving the two resulting equations.

EXERCISES 9.2   *Find the number that should be added to each of the following to make it a perfect square. See Example 2.*

1. $x^2 + 2x$

2. $y^2 - 4y$

3. $x^2 + 18x$

4. $m^2 - 3m$

5. $z^2 + 9z$

6. $p^2 + 22p$

7. $x^2 + 14x$

8. $r^2 + 7r$

9. $y^2 + 5y$

10. $q^2 - 8q$

Solve the following equations by completing the square. See Examples 1–4. You may have to simplify first.

11. $x^2 + 4x = -3$

12. $y^2 - 4y = 0$

13. $a^2 + 2a = 5$

14. $m^2 + 4m = 12$

15. $z^2 + 6z = -8$

16. $q^2 - 8q = -16$

17. $x^2 - 6x + 1 = 0$

18. $b^2 - 2b - 2 = 0$

19. $c^2 + 3c = 2$

20. $k^2 + 5k - 3 = 0$

21. $2m^2 + 4m = -7$

22. $3y^2 - 9y + 5 = 0$

23. $6q^2 - 8q + 3 = 0$

24. $4y^2 + 4y - 3 = 0$

25. $-x^2 + 6x = 4$

26. $3y^2 - 6y - 2 = 0$

27. $2m^2 - 4m - 5 = 0$

28. $-x^2 + 4 = 2x$

29. $3x^2 - 2x = 1$

30. $-x^2 - 4 = 2x$

31. $m^2 - 4m + 8 = 6m$

32. $2z^2 = 8z + 5 - 4z^2$

33. $3r^2 - 2 = 6r + 3$

34. $4p - 3 = p^2 + 2p$

35. $(x + 1)(x + 3) = 2$

36. $(x - 3)(x + 1) = 1$

9.3   Solving Quadratic Equations by the Quadratic Formula

- **Identify the letters *a*, *b*, and *c* in a quadratic equation.**
- **Use the quadratic formula to solve quadratic equations.**
- **Solve quadratic equations involving fractions.**

Completing the square can be used to solve any quadratic equation, but the method is not very handy. In this section, we will work out a general formula, the quadratic formula, which gives the solution for any quadratic equation.

To get the quadratic formula, start with the *standard form* of a quadratic equation,

$$ax^2 + bx + c = 0, \quad a \neq 0.$$

The restriction $a \neq 0$ is important to make sure that the equation is in fact quadratic. If $a = 0$, then the equation becomes $0x^2 + bx + c = 0$, or $bx + c = 0$. This is a linear, not a quadratic, equation.

EXAMPLE 1   Match the coefficents of each of the following quadratic equations with the letters *a*, *b*, and *c* of the general quadratic equation

$$ax^2 + bx + c = 0.$$

(a) $2x^2 + 3x - 5 = 0$

In this example $a = 2$, $b = 3$, and $c = -5$.

(b) $-x^2 + 2 = 6x$

First rewrite the equation to match the standard form $ax^2 + bx + c = 0$.

$$- x^2 + 2 = 6x$$
$$-x^2 - 6x + 2 = 0 \qquad \text{Add } -6x$$

Now we can identify $a = -1$, $b = -6$, and $c = 2$.

(c) $2(x + 3)(x - 1) = 0$

Here we must first multiply.

$$2(x + 3)(x - 1) = 0$$
$$2(x^2 + 2x - 3) = 0$$
$$2x^2 + 4x - 6 = 0$$

From this result, $a = 2$, $b = 4$, and $c = -6$.

We solve the equation $ax^2 + bx + c = 0$ by completing the square. First, we need the coefficient 1 for the x^2 term. To get this, multiply both sides by $\dfrac{1}{a}$, which gives

$$x^2 + \frac{b}{a}x + \frac{c}{a} = 0.$$

Next add $-\dfrac{c}{a}$ to both sides, to get

$$x^2 + \frac{b}{a}x = -\frac{c}{a}$$

Now complete the square on the left. To do this, take half the coefficient of x, that is $\dfrac{b}{2a}$. Square $\dfrac{b}{2a}$ to get $\dfrac{b^2}{4a^2}$. Next, add $\dfrac{b^2}{4a^2}$ to both sides of the equation.

$$x^2 + \frac{b}{a}x + \frac{b^2}{4a^2} = \frac{-c}{a} + \frac{b^2}{4a^2}$$

Rewrite the left-hand side as a perfect square.

$$\left(x + \frac{b}{2a}\right)^2 = \frac{-c}{a} + \frac{b^2}{4a^2}$$

Now simplify the right-hand side of the equation.

$$\left(x + \frac{b}{2a}\right)^2 = \frac{b^2}{4a^2} + \frac{-c}{a}$$

$$= \frac{b^2}{4a^2} + \frac{-4ac}{4a^2}$$

$$= \frac{b^2 - 4ac}{4a^2}$$

Take the square root of both sides.

$$x + \frac{b}{2a} = \sqrt{\frac{b^2 - 4ac}{4a^2}} \qquad \text{or} \qquad x + \frac{b}{2a} = -\sqrt{\frac{b^2 - 4ac}{4a^2}}$$

Simplify the radical.

$$\sqrt{\frac{b^2 - 4ac}{4a^2}} = \frac{\sqrt{b^2 - 4ac}}{\sqrt{4a^2}}$$

$$= \frac{\sqrt{b^2 - 4ac}}{2a}$$

Now we can write the solutions as follows:

$$x + \frac{b}{2a} = \frac{\sqrt{b^2 - 4ac}}{2a} \qquad \text{or} \qquad x + \frac{b}{2a} = \frac{-\sqrt{b^2 - 4ac}}{2a}$$

$$x = \frac{-b}{2a} + \frac{\sqrt{b^2 - 4ac}}{2a} \qquad\qquad x = \frac{-b}{2a} - \frac{\sqrt{b^2 - 4ac}}{2a}$$

$$x = \frac{-b + \sqrt{b^2 - 4ac}}{2a} \qquad\qquad x = \frac{-b - \sqrt{b^2 - 4ac}}{2a}$$

Hence, the solutions of the general quadratic equation $ax^2 + bx + c = 0$ $(a \neq 0)$ are

$$\frac{-b + \sqrt{b^2 - 4ac}}{2a} \qquad \text{and} \qquad \frac{-b - \sqrt{b^2 - 4ac}}{2a}$$

For convenience, the solutions are often expressed in compact form by using the symbol $\pm$ (read "plus or minus"). The result is called the **quadratic formula.**

$$x = \frac{-b \pm \sqrt{b^2 - 4ac}}{2a}.$$

EXAMPLE 2   Use the quadratic formula to solve $2x^2 - 7x - 9 = 0$.
   To begin, match the coefficients of the variables with the letter symbols of the general quadratic equation,

$$ax^2 + bx + c = 0.$$

Here, $a = 2$, $b = -7$, and $c = -9$. Substitute these numbers into the quadratic formula and simplify the result.

$$x = \frac{-b \pm \sqrt{b^2 - 4ac}}{2a}$$

$$= \frac{-(-7) \pm \sqrt{(-7)^2 - 4(2)(-9)}}{2(2)}$$

$$= \frac{7 \pm \sqrt{49 + 72}}{4}$$

$$= \frac{7 \pm \sqrt{121}}{4}$$

Since $\sqrt{121} = 11$,

$$x = \frac{7 \pm 11}{4}.$$

To write the two solutions separately, first take the plus sign:

$$x = \frac{7 + 11}{4}$$

$$= \frac{18}{4}$$

$$= \frac{9}{2}.$$

Then take the minus sign:

$$x = \frac{7 - 11}{4}$$

$$= \frac{-4}{4}$$

$$= -1.$$

The solutions of $2x^2 - 7x - 9 = 0$ are $\frac{9}{2}$ and -1.

EXAMPLE 3   Solve $x^2 = 2x + 1$.

To find a, b, and c add $-2x - 1$ to both sides of the equation to get

$$x^2 - 2x - 1 = 0.$$

Then $a = 1$, $b = -2$, and $c = -1$. The solution is found by substituting these values into the quadratic formula.

$$x = \frac{-b \pm \sqrt{b^2 - 4ac}}{2a}$$

$$= \frac{-(-2) \pm \sqrt{(-2)^2 - 4(1)(-1)}}{2(1)}$$

$$= \frac{2 \pm \sqrt{4 + 4}}{2}$$

$$= \frac{2 \pm \sqrt{8}}{2}$$

Since $\sqrt{8} = \sqrt{4 \cdot 2} = \sqrt{4} \cdot \sqrt{2} = 2\sqrt{2}$,

$$x = \frac{2 \pm 2\sqrt{2}}{2}.$$

And since $2 \pm 2\sqrt{2}$ factors as $2(1 \pm \sqrt{2})$,

$$x = \frac{2(1 \pm \sqrt{2})}{2}$$

$$= 1 \pm \sqrt{2}.$$

Therefore, the two solutions of this equation are
$$1 + \sqrt{2} \quad \text{and} \quad 1 - \sqrt{2}.$$

EXAMPLE 4   Solve the equation $x^2 + 5x + 8 = 0$.

Here $a = 1$, $b = 5$, and $c = 8$. Substitute into the quadratic formula and simplify the result.

$$x = \frac{-5 \pm \sqrt{5^2 - 4(1)(8)}}{2(1)}$$

$$= \frac{-5 \pm \sqrt{25 - 32}}{2}$$

$$= \frac{-5 \pm \sqrt{-7}}{2}$$

The radical $\sqrt{-7}$ is not a real number so the equation has no real number solutions.

EXAMPLE 5   Solve the equation

$$\frac{1}{10}t^2 = \frac{2}{5} - \frac{1}{2}t.$$

To eliminate the denominators, multiply both sides of the equation by the common denominator 10.

$$10\left(\frac{1}{10}t^2\right) = 10\left(\frac{2}{5} - \frac{1}{2}t\right)$$

$$t^2 = 4 - 5t$$

Add $-4 + 5t$ to both sides of the equation to get

$$t^2 + 5t - 4 = 0.$$

In this form, we can identify $a = 1$, $b = 5$, and $c = -4$. Use the quadratic formula to complete the solution.

$$t = \frac{-5 \pm \sqrt{25 - 4(1)(-4)}}{2(1)}$$

$$= \frac{-5 \pm \sqrt{25 + 16}}{2}$$

$$= \frac{-5 \pm \sqrt{41}}{2}$$

The solutions are

$$\frac{-5 + \sqrt{41}}{2} \quad \text{and} \quad \frac{-5 - \sqrt{41}}{2}.$$

EXERCISES 9.3 *Write each equation in standard form and then identify the values of* a, b, *and* c. *Do not try to solve. See Example 1.*

1. $3m^2 + 4m - 8 = 0$

2. $9k^2 + 2k - 3 = 0$

3. $-8y^2 - 2y - 3 = 0$

4. $-2p^2 + 3p - 8 = 0$

5. $2z^2 = 3z - 2$

6. $9t^2 - 2 = 4t$

7. $x^2 = 2$

8. $m^2 - 3 = 0$

9. $3r^2 - 8r = 0$

10. $5y^2 = 2y$

11. $(m - 3)(m + 4) = 0$

12. $(w + 6)^2 = 3$

13. $9(s - 1)(s + 2) = 8$

14. $(3y - 1)(2y + 5) = y$

Use the quadratic formula to solve each equation. Write all radicals in simplified form. Reduce answers to lowest terms. See Examples 2 and 3.

15. $p^2 + 2p - 2 = 0$

16. $6k^2 + 6k + 1 = 0$

17. $y^2 + 4y + 4 = 0$

18. $3r^2 - 5r + 1 = 0$

19. $z^2 = 13 - 12z$

20. $x^2 = 8x + 9$

21. $2w^2 + 12w + 5 = 0$

22. $k^2 = 20k - 19$

23. $5x^2 + 4x - 1 = 0$

24. $5n^2 + n - 1 = 0$

25. $2z^2 = 3z + 5$

26. $7r - 2r^2 + 30 = 0$

27. $z^2 + 6z + 9 = 0$

28. $x^2 - 2x + 1 = 0$

29. $4p^2 - 12p + 9 = 0$

30. $9r^2 + 6r + 1 = 0$

31. $5m^2 + 5m = 0$

32. $4y^2 - 8y = 0$

33. $6p^2 = 10p$

34. $3r^2 = 16r$

35. $m^2 - 20 = 0$

36. $k^2 - 5 = 0$

37. $9r^2 - 16 = 0$

38. $4y^2 - 25 = 0$

39. $2x^2 + 2x + 4 = 4 - 2x$

40. $3x^2 - 4x + 3 = 8x - 1$

Use the quadratic formula to solve each equation. See Examples 4 and 5.

41. $2y^2 + y + 7 = 0$

42. $m^2 + m + 1 = 0$

43. $2z^2 = 3z - 2$

44. $t^2 = 5t - 20$

45. $\frac{1}{2}x^2 = 1 - \frac{1}{6}x$

46. $\frac{3}{2}r^2 - r = \frac{4}{3}$

47. $\frac{2}{3}m^2 - \frac{4}{9}m - \frac{1}{3} = 0$

48. $\frac{3}{5}x - \frac{2}{5}x^2 = -1$

49. $\frac{r^2}{2} = r + \frac{1}{2}$

50. $\frac{m^2}{4} + \frac{3m}{2} + 1 = 0$

51. $k^2 = \frac{2k}{3} + \frac{2}{9}$

52. $\frac{2y^2}{7} + \frac{10}{7}y + 1 = 0$

53. $\frac{m^2}{2} = \frac{m}{2} - 1$

54. $\frac{3k^2}{8} - k = -\frac{17}{24}$

9.4 Graphing Parabolas

- **Identify parabolas.**
- **Graph quadratic equations.**
- **Find the vertex of a parabola.**

In Chapter 6, we graphed straight lines to represent the solutions of linear equations. Now we investigate the graphs of quadratic equations in two variables which have the form $y = ax^2 + bx + c$. Perhaps the simplest such quadratic equation is

$$y = x^2$$

(which is the same as $y = 1x^2 + 0x + 0$). The graph of this equation cannot be a straight line since only linear equations of the form

$$ax + by + c = 0$$

have graphs which are straight lines. However, we can graph $y = x^2$ in much the same way as we graphed straight lines, by selecting values for x and then finding the corresponding y-values.

EXAMPLE 1 Graph $y = x^2$.

If $x = 2$ in the equation $y = x^2$, then

$$y = 2^2$$
$$= 4.$$

Thus the point $(2, 4)$ belongs to the graph of $y = x^2$. (Recall that in an ordered pair such as $(2, 4)$, the x-value comes first and the y-value second.) We can complete a chart showing values of y for some values of x (which we choose arbitrarily).

Equation	Ordered pairs
$y = x^2$	$(-3, 9)$
	$(-2, 4)$
	$(-1, 1)$
	$(0, 0)$
	$(1, 1)$
	$(2, 4)$
	$(3, 9)$

If we plot these points on a coordinate system and draw a smooth curve through them, we get the graph shown in Figure 9.1 called a **parabola.** The point $(0, 0)$, the lowest point on this graph, is called the **vertex** of the parabola.

Every quadratic equation of the form

$$y = ax^2 + bx + c$$

has a graph which is a parabola. Because of its many useful properties, the

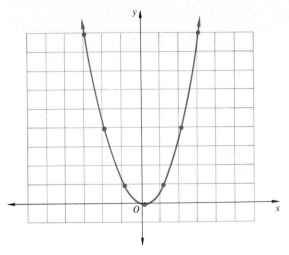

Figure 9.1

parabola occurs frequently in real-life applications. For example, if an object is thrown into the air, the path that the object follows is a parabola (discounting wind resistance). The cross-sections of radar, spotlight, and telescope reflectors also form parabolas.

EXAMPLE 2 Graph the parabola $y = -x^2$.

We could select values for x and then find the corresponding y-values. But note that for a given x-value, the y-value will be the negative of the corresponding y-value of the parabola $y = x^2$ discussed above. Hence this new parabola has the same shape as the one in the preceding figure, but is turned in the opposite direction. We say it opens downward (the graph in Figure 9.1 opens upward), as shown in Figure 9.2. Here the vertex, $(0, 0)$, is the *highest* point on the graph.

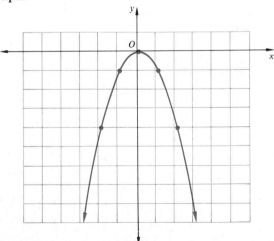

Figure 9.2

EXAMPLE 3 Graph the parabola $y = (x - 2)^2$.

Again we select values for x and find the corresponding y-values. For example, if we let $x = -1$, we have

$$y = (-1 - 2)^2$$
$$= (-3)^2$$
$$= 9.$$

Calculating other ordered pairs in the same way, we get the following:

Equation	*Ordered pairs*
$y = (x - 2)^2$	$(-1, 9)$
	$(0, 4)$
	$(1, 1)$
	$(2, 0)$
	$(3, 1)$
	$(4, 4)$
	$(5, 9)$

Plotting these points and joining them gives the graph shown in Figure 9.3. Note that the parabola of the figure has the same shape as our original parabola $(y = x^2)$, but is shifted two units to the right. The vertex here is $(2, 0)$.

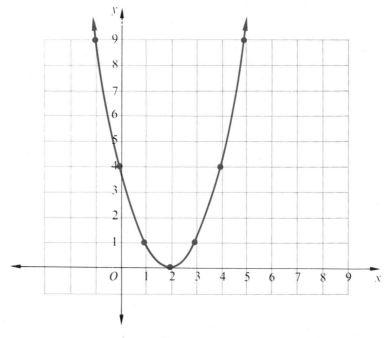

Figure 9.3

EXAMPLE 4 Graph the parabola $y = -3(x + 4)^2$.

If we make a table of values and plot the points, we get the graph shown in

Figure 9.4. The graph opens downward, is shifted four units to the left, and is narrower than the graph of $y = x^2$. The vertex is $(-4, 0)$.

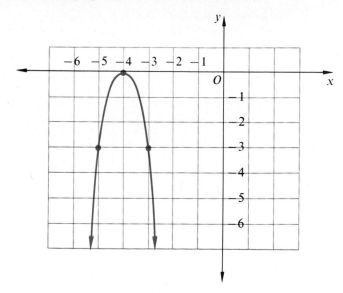

Figure 9.4

EXAMPLE 5 Graph the parabola $y = x^2 - 3$.

The graph is shown in Figure 9.5. Note that this time the graph is shifted three units downward, as compared to the graph of $y = x^2$. The vertex is $(0, -3)$.

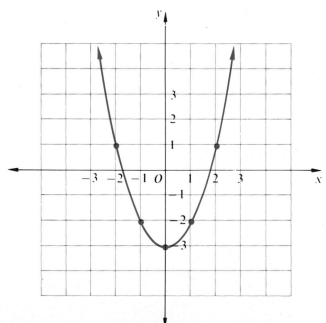

Figure 9.5

EXAMPLE 6 Graph $y = (x - 1)^2 + 4$.

This parabola is shifted 1 unit to the right and 4 units up. The vertex is at $(1, 4)$. See Figure 9.6.

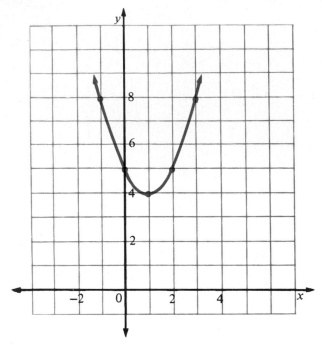

Figure 9.6

The graph of

$$y = a(x - h)^2 + k$$

is a parabola with vertex at (h, k).

The parabola opens upward if $a > 0$, and downward if $a < 0$.

The parabola is "fatter" than $y = x^2$ if $0 < |a| < 1$, while the parabola is "thinner" than $y = x^2$ if $|a| > 1$.

EXERCISES 9.4 *Sketch the graph of each parabola. Identify each vertex. See Examples 1–6.*

1. $y = 2x^2$

2. $y = -2x^2$

3. $y = (x + 1)^2$

4. $y = (x - 2)^2$

5. $y = -(x + 1)^2$

6. $y = -(x - 2)^2$

7. $y = x^2 + 1$

8. $y = x^2 - 6$

9. $y = -x^2 - 2$ 10. $y = -x^2 + 4$

11. $y = 8 - x^2$ 12. $y = -2 - x^2$

13. $y = (x - 2)^2 + 3$ 14. $y = (x + 5)^2 - 4$

15. $y = (x + 2)^2 + 1$ 16. $y = (x - 2)^2 - 3$

17. $y = (x - 4)^2 - 2$ 18. $y = (x + 3)^2 + 4$

19. $y = 2(x + 2)^2 - 3$ 20. $y = 3(x - 1)^2 + 4$

21. $y = -(x - 3)^2 - 2$ 22. $y = -(x + 4)^2 - 5$

23. $y = -3(x - 5)^2 + 4$ 24. $y = -2(x + 2)^2 - 1$

Chapter 9   Test

[9.1]   *Solve by the square root method.*

1. $m^2 = 5$ 2. $(p - 3)^2 = 49$ 3. $(3z - 2)^2 = 35$

[9.2]   *Solve by completing the square.*

4. $2k^2 - 5k = 0$

5. $5r^2 = 2 - 9r$

[9.3]   *Solve by using the quadratic formula.*

6. $x^2 - 8x + 16 = 0$ 7. $3y^2 + 2 = 7y$

8. $3n^2 - 5n + 1 = 0$ 9. $4p^2 - 12p - 9 = 0$

10. $8r^2 - 10r - 3 = 0$ 11. $9p^2 + 6p = -1$

12. $\dfrac{m^2}{2} + \dfrac{1}{3} = \dfrac{2}{3} m$ 13. $y^2 - \dfrac{5}{3}y + \dfrac{1}{3} = 0$

[9.4]   *Draw a graph of the following. Give the vertex of each.*

14. $y = x^2 - 4$ 15. $y = (x + 1)^2 - 5$

Prime Factors of the numbers 2 through 100

$2 = 2$	$26 = 2 \cdot 13$	$51 = 3 \cdot 17$	$76 = 2^2 \cdot 19$
$3 = 3$	$27 = 3^3$	$52 = 2^2 \cdot 13$	$77 = 7 \cdot 11$
$4 = 2^2$	$28 = 2^2 \cdot 7$	$53 = 53$	$78 = 2 \cdot 3 \cdot 13$
$5 = 5$	$29 = 29$	$54 = 2 \cdot 3^3$	$79 = 79$
$6 = 2 \cdot 3$	$30 = 2 \cdot 3 \cdot 5$	$55 = 5 \cdot 11$	$80 = 2^4 \cdot 5$
$7 = 7$	$31 = 31$	$56 = 2^3 \cdot 7$	$81 = 3^4$
$8 = 2^3$	$32 = 2^5$	$57 = 3 \cdot 19$	$82 = 2 \cdot 41$
$9 = 3^2$	$33 = 3 \cdot 11$	$58 = 2 \cdot 29$	$83 = 83$
$10 = 2 \cdot 5$	$34 = 2 \cdot 17$	$59 = 59$	$84 = 2^2 \cdot 3 \cdot 7$
$11 = 11$	$35 = 5 \cdot 7$	$60 = 2^2 \cdot 3 \cdot 5$	$85 = 5 \cdot 17$
$12 = 2^2 \cdot 3$	$36 = 2^2 \cdot 3^2$	$61 = 61$	$86 = 2 \cdot 43$
$13 = 13$	$37 = 37$	$62 = 2 \cdot 31$	$87 = 3 \cdot 29$
$14 = 2 \cdot 7$	$38 = 2 \cdot 19$	$63 = 3^2 \cdot 7$	$88 = 2^3 \cdot 11$
$15 = 3 \cdot 5$	$39 = 3 \cdot 13$	$64 = 2^6$	$89 = 89$
$16 = 2^4$	$40 = 2^3 \cdot 5$	$65 = 5 \cdot 13$	$90 = 2 \cdot 3^2 \cdot 5$
$17 = 17$	$41 = 41$	$66 = 2 \cdot 3 \cdot 11$	$91 = 7 \cdot 13$
$18 = 2 \cdot 3^2$	$42 = 2 \cdot 3 \cdot 7$	$67 = 67$	$92 = 2^2 \cdot 23$
$19 = 19$	$43 = 43$	$68 = 2^2 \cdot 17$	$93 = 3 \cdot 31$
$20 = 2^2 \cdot 5$	$44 = 2^2 \cdot 11$	$69 = 3 \cdot 23$	$94 = 2 \cdot 47$
$21 = 3 \cdot 7$	$45 = 3^2 \cdot 5$	$70 = 2 \cdot 5 \cdot 7$	$95 = 5 \cdot 19$
$22 = 2 \cdot 11$	$46 = 2 \cdot 23$	$71 = 71$	$96 = 2^5 \cdot 3$
$23 = 23$	$47 = 47$	$72 = 2^3 \cdot 3^2$	$97 = 97$
$24 = 2^3 \cdot 3$	$48 = 2^4 \cdot 3$	$73 = 73$	$98 = 2 \cdot 7^2$
$25 = 5^2$	$49 = 7^2$	$74 = 2 \cdot 37$	$99 = 3^2 \cdot 11$
	$50 = 2 \cdot 5^2$	$75 = 3 \cdot 5^2$	$100 = 2^2 \cdot 5^2$

Squares and Square Roots

n	n^2	$\sqrt{n}$	$\sqrt{10n}$	n	n^2	$\sqrt{n}$	$\sqrt{10n}$
1	1	1.000	3.162	51	2601	7.141	22.583
2	4	1.414	4.472	52	2704	7.211	22.804
3	9	1.732	5.477	53	2809	7.280	23.022
4	16	2.000	6.325	54	2916	7.348	23.238
5	25	2.236	7.071	55	3025	7.416	23.452
6	36	2.449	7.746	56	3136	7.483	23.664
7	49	2.646	8.367	57	3249	7.550	23.875
8	64	2.828	8.944	58	3364	7.616	24.083
9	81	3.000	9.487	59	3481	7.681	24.290
10	100	3.162	10.000	60	3600	7.746	24.495
11	121	3.317	10.488	61	3721	7.810	24.698
12	144	3.464	10.954	62	3844	7.874	24.900
13	169	3.606	11.402	63	3969	7.937	25.100
14	196	3.742	11.832	64	4096	8.000	25.298
15	225	3.873	12.247	65	4225	8.062	25.495
16	256	4.000	12.649	66	4356	8.124	25.690
17	289	4.123	13.038	67	4489	8.185	25.884
18	324	4.243	13.416	68	4624	8.246	26.077
19	361	4.359	13.784	69	4761	8.307	26.268
20	400	4.472	14.142	70	4900	8.367	26.458
21	441	4.583	14.491	71	5041	8.426	26.646
22	484	4.690	14.832	72	5184	8.485	26.833
23	529	4.796	15.166	73	5329	8.544	27.019
24	576	4,899	15.492	74	5476	8.602	27.203
25	625	5.000	15.811	75	5625	8.660	27.386
26	676	5.099	16.125	76	5776	8.718	27.568
27	729	5.196	16.432	77	5929	8.775	27.749
28	784	5.292	16.733	78	6084	8.832	27.928
29	841	5.385	17.029	79	6241	8.888	28.107
30	900	5.477	17.321	80	6400	8.944	28.284
31	961	5.568	17.607	81	6561	9.000	28.460
32	1024	5.657	17.889	82	6724	9.055	28.636
33	1089	5.745	18.166	83	6889	9.110	28.810
34	1156	5.831	18.439	84	7056	9.165	28.983
35	1225	5.916	18.708	85	7225	9.220	29.155
36	1296	6.000	18.974	86	7396	9.274	29.326
37	1369	6.083	19.235	87	7569	9.327	29.496
38	1444	6.164	19.494	88	7744	9.381	29.665
39	1521	6.245	19.748	89	7921	9.434	29.833
40	1600	6.325	20.000	90	8100	9.487	30.000
41	1681	6.403	20.248	91	8281	9.539	30.166
42	1764	6.481	20.494	92	8464	9.592	30.332
43	1849	6.557	20.736	93	8649	9.644	30.496
44	1936	6.633	20.976	94	8836	9.695	30.659
45	2025	6.708	21.213	95	9025	9.747	30.822
46	2116	6.782	21.448	96	9216	9.798	30.984
47	2209	6.856	21.679	97	9409	9.849	31.145
48	2304	6.928	21.909	98	9604	9.899	31.305
49	2401	7.000	22.136	99	9801	9.950	31.464
50	2500	7.071	22.361	100	10000	10.000	31.623

Appendices

Appendix A Fractions

- **Reduce fractions to lowest terms.**
- **Multiply two fractions.**
- **Divide two fractions.**
- **Write a fraction as an equal fraction having a given denominator.**
- **Add fractions.**
- **Subtract fractions.**

In everyday life, the numbers we most often see are the whole numbers 0, 1, 2, 3, 4, 5, and so on, and the **fractions,** $\frac{1}{2}, \frac{2}{3}, \frac{11}{12}, \frac{15}{17}, \frac{9}{2}$, and so on. In a fraction, the number on the top is the **numerator** and the number on the bottom is the **denominator.**

A fraction is a **proper fraction** if the numerator is smaller than the denominator; otherwise it is an **improper fraction.** For example,

$$\frac{3}{4}, \quad \frac{7}{8}, \quad \frac{9}{10}, \quad \frac{125}{126} \text{ are proper fractions, and}$$

$$\frac{5}{4}, \quad \frac{17}{15}, \quad \frac{28}{3} \text{ are improper fractions.}$$

An improper fraction can also be expressed as a **mixed number,** which is a combination of a whole number and a proper fraction. For instance, $\frac{4}{3}$, an improper fraction, can be written as $1\frac{1}{3}$, since $1\frac{1}{3}$ equals $\frac{3}{3} + \frac{1}{3} = \frac{4}{3}$.

Much work with fractions can be simplified by **prime factorization.** A **prime number** is a whole number greater than 1 that is divisible only by itself and 1. The first few primes are

$$2, 3, 5, 7, 11, 13, 17, 19, 23,$$

and so on. To find the prime factorization of a number, write the number as a product of primes, as shown in the next example.

EXAMPLE 1   Find the prime factorization of each of the following.

(a) 20

Divide by the first prime number, 2.

$$20 = 2 \cdot 10$$

Divide 10 by 2:

$$20 = 2 \cdot 2 \cdot 5$$

All these numbers are prime, so that the prime factorization of 20 is $2 \cdot 2 \cdot 5$. This result is often written in shortcut form with **exponents:** $20 = 2^2 \cdot 5$

(b) $72 = 2 \cdot 36$ Divide by 2

$ = 2 \cdot 2 \cdot 18$

$ = 2 \cdot 2 \cdot 2 \cdot 9$

$ = 2 \cdot 2 \cdot 2 \cdot 3 \cdot 3$ Divide by 3

$ = 2^3 \cdot 3^2$ Write with exponents

(c) $280 = 2 \cdot 140$

$ = 2 \cdot 2 \cdot 70$

$ = 2 \cdot 2 \cdot 2 \cdot 35$

$ = 2 \cdot 2 \cdot 2 \cdot 5 \cdot 7$

$ = 2^3 \cdot 5 \cdot 7$

A table giving the prime factorizations of all whole numbers from 2 through 100 is included on page 318.

A fraction is reduced to **lowest terms** when both numerator and denominator cannot be divided by a number other than 1. A number can be reduced to lowest terms by using prime factorization.

EXAMPLE 2   Reduce to lowest terms.

(a) $\dfrac{12}{15}$

Find the prime factorization of both 12 and 15.

$$\frac{12}{15} = \frac{2^2 \cdot 3}{3 \cdot 5}$$

$$= \frac{2 \cdot 2 \cdot 3}{3 \cdot 5}$$

Divide numerator and denominator by the numbers that appear in both; 3 here. This gives

$$\frac{12}{15} = \frac{2 \cdot 2}{5}$$

$$= \frac{4}{5}$$

(b) $\dfrac{24}{72} = \dfrac{2^3 \cdot 3}{2^3 \cdot 3^2}$

$$= \frac{2 \cdot 2 \cdot 2 \cdot 3}{2 \cdot 2 \cdot 2 \cdot 3 \cdot 3}$$

$$= \frac{1}{3}$$

In this section, we study the basic operations on fractions, namely addition, subtraction, multiplication, and division. The easiest operation for fractions is multiplication, so we begin with it.

To *multiply* two fractions, first multiply their numerators and then multiply their denominators. In symbols, if $\dfrac{a}{b}$ and $\dfrac{c}{d}$ are fractions, then

$$\frac{a}{b} \cdot \frac{c}{d} = \frac{a \cdot c}{b \cdot d}.$$

The dot, $\cdot$, indicates multiplication. For example,

$$3 \cdot 5 = 15 \qquad \text{and} \qquad 7 \cdot 8 = 56.$$

When two numbers are multiplied, the answer is called the **product** of the two numbers.

EXAMPLE 3   Find the product of $\dfrac{3}{8}$ and $\dfrac{4}{9}$ and express the answer in lowest terms.

First, multiply $\dfrac{3}{8}$ and $\dfrac{4}{9}$.

$$\frac{3}{8} \cdot \frac{4}{9} = \frac{3 \cdot 4}{8 \cdot 9}$$

$$= \frac{12}{72}$$

Reduce the answer to lowest terms.

$$\frac{12}{72} = \frac{2 \cdot 2 \cdot 3}{2 \cdot 2 \cdot 2 \cdot 3 \cdot 3}$$

$$= \frac{1}{6}$$

To *divide* two fractions, we invert the second fraction and replace the division sign with a multiplication sign, as shown in the following definition.

$$\frac{a}{b} \div \frac{c}{d} = \frac{a}{b} \cdot \frac{d}{c}$$

The reason this works is explained in Chapter 5. The answer to a division problem is called a **quotient.** For example, the quotient of 20 and 10 is 2, since $20 \div 10 = 2$.

EXAMPLE 4   Find the following quotients and reduce to lowest terms.

(a) $\dfrac{3}{4} \div \dfrac{8}{5} = \dfrac{3}{4} \cdot \dfrac{5}{8}$

$$= \frac{15}{32}$$

(b) $\dfrac{3}{4} \div \dfrac{5}{8} = \dfrac{3}{4} \cdot \dfrac{8}{5}$

$$= \frac{24}{20}$$

$$= \frac{6}{5}$$

To add or subtract fractions, we must first make sure that the fractions all have the same denominators. This also can be done with prime factorizations, as the next example shows.

EXAMPLE 5   Find the least common denominators for each of the following fractions.

(a) $\dfrac{3}{8}, \dfrac{5}{12}$

The **least common denominator** is the smallest number that both denominators divide into. To find it, first write the prime factorization of each denominator.

$$8 = 2^3$$

$$12 = 2^2 \cdot 3$$

The least common denominator is found by using each prime from the factorization the **most** number of times it appears. Since 2 appears 3 times in the prime factorization of 8, and 3 appears at most 1 time,

$$\text{least common denominator} = 2^3 \cdot 3 = 24$$

(b) $\dfrac{1}{12}, \dfrac{3}{10}, \dfrac{5}{18}$

Write the prime factorizations.

$12 = 2^2 \cdot 3$ ←   2 appears twice

$10 = 2 \cdot 5$ ←   5 appears once   list the most number

$18 = 2 \cdot 3^2$ ←   3 appears twice   of times each prime appears

The least common denominator is $2^2 \cdot 3^2 \cdot 5 = 180$.

Once we find the least common denominator, we must rewrite each fraction in the problem so that it has this common denominator. For example, suppose we need to rewrite $\dfrac{3}{4}$ as a fraction with denominator 32.

$$\frac{3}{4} = \frac{?}{32}$$

In this case, we need to ask ourselves what number times 4 will equal 32? Since $4 \cdot 8 = 32$, 8 is the number we use to rewrite $\dfrac{3}{4}$. We want the value of the original fraction, $\dfrac{3}{4}$, to stay the same, so we must multiply both the numerator and the denominator by the *same* number, 8.

$$\frac{3}{4} = \frac{3 \cdot 8}{4 \cdot 8}$$

$$= \frac{24}{32}$$

EXAMPLE 6   Write each of the following as fractions having the indicated denominators.

(a) $\dfrac{5}{8} = \dfrac{?}{72}$

Since 8 divided into 72 is 9, we multiply the numerator and denominator by 9.

$$\frac{5}{8} = \frac{5 \cdot 9}{8 \cdot 9}$$

$$= \frac{45}{72}$$

(b) $\dfrac{2}{3} = \dfrac{?}{18}$

Since 3 divided into 18 is 6, we can multiply the numerator and denominator by 6 to get a common denominator.

$$\frac{2}{3} = \frac{2 \cdot 6}{3 \cdot 6}$$

$$= \frac{12}{18}$$

The **sum** of two fractions having the same denominator is found by adding the numerators. If $\dfrac{a}{b}$ and $\dfrac{c}{b}$ are fractions, then

$$\frac{a}{b} + \frac{c}{b} = \frac{a + c}{b}.$$

For example,

$$\frac{3}{7} + \frac{2}{7} = \frac{3 + 2}{7} \qquad \text{and} \qquad \frac{2}{10} + \frac{5}{10} = \frac{2 + 5}{10}$$

$$= \frac{5}{7} \qquad\qquad\qquad\qquad = \frac{7}{10}.$$

Usually, the two fractions to be added do not have the same denominators. In this case, work the problem as shown in the next example.

EXAMPLE 7   Add the pairs of fractions.

(a) $\dfrac{1}{2} + \dfrac{1}{3}$

We cannot add until the fractions have the same denominator. One number that we can use as a common denominator is 6, since both 2 and 3 divide into 6. Write both $\dfrac{1}{2}$ and $\dfrac{1}{3}$ as fractions with denominator 6.

$$\frac{1}{2} = \frac{1 \cdot 3}{2 \cdot 3} \qquad \text{and} \qquad \frac{1}{3} = \frac{1 \cdot 2}{3 \cdot 2}$$

$$= \frac{3}{6} \qquad\qquad\qquad\qquad = \frac{2}{6}$$

Now we can add.

$$\frac{1}{2} + \frac{1}{3} = \frac{3}{6} + \frac{2}{6}$$

$$= \frac{3 + 2}{6}$$

$$= \frac{5}{6}$$

(b) $\dfrac{3}{10} + \dfrac{5}{12}$

A common denominator here is 60, since both 10 and 12 divide into 60.

$$\dfrac{3}{10} = \dfrac{3 \cdot 6}{10 \cdot 6} \qquad \text{and} \qquad \dfrac{5}{12} = \dfrac{5 \cdot 5}{12 \cdot 5}$$

$$= \dfrac{18}{60} \qquad\qquad\qquad = \dfrac{25}{60}$$

Finally,

$$\dfrac{3}{10} + \dfrac{5}{12} = \dfrac{18}{60} + \dfrac{25}{60}$$

$$= \dfrac{18 + 25}{60}$$

$$= \dfrac{43}{60}.$$

(c) $3\dfrac{1}{2} + 2\dfrac{3}{4}$

Change both mixed numbers to improper fractions as follows.

$$3\dfrac{1}{2} = 3 + \dfrac{1}{2} \qquad \text{and} \qquad 2\dfrac{3}{4} = 2 + \dfrac{3}{4}$$

$$= \dfrac{6}{2} + \dfrac{1}{2} \qquad\qquad\qquad = \dfrac{8}{4} + \dfrac{3}{4}$$

$$= \dfrac{7}{2} \qquad\qquad\qquad\qquad = \dfrac{11}{4}$$

Then $3\dfrac{1}{2} + 2\dfrac{3}{4} = \dfrac{7}{2} + \dfrac{11}{4}$

$$= \dfrac{14}{4} + \dfrac{11}{4}$$

$$= \dfrac{25}{4} \text{ or } 6\dfrac{1}{4}$$

Subtraction of fractions is very similar to addition. Just subtract the numerators instead of adding them, according to the following definition.

$$\dfrac{a}{b} - \dfrac{c}{b} = \dfrac{a - c}{b}.$$

EXAMPLE 8 Subtract the following pairs of fractions.

(a) $\dfrac{5}{8} - \dfrac{3}{8} = \dfrac{5 - 3}{8}$

$$= \dfrac{2}{8}$$

$$= \frac{1}{4} \qquad \text{Reduced}$$

(b) $\frac{3}{4} - \frac{1}{3}$

A common denominator is 12.

$$\frac{3}{4} - \frac{1}{3} = \frac{9}{12} - \frac{4}{12}$$

$$= \frac{9 - 4}{12}$$

$$= \frac{5}{12}$$

(c) $\frac{7}{9} - \frac{1}{6} = \frac{14}{18} - \frac{3}{18}$

$$= \frac{14 - 3}{18}$$

$$= \frac{11}{18}$$

In this case, 18 is a common denominator of both 9 and 6.

(d) $2\frac{1}{2} - 1\frac{3}{4}$

First, change the mixed numbers $2\frac{1}{2}$ and $1\frac{3}{4}$ into improper fractions.

$$2\frac{1}{2} = 2 + \frac{1}{2} \quad \text{and} \quad 1\frac{3}{4} = 1 + \frac{3}{4}$$

$$= \frac{4}{2} + \frac{1}{2} \qquad\qquad = \frac{4}{4} + \frac{3}{4}$$

$$= \frac{5}{2} \qquad\qquad\qquad = \frac{7}{4}$$

Then

$$2\frac{1}{2} - 1\frac{3}{4} = \frac{5}{2} - \frac{7}{4}.$$

Multiply $\frac{5}{2}$ by $\frac{2}{2}$ to get a common denominator of 4.

$$\frac{5}{2} \cdot \frac{2}{2} = \frac{10}{4}$$

Finally,

$$\frac{10}{4} - \frac{7}{4} = \frac{3}{4}.$$

EXERCISES APPENDIX A

Reduce fractions to lowest terms. See Example 2.

1. $\dfrac{7}{14}$ 2. $\dfrac{3}{9}$ 3. $\dfrac{10}{12}$ 4. $\dfrac{8}{10}$

5. $\dfrac{16}{18}$ 6. $\dfrac{14}{20}$ 7. $\dfrac{50}{75}$ 8. $\dfrac{32}{48}$

9. $\dfrac{72}{108}$ 10. $\dfrac{96}{120}$

Find the products or quotients. Reduce answers to lowest terms. See Examples 3 and 4.

11. $\dfrac{3}{4} \cdot \dfrac{9}{5}$ 12. $\dfrac{3}{8} \cdot \dfrac{2}{7}$

13. $\dfrac{1}{10} \cdot \dfrac{6}{5}$ 14. $2 \cdot \dfrac{1}{3}$

15. $\dfrac{9}{4} \cdot \dfrac{8}{15}$ 16. $\dfrac{3}{5} \cdot \dfrac{5}{3}$

17. $\dfrac{3}{8} \div \dfrac{5}{4}$ 18. $\dfrac{9}{16} \div \dfrac{3}{8}$

19. $\dfrac{5}{12} \div \dfrac{15}{4}$ 20. $\dfrac{15}{16} \div \dfrac{30}{8}$

21. $\dfrac{15}{32} \cdot \dfrac{8}{25}$ 22. $\dfrac{24}{25} \cdot \dfrac{50}{3}$

23. $\dfrac{2}{3} \cdot \dfrac{5}{8}$ 24. $\dfrac{2}{4} \cdot \dfrac{3}{9}$

25. $\dfrac{13}{2} \cdot \dfrac{2}{3}$ 26. $\dfrac{9}{4} \cdot \dfrac{8}{7}$

27. $\dfrac{28}{3} \cdot \dfrac{6}{2}$ 28. $\dfrac{121}{9} \cdot \dfrac{18}{11}$

Add or subtract. Reduce answers to lowest terms. See Examples 7 and 8.

29. $\dfrac{1}{12} + \dfrac{3}{12}$ 30. $\dfrac{2}{3} + \dfrac{2}{3}$

31. $\dfrac{1}{10} + \dfrac{6}{10}$ 32. $\dfrac{3}{4} + \dfrac{8}{4}$

33. $\dfrac{4}{9} + \dfrac{2}{3}$ 34. $\dfrac{3}{5} + \dfrac{2}{15}$

35. $\dfrac{8}{11} + \dfrac{3}{22}$ 36. $\dfrac{9}{10} - \dfrac{3}{5}$

37. $\dfrac{2}{3} - \dfrac{3}{5}$ 38. $\dfrac{8}{12} - \dfrac{5}{9}$

39. $\dfrac{5}{6} - \dfrac{3}{10}$ 40. $\dfrac{11}{4} - \dfrac{11}{8}$

41. $3\frac{1}{4} + 6\frac{1}{8}$

42. $5\frac{2}{3} + \frac{1}{4}$

43. $4\frac{1}{2} + \frac{2}{3}$

44. $7\frac{5}{8} + 3\frac{3}{4}$

45. $6\frac{2}{3} - 5\frac{1}{4}$

46. $8\frac{8}{9} - 7\frac{4}{5}$

47. $\frac{2}{5} + \frac{1}{3} + \frac{9}{10}$

48. $\frac{3}{8} + \frac{5}{6} + \frac{2}{3}$

49. $\frac{5}{7} + \frac{1}{4} - \frac{1}{2}$

50. $\frac{2}{3} + \frac{1}{6} - \frac{1}{2}$

Work the following word problems.

51. John Rizzo paid $\frac{1}{8}$ of a debt in January, $\frac{1}{3}$ in February, and $\frac{1}{4}$ in March. What portion of the debt was paid in these three months?

52. A rectangle is $\frac{5}{16}$ yard on each of two sides, and $\frac{7}{12}$ yard on each of the other two sides. Find the total distance around the rectangle.

53. The Eastside Wholesale Market sold $3\frac{1}{4}$ tons of broccoli last month, $2\frac{3}{8}$ tons of spinach, $7\frac{1}{2}$ tons of corn, and $1\frac{5}{16}$ tons of turnips. Find the total number of tons of vegetables sold by the firm during the month.

54. Sharkey's Casino decided to expand by buying a piece of property next to the casino. The property has an irregular shape, with five sides. The lengths of the five sides are $146\frac{1}{2}$ feet, $98\frac{3}{4}$ feet, 196 feet, $76\frac{5}{8}$ feet, and $100\frac{7}{8}$ feet. Find the total distance around the piece of property.

55. Joann Kaufmann worked 40 hours during a certain week. She worked $8\frac{1}{4}$ hours on Monday, $6\frac{3}{8}$ hours on Tuesday, $7\frac{2}{3}$ hours on Wednesday, and $8\frac{3}{4}$ hours on Thursday. How many hours did she work on Friday?

56. A concrete truck is loaded with $9\frac{7}{8}$ cubic yards of concrete. The driver gives out $1\frac{1}{2}$ cubic yards at the first stop and $2\frac{3}{4}$ cubic yards at the second stop. At a third stop, the customer needs $3\frac{5}{12}$ cubic yards. How much concrete is there left in the truck?

57. Rosario wants to make 16 dresses to sell at the company bazaar. Each dress needs $2\frac{1}{4}$ yards of material. How many yards should be bought?

58. Lindsay allows $1\frac{3}{5}$ bottles of beverage for each guest at a party. If he expects 35 guests, how many bottles of beverage will he need?

Appendix B The Metric System

- **Convert from one metric unit of measure to another.**
- **Convert measurements from English to metric and from metric to English.**

In the United States today, length is measured in inches, feet, or miles. Weight is measured in ounces (there are two kinds of ounces), pounds, or tons (there are long tons and short tons). Volume is measured in pints, quarts, or gallons. These weights and measures make up the **English system** of measures. The United States will gradually switch to the **metric system,** which is used in almost every country in the world. Many industries are now working on the switch to the metric system, which will be in effect in the U.S. by the mid-1980's. Many automobiles are now made to metric specifications.

The metric system was developed in France in 1789. The name comes from the basic unit of length, the **meter** (abbreviated m), which is a little longer than a yard.

The meter can be subdivided into smaller parts for measuring shorter distances. The most common subdivisions are the **millimeter,** or 1/1000 meter, and the **centimeter,** 1/100 meter. Millimeters are abbreviated mm and centimeters are abbreviated cm.

A dime is about 2 mm thick. Film for instamatic cameras is 35 mm wide. Many common parts of the body can be measured with centimeters and millimeters. A man is perhaps 150 cm tall, and a woman's waist might be 66 cm around. Some manufacturers of clothing use metric sizes—a size 40 suit becomes a size 102 suit in metric.

A major advantage of the metric system of measurement is the ease in converting from one unit of measure to another. This is illustrated in Examples 1–4.

EXAMPLE 1 Convert as indicated.

(a) 28 cm to mm

One centimeter is made up of 10 mm. Thus, 28 cm is

$$28 \times 10 = 280 \text{ mm}$$

(b) 6 m to cm

$$6 \text{ m} = 6 \cdot 100 \text{ cm}$$
$$= 600 \text{ cm}$$

(c) 3.823 m to mm

$$3.823 \text{ m} = 3.823(1000 \text{ mm})$$
$$= 3823 \text{ mm}$$

EXAMPLE 2   Convert as indicated.

(a) 250 mm to m

One meter is 1000 mm.

$$250 \text{ mm} = \frac{250}{1000} \text{ m}$$
$$= .250 \text{ m}$$

(b) 375 mm to cm

$$375 \text{ mm} = \frac{375}{10} \text{ cm}$$
$$= 37.5 \text{ cm}$$

(c) 8.42 cm to m

$$8.42 \text{ cm} = \frac{8.42}{100} \text{ m}$$
$$= .0842 \text{ m}$$

Longer distances are measured in **kilometers** (km), or one thousand meters. A kilometer is about 5/8 of a mile. The table here shows distances in kilometers between various cities.

Some Highway Distances in Kilometers

	Seattle	Los Angeles	Denver	Houston	St. Louis	Chicago	Cleveland	Atlanta	Miami	Washington	New York	Boston
Seattle		1842	2167	3704	3393	3319	3868	4434	5504	4422	4673	4885
Los Angeles	1842		1825	2499	2973	3371	3894	3535	4364	4254	4690	4911
Denver	2167	1825		1651	1377	1635	2183	2254	3290	2729	4580	3200
Houston	3704	2499	1651		1278	1746	2066	1310	1957	2269	2632	3083
St. Louis	3393	2973	1377	1278		463	879	898	1968	1289	1554	1895
Chicago	3319	3371	1635	1746	463		552	1175	2188	1146	1352	1569
Cleveland	3868	3894	2183	2066	879	552		1104	2097	565	816	1017
Atlanta	4434	3535	2254	1310	898	1175	1104		1070	1014	1376	1718
Miami	5504	4364	3290	1957	1968	2188	2097	1070		1778	2140	2481
Washington	4422	4254	2729	2269	1289	1146	565	1014	1778		368	703
New York	4673	4690	4580	2632	1554	1352	816	1376	2140	368		348
Boston	4885	4911	3200	3083	1895	1569	1017	1718	2481	703	348	

EXAMPLE 3 Convert as indicated.

(a) 9.7 km to m

Since 1000 m = 1 km, we have

$$9.7 \text{ km} = 9.7(1000)$$
$$= 9700 \text{ m}$$

(b) 8680 m to km

$$8680 \text{ m} = \frac{8680}{1000} \text{ km}$$
$$= 8.680 \text{ km}$$

(c) 25,600 m to km

$$25{,}600 \text{ m} = 25.6 \text{ km}$$

Weights in the metric system are based on the **gram** (g). A nickel weighs about 5g, for example. Since a gram is such a small weight, milligrams (1/1000 g) and centigrams (1/100 g) are mainly used to measure very small weights in science. A **kilogram,** or 1000 grams, is about 2.2 pounds. Kilograms (abbreviated kg) are sometimes called *kilos*.

EXAMPLE 4 Convert as indicated.

(a) 2500 g to kg
1000 g = 1 kg. Thus,

$$2500 \text{ g} = \frac{2500}{1000} \text{ kg}$$
$$= 2.5 \text{ kg}$$

(b) .38 kg to g

$$.38 \text{ kg} = .38 \cdot 1000 \text{g}$$
$$= 380 \text{ g}$$

(c) 275 mg to g

$$275 \text{ mg} = \frac{275}{1000} \text{ g}$$
$$= .275 \text{ g}$$

(d) 896 cg to g

$$896 \text{ cg} = \frac{896}{100} \text{ g}$$
$$= 8.96 \text{ g}$$

Volume is measured in **liters** (l). A liter is about a quart. Milliliters (1/1000 liter), centiliters (1/100 liter), and kiloliters (1000 liters) are used mainly in science.

In summary, the metric system uses the following four common prefixes:

Prefix	Definition	Example
milli-	1/1000	1 millimeter = 1/1000 meter
centi-	1/100	1 centiliter = 1/100 liter
deci-	1/10	1 decigram = 1/10 gram
kilo-	1000	1 kilogram = 1000 grams

Eventually, people will think in the metric system as easily as they now think in the English system. To help you "think metric," you should get in the habit of estimating in the metric system. As an aid, use the *approximate* conversion table shown below.

METRIC TO ENGLISH   **ENGLISH TO METRIC**

From	to	Multiply by	From	to	Multiply by
meters	yards	1.094	yards	meters	.9144
meters	feet	3.281	feet	meters	.3048
meters	inches	39.37	inches	meters	.0254
kilometers	miles	.6214	miles	kilometers	1.6093
grams	pounds	.00220	pounds	grams	454
kilograms	pounds	2.20	pounds	kilograms	.454
liters	quarts	1.057	quarts	liters	.946
liters	gallons	.264	gallons	liters	3.785

EXAMPLE 5   Convert as indicated.

(a) 2 yards to meters

Look in the table, for "From yards to meters." You should find the number .9144. Multiply

$$2 \text{ yards} = (2).9144 \text{ meters}$$
$$= 1.8288 \text{ m}$$

(b) 120 miles to km

Look at "From miles to kilometers," finding 1.6093.

$$120 \text{ miles} = 120 \cdot 1.6093 \text{ km}$$
$$= 193.116 \text{ km}$$

(c) 25 gallons to l

$$25 \text{ gallons} = 25 \cdot 3.785 \text{ l}$$
$$= 94.625 \text{ l}$$

(d) 58 pounds to kilograms

$$58 \text{ pounds} = (58).454 \text{ kg}$$
$$= 26.332 \text{ kg}$$

EXAMPLE 6 Convert as indicated.

(a) 72 meters to yards

Look for "From meters to yards" in the table above.

$$72 \text{ m} = (72)1.094 \text{ yards}$$
$$= 78.768 \text{ yards}$$

(b) 400 km to miles

$$400 \text{ km} = 400 \cdot .6214 \text{ miles}$$
$$= 248.56 \text{ miles}$$

(c) 2000 g to pounds

$$2000 \text{ g} = (2000).00220 \text{ pounds}$$
$$= 4.4 \text{ pounds}$$

(d) 850 l to quarts

$$850 \text{ l} = (850)1.057 \text{ quarts}$$
$$= 898.45 \text{ quarts}$$

EXERCISES APPENDIX B *Make the indicated conversions within the metric system. See Examples 1–4.*

1. 20 m to mm
2. 7.6 m to cm
3. 7 cm to mm
4. 9.63 cm to mm
5. 80 mm to cm
6. 500 mm to cm
7. 320 mm to m
8. 9760 cm to m
9. 5200 m to km
10. 15,000 m to km
11. 7.8 km to m
12. 49.8 km to m
13. 6 kg to g
14. 15.9 kg to g
15. 1.92 kg to g
16. 3.24 kg to g
17. 8200 g to kg
18. 16,200 g to kg
19. 69.4 mg to cg
20. 1749 cg to g
21. 8.1 g to cg
22. .042 g to mg

23. 9 l to ml

24. 2.98 l to ml

25. 57,000 ml to l

26. 800 ml to l

27. 29.6 ml to cl

28. 34.1 ml to cl

Use the table in the text to make each conversion. See Examples 5 and 6. Round to the nearest tenth.

29. 12 yards to m

30. 32.1 yards to m

31. 6.7 feet to m

32. 46 feet to m

32. 25 inches to m

34. 77 inches to m

35. 122 miles to km

36. 400 miles to km

37. 8.4 pounds to g

38. 1.3 pounds to g

39. 110 pounds to kg

40. 680 pounds to kg

41. 8 quarts to l

42. 13 quarts to l

43. 76 gallons to l

44. 12 gallons to l

45. 36 m to yards

46. 80 m to yards

47. 40 m to feet

48. 11 m to feet

49. 600 km to miles

50. 850 km to miles

51. 680 g to pounds

52. 12,700 g to pounds

53. 4.9 kg to pounds

54. 10.1 kg to pounds

55. 8 l to quarts

56. 14.1 l to quarts

57. 76.8 l to gallons

58. 130 l to gallons

Estimate each of the following.

59. Find your height in cm.

60. Find your height in mm.

61. Find the length of your longest finger in cm.

62. What are the dimensions of the cover of this book in mm?

63. Give your jeans size (waist and length) in cm.

64. What is your weight in kg?

65. What is the distance in km between the two largest cities in your state?

66. How many liters are in a six-pack of 12-ounce cans of soda pop?

Appendix C Further Methods of Factoring

- **Factor the difference of two cubes.**
- **Factor the sum of two cubes.**
- **Factor by grouping.**

In Chapter 4 we factored the difference of two squares, $x^2 - y^2 = (x + y)(x - y)$; here we factor the **difference of two cubes:**

$$x^3 - y^3 = (x - y)(x^2 + xy + y^2).$$

EXAMPLE 1   (a) $m^3 - 125 = m^3 - 5^3$

$$= (m - 5)(m^2 + 5m + 5^2)$$
$$- (m - 5)(m^2 + 5m + 25)$$

(b) $8p^3 - 27 = (2p)^3 - 3^3$

$$= (2p - 3)[(2p)^2 + 3(2p) + 3^2]$$
$$= (2p - 3)(4p^2 + 6p + 9)$$

(c) $125t^3 - 216s^6 = (5t)^3 - (6s^2)^3$

$$= (5t - 6s^2)[(5t)^2 + (5t)(6s^2) + (6s^2)^2]$$
$$= (5t - 6s^2)(25t^2 + 30ts^2 + 36s^4)$$

A common error when factoring the difference of two cubes is to try to factor $x^2 + xy + y^2$. It is easy to confuse this factor with a perfect square trinomial, $x^2 + 2xy + y^2$. Because of the lack of a 2 in $x^2 + xy + y^2$, it is very unusual to be able to factor $x^2 + xy + y^2$ further.

A *sum* of two squares, such as $m^2 + 25$, cannot be factored, but we can factor the **sum of two cubes:**

$$x^3 + y^3 = (x + y)(x^2 - xy + y^2).$$

EXAMPLE 2   (a) $k^3 + 27 = k^3 + 3^3$

$$= (k + 3)(k^2 - 3k + 3^2)$$
$$= (k + 3)(k^2 - 3k + 9)$$

(b) $8m^3 + 125 = (2m)^3 + 5^3$

$$= (2m + 5)[(2m)^2 - (2m)(5) + 5^2]$$
$$= (2m + 5)(4m^2 - 10m + 25)$$

(c) $1000a^6 + 27b^3 = (10a^2)^3 + (3b)^3$

$$= (10a^2 + 3b)[(10a^2)^2 - (10a^2)(3b) + (3b)^2]$$
$$= (10a^2 + 3b)(100a^4 - 30a^2b + 9b^2)$$

Let us summarize the methods for factoring the sum and difference of two cubes:

$$x^3 - y^3 = (x - y)(x^2 + xy + y^2) \quad \text{difference of two cubes}$$
$$x^3 + y^3 = (x + y)(x^2 - xy + y^2) \quad \text{sum of two cubes}$$

Some polynomials that cannot be factored by any other method can be **factored by grouping.** For example, in the polynomial

$$kx - ky + mx - my,$$

$kx - ky$ may be factored as $k(x - y)$, while $mx - my$ can be written as $m(x - y)$. Thus,

$$kx - ky + mx - my = k(x - y) + m(x - y).$$

Both $k(x - y)$ and $m(x - y)$ have $(x - y)$ as a common factor, so

$$kx - ky + mx - my = (x - y)(k + m).$$

To check that $kx - ky + mx - my$ can be factored as $(x - y)(k + m)$, multiply $x - y$ and $k + m$.

EXAMPLE 3   (a) $9b - 9c + rb - rc = 9(b - c) + r(b - c)$
$$= (b - c)(9 + r)$$

(b) $mp + 2p - 3m - 6 = p(m + 2) - 3(m + 2)$
$$= (m + 2)(p - 3)$$

(c) $a^2 - b^2 - 6a - 6b = (a + b)(a - b) - 6(a + b)$
$$= (a + b)(a - b - 6)$$

(d) To factor $3x - 3y - ax + ay$ we could factor $3x - 3y$ as $3(x - y)$, and $-ax + ay$ as $a(-x + y)$. However, $3(x - y)$ and $a(-x + y)$ do not have a common factor. It is better to factor $-ax + ay$ as $-a(x - y)$. This gives

$$3x - 3y - ax + ay = 3(x - y) - a(x - y)$$
$$= (x - y)(3 - a).$$

EXERCISES
APPENDIX C   *Factor each sum or difference of cubes. See Examples 1 and 2.*

1. $y^3 + 1$ 2. $m^3 - 1$

3. $r^3 - t^3$ 4. $a^3 + b^3$

5. $8a^3 + 1$ 6. $8a^3 - 1$

7. $27x^3 - 125$ 8. $64p^3 + 27$

9. $8p^3 + q^3$

10. $125y^3 - 8x^3$

11. $27a^3 - 64b^3$

12. $125t^3 + 8s^3$

13. $64x^3 + 125y^3$

14. $216z^3 - w^3$

15. $125m^3 - 8p^3$

16. $343r^3 + 1000s^3$

17. $1000z^3 + 27x^3$

18. $64y^3 - 1331w^3$

19. $64y^6 + 1$

20. $m^6 - 8$

21. $8k^6 - 27q^3$

22. $125z^3 + 64r^6$

23. $1000a^3 - 343b^9$

24. $27r^9 + 125s^3$

Factor each polynomial by grouping. See Example 3.

25. $ax + 2bx + ay + 2by$

26. $3x + 3y + 7ax + 7ay$

27. $2b + 2c + ab + ac$

28. $3am + 3ap + 2bm + 2bp$

29. $3a^3 + 3ab^2 + 2a^2b + 2b^3$

30. $16m^3 - 4m^2p^2 - 4mp + p^3$

31. $1 - a + ab - b$

32. $2pq^2 - 8q^2 + p - 4$

33. $8 - 6y^3 - 12y + 9y^4$

34. $x^3y^2 + x^3 - 3y^2 - 3$

Answers to Selected Problems

CHAPTER 1

Section 1.1 (page 4)

1. 54   **3.** 912   **5.** 544   **7.** 99   **9.** 126   **11.** 276   **13.** 10   **15.** $\dfrac{2}{21}$ **17.** 6

19. 50   **21.** $<$ and $\leq$ **23.** $\geq, >$ **25.** $\leq, \geq$ **27.** $\geq, >$ **29.** $\geq, >$ **31.** $\leq, <$

33. $7 = 5 + 2$ **35.** $3 < \dfrac{50}{5}$ **37.** $12 \neq 5$ **39.** $0 \geq 0$ **41.** True   **43.** True   **45.** True

47. True   **49.** True   **51.** False   **53.** False   **55.** False   **57.** False   **59.** $14 > 6$
61. $3 \leq 15$ **63.** $8 < 9$ **65.** $6 \geq 0$ **67.** $15 \leq 18$

Section 1.2 (page 8)

1. 36   **3.** 64   **5.** 289   **7.** 125   **9.** 1296   **11.** 32   **13.** 729   **15.** $\dfrac{1}{4}$ **17.** $\dfrac{8}{125}$

19. False   **21.** True   **23.** True   **25.** False   **27.** False   **29.** True   **31.** False
33. True   **35.** True   **37.** False   **39.** False   **41.** False   **43.** True   **45.** True
47. False   **49.** False   **51.** $10 - (7 - 3) = 6$ **53.** no parentheses needed, or $(3 \cdot 5) + 7 = 22$
55. $3 \cdot (5 - 4) = 3$ **57.** $(3 \cdot 5) + (2 \cdot 4) = 23$, or use no parentheses at all   **59.** $(3 \cdot 5 + 2) \cdot 4 = 68$
61. $(3 \cdot 5) - (2 \cdot 4) = 7$, or use no parentheses at all   **63.** $(100 \div 20) \div 5 = 1$, or use no parentheses at all
65. $100 \div (20 \div 5) = 25$ **67.** $(2^2 + 4) \cdot 2 = 16$ **69.** $(3^3 - 2) \cdot 4 = 100$

Section 1.3 (page 12)

1. (a) 12   (b) 24   **3.** (a) 15   (b) 75   **5.** (a) 14   (b) 38   **7.** (a) $\dfrac{4}{3}$ (b) $\dfrac{16}{3}$ **9.** (a) $\dfrac{2}{3}$ (b) $\dfrac{4}{3}$

11. (a) $\dfrac{5}{2}$ (b) $\dfrac{17}{14}$ **13.** (a) 30   (b) 690   **15.** 6   **17.** 43   **19.** 24   **21.** 6   **23.** $\dfrac{19}{6}$

25. 10   **27.** 2   **29.** $\dfrac{5}{6}$ **31.** 20   **33.** 28   **35.** 6   **37.** $8x$ **39.** $2x$ **41.** $x + 6$ or

$6 + x$ **43.** $8 - x$ **45.** $3x + 8$ or $8 + 3x$ **47.** $15 - 2x$ **49.** yes   **51.** no   **53.** yes
55. yes   **57.** no   **59.** yes   **61.** yes   **63.** $x + 8 = 12; 4$ **65.** $x + 2 = 10; 8$ **67.** $2x + 5 = 13; 4$
69. $3x = 2x + 2; 2$ **71.** $\dfrac{20}{5x} = 2; 2$

Section 1.4 (page 18)
1. -8 **3.** 9   **5.** 2   **7.** -15 **9.** -8 **11.** -5 **13.** -12 **15.** -8 **17.** 3
19. $|-3|$ or 3   **21.** $-|-6|$ or -6 **23.** True   **25.** True   **27.** False   **29.** True
31. True   **33.** True   **35.** True   **37.** True   **39.** True   **41.** False   **43.** True

45.
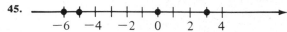

47.

49.
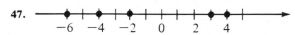

51.

Section 1.5 (page 22)
1. 2   **3.** -2 **5.** -8 **7.** -11 **9.** -12 **11.** 4   **13.** 12   **15.** 5   **17.** 2
19. -9 **21.** 13   **23.** -11 **25.** $\dfrac{1}{2}$ **27.** $-\dfrac{19}{24}$ **29.** $-\dfrac{3}{4}$ **31.** $-.5$ **33.** -7.7
35. -8 **37.** 0   **39.** -20 **41.** True   **43.** False   **45.** False   **47.** True
49. False   **51.** True   **53.** True   **55.** False   **57.** True   **59.** -2 **61.** -3 **63.** -2
65. -2 **67.** 2   **69.** \$9   **71.** -135 feet   **73.** 90   **75.** $13°$

Section 1.6 (page 25)
1. -3 **3.** -4 **5.** -8 **7.** -14 **9.** 9   **11.** 17   **13.** -4 **15.** 4   **17.** 1
19. $\dfrac{3}{4}$ **21.** $-\dfrac{11}{8}$ **23.** $\dfrac{15}{8}$ **25.** 11.6   **27.** -9.9 **29.** 10   **31.** -5 **33.** 11
35. -10 **37.** -18 **39.** 2   **41.** -16 **43.** -12 **45.** $12 - (-6); 18$ **47.** $-25 - (-4);$
-21 **49.** $-24 - (-27); 3$ **51.** -15 **53.** 14,776

Section 1.7 (page 29)
1. 12   **3.** -12 **5.** 5   **7.** 44   **9.** 120   **11.** -48 **13.** -30 **15.** -65 **17.** 0
19. -165 **21.** $\dfrac{5}{12}$ **23.** $-.102$ **25.** -14 **27.** -3 **29.** -36 **31.** 12   **33.** 5
35. 12   **37.** 18   **39.** -14 **41.** -10 **43.** 45   **45.** 12   **47.** 16   **49.** 17
51. -28 **53.** 12   **55.** -360 **57.** 0   **59.** -30 **61.** 44   **63.** -2 **65.** 0
67. -2 **69.** -2 **71.** -2

Section 1.8 (page 33)
1. $\dfrac{1}{9}$ **3.** $-\dfrac{1}{4}$ **5.** $\dfrac{3}{2}$ **7.** $-\dfrac{10}{9}$ **9.** none   **11.** $-\dfrac{17}{6}$ **13.** -2 **15.** -3 **17.** -6
19. -5 **21.** 2   **23.** 15   **25.** 36   **27.** 0   **29.** $\dfrac{2}{3}$ **31.** 2.1   **33.** -5 **35.** -4
37. -10 **39.** 5   **41.** -4 **43.** -60 **45.** -6 **47.** 2   **49.** 4   **51.** 3
53. -3 **55.** 8   **57.** -2 **59.** -1 **61.** No such number (denominator is 0)   **63.** 3

65. 2   **67.** −8   **69.** −6   **71.** 0   **73.** 8   **75.** −4   **77.** $6x = -42; -7$

79. $\frac{x}{5} = -1; -5$ **81.** $\frac{x}{3} = -3; -9$ **83.** $\frac{x}{2} = -4; -8$ **85.** $\frac{6}{x+1} = 3; 1$

Section 1.9   (page 40)

1. Commutative   **3.** Associative   **5.** Commutative   **7.** Commutative   **9.** Closure
11. Inverse   **13.** Identity   **15.** Inverse   **17.** Identity   **19.** Distributive   **21.** $k + 9$
23. m **25.** $3r + 3m$ **27.** 1   **29.** 0   **31.** $-5 + 5$, or 0   **33.** $-3r - 6$ **35.** 9
37. $k + [5 + (-6)] = k - 1$ **39.** $4z + (2r + 3k)$ **41.** $5m + 10$ **43.** $-4r - 8$ **45.** $-8k + 16$
47. $-9a - 27$ **49.** $4r + 32$ **51.** $-16 + 2k$ **53.** $10r + 12m$ **55.** $-12x + 16y$
57. $5(8 + 9) = 5(17) = 85$ **59.** $7(2 + 8) = 7(10) = 70$ **61.** $9(p + q)$ **63.** $5(7z + 8w)$
65. $-3k - 5$ **67.** $-4y + 8$ **69.** $4 - p$ **71.** $1 + 15r$ **73.** (a) yes (b) no (c) yes
75. (a) yes (b) yes (c) yes   **77.** (a) yes (b) no (c) yes   **79.** (a) no (b) no (c) yes

Chapter 1   Test   (page 42)

1. True   **2.** False   **3.** False   **4.** True   **5.** False   **6.** True   **7.** False   **8.** False
9. 34   **10.** 4   **11.** −5   **12.** 3   **13.** $-|-8|$ **14.** 0   **15.** 4   **16.** −9   **17.** 32
18. −4   **19.** 2   **20.** 1   **21.** 6   **22.** −72   **23.** 18   **24.** 25   **25.** −15   **26.** −9
27. 1   **28.** 3   **29.** F, H   **30.** B   **31.** C, D   **32.** A, G   **33.** E

CHAPTER 2

Section 2.1   (page 46)

1. 15   **3.** −22   **5.** 35   **7.** −9   **9.** 1   **11.** −1   **13.** like   **15.** unlike   **17.** like
19. like   **21.** like   **23.** unlike   **25.** $17y$ **27.** $-6a$ **29.** $13b$ **31.** $7k + 15$
33. $m - 1$ **35.** $-4y$ **37.** $2x + 6$ **39.** $20 - 7m$ **41.** $z + 20$ **43.** $-15 + x$
45. $-8 + 23x$ **47.** $9y^2$ **49.** $9p^2 - 14p^3$ **51.** $30t + 66$ **53.** $-3n - 15$ **55.** $16r - 35$
57. $4r + 15$ **59.** $12k - 5$ **61.** $-2k - 3$ **63.** $2 - x$ **65.** $10x$ **67.** $-32 - 47x$

Section 2.2   (page 51)

1. 10   **3.** −2   **5.** 10   **7.** −8   **9.** −5   **11.** −2   **13.** 4   **15.** −5   **17.** −11
19. −6   **21.** $\frac{1}{2}$ **23.** −5   **25.** −2   **27.** $\frac{7}{6}$ **29.** −5   **31.** 7   **33.** 8   **35.** −10
37. −9   **39.** 0   **41.** 6   **43.** −2   **45.** 17   **47.** 18   **49.** 26   **51.** $3x = 17 + 2x; 17$
53. $5x + 3x = 7x + 9; 9$ **55.** $6(2x + 5) = 13x - 8; 38$

Section 2.3   (page 56)

1. 5   **3.** 25   **5.** −8   **7.** −7   **9.** −4   **11.** −9   **13.** 0   **15.** −6   **17.** 4
19. 4   **21.** 8   **23.** 20   **25.** −3   **27.** 4   **29.** −3   **31.** 7   **33.** 32   **35.** 49
37. 9   **39.** 8   **41.** −80   **43.** $\frac{15}{2}$ **45.** $\frac{49}{2}$ **47.** 3   **49.** −6   **51.** $\frac{x}{4} = 6; 24$

53. $\frac{x}{4} = \$62; \$248$

Section 2.4   (page 61)

1. 2   **3.** −4   **5.** 9   **7.** −2   **9.** −1   **11.** −4   **13.** −12.5   **15.** $-\frac{13}{4}$ **17.** −3

19. 18   **21.** 8   **23.** −2   **25.** 6   **27.** −5   **29.** 0   **31.** 5   **33.** 0   **35.** $-\frac{1}{5}$

37. $-\frac{5}{7}$ **39.** 1.4   **41.** −5.2   **43.** $\frac{9}{2}$ **45.** $\frac{3}{7}$ **47.** $3(x - 17) = 102; 51$

49. $8 - 3(x + 4) = 2; -2$

Section 2.5 (page 66)
1. $8 + x$ or $x + 8$ **3.** $-1 + x$ or $x + (-1)$ **5.** $x + (-18)$ **7.** $x - 5$ **9.** $x - 9$ **11.** $9x$
13. $3x$ **15.** $\dfrac{x}{6}$ **17.** $\dfrac{x}{-4}$ **19.** $8(x + 3)$ **21.** $\dfrac{1}{x} - x$ **23.** $8(x - 8)$ **25.** Let x be the number;
$3x - 2 = 22$; 8 **27.** Let x be the number; $4(x + 3) = 36$; 6 **29.** Let x be the number; $2x + x = 90$; 30
31. Let x be the number; $x - 6 = 7x$; -1 **33.** Let x be the number; $5x + 2x = 10$; $\dfrac{10}{7}$ **35.** 10, 11
37. 15, 16, 17 **39.** 15, 17, 19 **41.** 19 inches **43.** 48 **45.** 36 **47.** 613 **49.** 36 quart cartons

Section 2.6 (page 72)
1. $P = 128$ **3.** $A = 36$ **5.** $V = 60$ **7.** $t = 4$ **9.** $h = 8$ **11.** $L = 14$ **13.** $h = 10$
15. $A = 21$ **17.** $r = 1.5$ **19.** $A = 254.34$ **21.** $V = 113.04$ **23.** $t = 2$ **25.** $h = 3$
27. $h = 7$ **29.** $h = 1$ **31.** $L = \dfrac{A}{W}$ **33.** $t = \dfrac{d}{r}$ **35.** $h = \dfrac{V}{lw}$ **37.** $t = \dfrac{I}{pr}$
39. $b = \dfrac{2A}{h}$ **41.** $w = \dfrac{P - 2l}{2}$ **43.** $\dfrac{2A}{h} - B = b$ **45.** $l = \dfrac{r}{2A}$ **47.** $g = \dfrac{mv^2}{2k}$ **49.** $a = \dfrac{S - a}{S}$
51. $r^2 = \dfrac{A}{4\pi}$ **53.** $r^2 = \dfrac{V}{\pi h}$ **55.** 10 meters **57.** 37.68 feet **59.** 24 kilometers

Section 2.7 (page 76)
1. 4 **3.** 3 **5.** 16, 18, 21 **7.** 5 **9.** 25 fives, 30 twenties **11.** 18 of the 16¢, 20 of the 29¢
13. 50 fives, 25 tens, 8 twenties **15.** \$8000 at 8%, \$12,000 at 12% **17.** \$15,000 at 12%, \$9000 at 7%
19. \$8000 at 8%, \$19,000 at 10% **21.** 2 hours **23.** $2\frac{1}{2}$ hours **25.** 3 hours **27.** 40 gallons
29. 20 pounds **31.** 160 kilograms **33.** 3 days **35.** \$2500 at $5\frac{1}{2}$%, 7,500 at $6\frac{1}{2}$% **37.** 25 miles per hour

Section 2.8 (page 84)
1.

4

3.
—5

5.
3

7.
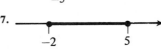
-2 5

9.
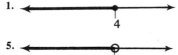
3   5

11. $a < 2$ **13.** $z \geq 1$ **15.** $p \leq 12$ **17.** $k \geq 5$

19. $x \leq 0$ **21.** $x < 6$ **23.** $k \leq -9$ **25.** $n \leq -11$;
-11

27. $z > 5$;
5

29. $y < 5$;
5

31. $k \geq 44$;
44

33. $k > -21$;
-21

35. $6 \leq p \leq 13$;
6   13

37. $5 < y < 12$;
5   12

39. $-21 \leq p \leq -13$;
-21 -13

41. $4x + 8 < 3x + 5$; $x < -3$

43. $2x - x \leq 7$; 7 meters **45.** 15, 60

Section 2.9 (page 89)
1. $x < 9$;
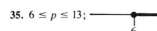
9

3. $r \geq -3$;
-3

5. $k \geq -6$;
-6

7. $y < -9$;
-9

9. $m < 7$; ‹───────────○──────›
7

11. $r > \dfrac{8}{3}$; ───────○──────────›
$8/3$

13. $k \geq -5$; ─────●──────────›
-5

15. $r < 10$; ‹──────────○──────
10

17. $q > -2$; ───────○──────────›
-2

19. $p > -5$; ───────○──────────›
-5

21. $k \leq 0$; ‹──────────●──────
0

23. $x < -11$; ‹──────────○──────
-11

25. $r \geq -1$; ───────●──────────›
-1

27. $p \leq \dfrac{8}{3}$; ‹──────────●──────
$8/3$

29. $-1 \leq x \leq 6$; ─────●──────●───›
-1 6

31. $1 < m < \dfrac{13}{6}$; ────○────────○──›
1 $\frac{13}{6}$

33. $0 \leq q \leq \dfrac{17}{5}$; ─────●──────●───›
0 $\frac{17}{5}$

35. $-26 \leq z \leq 6$; ─────●──────●───›
-26 6

37. 83 or more   **39.** any number greater than $\dfrac{11}{5}$ **41.** 38 meters   **43.** \$550

45. all numbers greater than or equal to -16 **47.** 30 meters

Chapter 2   Test   (page 91)
1. $4x + 2$ **2.** k **3.** $-r$ **4.** $z - 10$ **5.** $7m - 1$ **6.** 4   **7.** 5   **8.** -5 **9.** 0

10. 10   **11.** $-11/2$ **12.** -3 **13.** -5 **14.** \$100   **15.** $p = \dfrac{I}{rt}$ **16.** $h = \dfrac{2A}{b + B}$

17. 64 inches, 31 inches   **18.** 3   **19.** 5 miles per hour   **20.** Hank is 15, Don is 35

21. $x \leq 4$ ‹──────────●──────
4

22. $m > 7$ ───────○──────────›
7

23. $k > 2$ ───────○──────────›
2

24. $k \leq 1$ ‹──────────●──────
1

25. 40 inches

CHAPTER 3

Section 3.1   (page 97)
1. Base is 5, exponent is 12   **3.** Base is $3m$, exponent is 4   **5.** Base is 125, exponent is 3
7. Base is -24, exponent is 2   **9.** Base is m, exponent is 2   **11.** 3^5 **13.** 5^4 **15.** $(-2)^5$ **17.** $1/4^5$

19. $1/3^4$ **21.** 90   **23.** 80   **25.** 36   **27.** 2   **29.** 2   **31.** $\dfrac{1}{27}$ **33.** $\dfrac{1}{25}$

35. $\dfrac{1}{9}$ **37.** $\dfrac{1}{36}$ **39.** $\dfrac{1}{7}$ **41.** 32   **43.** 2   **45.** $\dfrac{27}{8}$ **47.** $\dfrac{5}{6}$ **49.** $\dfrac{9}{20}$ **51.** 4^5

53. 9^8 **55.** $1/3^3$ **57.** $1/4^2$ **59.** $(-3)^5$ **61.** $(-2)^9$ **63.** 4^5 **65.** $1/4^2$ **67.** $1/8^6$

69. $1/6^6$ **71.** 14^3 **73.** 8^2 **75.** $1/3^2$

Section 3.2   (page 102)
1. 6^6 **3.** $1/9^6$ **5.** 3^{10} **7.** y^5 **9.** a^3 **11.** $1/k^4$ **13.** $1/4^9$ **15.** $1/5^9$ **17.** m^5

19. $1/m$ **21.** $1/r$ **23.** a^7 **25.** 5^3m^3 **27.** $3^4m^4n^4$ **29.** $(-3)^2x^{10}$ **31.** $5^3p^6q^3$
33. $3^2/x^{10}$ **35.** $9^2/y^{10}$ **37.** $a^3/5^3$ **39.** $3^5m^5n^5/2^5$ **41.** b/a **43.** $25/m^2$ **45.** x^5
47. $1/b^2$ **49.** $125/(27x^2)$ **51.** $a^{11}/(2b^5)$ **53.** $108/(y^5z^3)$ **55.** $9z^2/(400x^3)$

Section 3.3 (page 105)
1. 6.835×10^9 **3.** 8.36×10^{12} **5.** 2.15×10^2 **7.** 2.5×10^4 **9.** 3.5×10^{-2}
11. 1.01×10^{-2} **13.** 1.2×10^{-5} **15.** 8,100,000,000 **17.** 9,132,000 **19.** 324,000,000
21. .00032 **23.** .041 **25.** 800,000 **27.** .000004 **29.** 420 **31.** 1440 **33.** 3,000,000
35. .2 **37.** 1300 **39.** .18 **41.** 4×10^{-4}; 8×10^{-4} **43.** 3.68×10^{15} **45.** 1000; .06102
47. 35,000

Section 3.4 (page 110)
1. $8m^5$ **3.** $-r^5$ **5.** Cannot be simplified, since the terms are not like terms (exponents are different)
7. x^5 **9.** $-p^7$ **11.** $6y^2$ **13.** 0 **15.** $9y^4 + 7y^2$ **17.** $14z^5 - 9z^3 + 8z^2$ **19.** $2p^7 - 8p^6 +$
$5p^4 - 9p$ **21.** Cannot be simplified further; it is of degree 4 since the highest exponent is 4, and it is a binomial
since it contains two terms. **23.** Simplified already, degree 9, trinomial **25.** Simplified already, degree 8,
trinomial **27.** Simplifies to $1x^5$ or just x^5, degree 5, monomial **29.** 0, monomial **31.** 0, 6
33. 36, -12 **35.** 19, -2 **37.** $-5, 1$ **39.** $-20, 7$ **41.** -9 **43.** -3 **45.** -27
47. 270 **49.** -135 **51.** Always **53.** Never **55.** Never

Section 3.5 (page 114)
1. $5m^2 + 3m$ **3.** $4x^4 - 4x^2$ **5.** $-n^5 - 12n^3 - 2$ **7.** $12m^3 + m^2 + 12m - 14$ **9.** $15m^2 - 3m + 4$
11. $8b^2 + 2b + 7$ **13.** $-r^2 - 2r$ **15.** $5m^2 - 14m$ **17.** $-6s^2 + 5s + 1$ **19.** $4s + 2s^2$
21. $4x^3 + 2x^2 + 5x$ **23.** $-11y^4 + 8y^2 + 3y$ **25.** $a^4 - a^2 + 1$ **27.** $5m^2 + 8m - 10$
29. $(4 + x^2) + (-9x + 2) > 8$ **31.** $(5 + x^2) + (3 - 2x) \neq 5$

Section 3.6 (page 117)
1. $-32x^7$ **3.** $15y^{11}$ **5.** $30a^9$ **7.** $6m^2 + 4m$ **9.** $-6p^4 + 12p^3$ **11.** $16z^2 - 24z^3 - 24z^4$
13. $6y + 4y^2 + 10y^5$ **15.** $m^2 + 12m + 35$ **17.** $x^2 - 25$ **19.** $t^2 - 16$ **21.** $6p^2 - p - 5$
23. $16m^2 - 9$ **25.** $6b^2 + 46b - 16$ **27.** $16 + 2a - 3a^2$ **29.** $-8 + 6k - k^2$ **31.** $12x^3 + 26x^2 +$
$10x + 1$ **33.** $81a^3 + 27a^2 + 11a + 2$ **35.** $20m^4 - m^3 - 8m^2 - 17m - 15$ **37.** $6x^6 - 3x^5 - 4x^4 +$
$4x^3 - 5x^2 + 8x - 3$ **39.** $5x^4 - 13x^3 + 20x^2 + 7x + 5$ **41.** $x^2 + 14x + 49$ **43.** $a^2 - 8a + 16$
45. $4p^2 - 20p + 25$ **47.** $25k^2 + 80k + 64$ **49.** $m^3 - 15m^2 + 75m - 125$ **51.** $8a^3 + 12a^2 + 6a + 1$
53. $k^4 + 4k^3 + 6k^2 + 4k + 1$

Section 3.7 (page 122)
1. $r^2 + 2r - 3$ **3.** $x^2 - 10x + 21$ **5.** $6x^2 + x - 2$ **7.** $6z^2 - 13z - 15$ **9.** $2a^2 + 9a + 4$
11. $8r^2 + 2r - 3$ **13.** $6a^2 + 8a - 8$ **15.** $20 + 9x - 20x^2$ **17.** $-12 + 5r + 2r^2$
19. $15 + a - 2a^2$ **21.** $p^2 + 4pq + 3q^2$ **23.** $10y^2 - 3yz - z^2$ **25.** $8y^2 + 31yz - 45z^2$ **27.** $-8r^2 +$
$2rs + 45s^2$ **29.** $m^2 + 4m + 4$ **31.** $25 + 10x + x^2$ **33.** $x^2 + 4xy + 4y^2$ **35.** $4z^2 - 20zx + 25x^2$
37. $25p^2 + 20pq + 4q^2$ **39.** $16a^2 + 40ab + 25b^2$ **41.** $p^2 - 4$ **43.** $4b^2 - 25$ **45.** $m^2 - n^2$
47. $r^2 - z^2$ **49.** $36a^2 - p^2$ **51.** $4m^2 - 25$ **53.** $49y^2 - 100$ **55.** $(3 + x)^2 = 5$
57. $(3 + x)(x - 4) > 7$

Section 3.8 (page 125)
1. $2x$ **3.** $2a^2$ **5.** $\dfrac{9k^3}{m}$ **7.** $30m^3 - 10m$ **9.** $60m^5 - 30m^2 + 40m$ **11.** $3m^4 - 2m^2 + m$

13. $4m^2 - 2m + 3$ **15.** $\dfrac{m}{2} + \dfrac{1}{2} + \dfrac{1}{2m}$ **17.** $x^2 + 3x$ **19.** $4x^2 - x + 1$ **21.** $9x - 3x^2 + 6x^3$

23. $\dfrac{12}{x} + 8 + x$ **25.** $\dfrac{x}{3} + 2 - \dfrac{1}{3x}$ **27.** $4k^3 - 6k^2 - k + \dfrac{7}{2} - \dfrac{3}{2k}$ **29.** $-10p^3 + 5p^2 - 3p + \dfrac{3}{p}$

31. $\dfrac{2}{x^3} + \dfrac{4}{x^2} + \dfrac{5}{2x}$ **33.** $4y^3 - 2 + \dfrac{3}{y}$ **35.** $\dfrac{12}{x} - \dfrac{6}{x^2} + \dfrac{14}{x^3} - \dfrac{10}{x^4}$ **37.** $12x^5 + 9x^4 - 12x^3 + 6x^2$

39. $-63y^4 - 21y^3 - 35y^2 + 14y$

Section 3.9 (page 129)

1. $x + 2$ **3.** $2y - 5$ **5.** $p - 4$ **7.** $r - 5$ **9.** $6m - 1$ **11.** $a - 7$ **13.** $x + 2 + \dfrac{1}{2x + 1}$

15. $a - 2 + \dfrac{6}{2a + 1}$ **17.** $d - 3 + \dfrac{17}{2d + 4}$ **19.** $x^2 - x + 2$ **21.** $4k^3 - k + 2$ **23.** $3y + 1$

25. $x^2 + 1 + \dfrac{-6x + 2}{x^2 - 2}$ **27.** $x^2 + x + 1$ **29.** $x^2 - 1$

Chapter 3   Test   (page 130)

1. $1/81$ **2.** 1 **3.** 6^6 **4.** $1/5^1$ or $1/5$ **5.** $1/2^{12}$ **6.** 8^8 **7.** p^{24} **8.** 4×10^6
9. 2.45×10^8 **10.** 3.79×10^{-4} **11.** $.0048$ **12.** 400 **13.** $-x^2 + 6x$; degree 2; binomial
14. $2m^4 + 11m^3 - 8m^2$; degree 4; trinomial   **15.** $3x^3 - 4x^2 + 2x - 1$; degree 3; none of these
16. 12 **17.** 12 **18.** $10x^3 - 2x^2 - 8x$ **19.** $x^5 - x^2 - 2x + 12$ **20.** $3y^2 - 2y - 2$
21. $6m^5 + 12m^4 - 18m^3 + 42m^2$ **22.** $r^2 - 3r - 10$ **23.** $6t^2 - t - 12$ **24.** $4k^2 + 28k + 49$
25. $25r^2 - 30rs + 9s^2$ **26.** $m^2 - 64$ **27.** $36p^2 - 64q^2$ **28.** $2x^3 + x^2 - 16x + 15$ **29.** $3y^2 - 5y + 2$
30. $2r^2 + 5r - 3 + 8/(5r)$ **31.** $3a + 2$ **32.** $3y - 6 + 7/(4y + 3)$ **33.** $3x^2 + 4x + 2$

CHAPTER 4

Section 4.1 (page 136)

1. $1, 2, 7, 14$ **3.** $1, 3, 9, 27$ **5.** $1, 3, 5, 9, 15, 45$ **7.** $1, 2, 3, 4, 5, 6, 10, 12, 15, 20, 30, 60$
9. $1, 2, 4, 5, 10, 20, 25, 50, 100$ **11.** $1, 29$ **13.** $2^3 \cdot 3 \cdot 5$ **15.** $2^2 \cdot 3^2 \cdot 5$ **17.** $5^2 \cdot 11$
19. $5^2 \cdot 19$ **21.** 12 **23.** $10p^2$ **25.** 1 **27.** $6m^2n$ **29.** 2 **31.** x **33.** $3m^2$
35. $2z^4$ **37.** xy^2 **39.** $2mn^4$ **41.** $7x^3y^2$ **43.** $12(x + 2)$ **45.** $3(1 + 12d)$ **47.** $9a(a - 2)$
49. $5y^5(13y^4 - 7)$ **51.** $11p^4(11p - 3)$ **53.** No common factor other than 1   **55.** $9m^2(1 + 10m)$
57. $19y^2p^2(y + 2p)$ **59.** $6x^2y(3y^2 - 4x^2)$ **61.** $13y^3(y^3 + 2y^2 - 3)$ **63.** $8a(2a^2 + a + 3)$
65. $9qp^3(5q^3p^2 - 4p^3 + 9q)$ **67.** $ab^3(a^2b^2 - ab^4 + 1)$ **69.** $5z^3a^3(25z^2 - 12za^2 + 17a)$
71. $11y^3(3y^5 - 4y^9 + 7 + y)$

Section 4.2 (page 140)

1. $x + 3$ **3.** $r + 8$ **5.** $t - 12$ **7.** $x - 8$ **9.** $m + 6$ **11.** $p - 1$ **13.** $x + 3$
15. $(x + 5)(x + 1)$ **17.** $(a + 4)(a + 5)$ **19.** $(x - 1)(x - 7)$ **21.** Cannot be factored
23. $(y - 2)(y - 4)$ **25.** $(s - 5)(s + 7)$ **27.** Cannot be factored   **29.** $(b - 3)(b - 8)$
31. $(y + 3)(y - 7)$ **33.** Cannot be factored   **35.** $(z + 5)(z - 8)$ **37.** $3m(m + 3)(m + 1)$
39. $6(a + 2)(a - 10)$ **41.** $3j(j - 4)(j - 6)$ **43.** $3x^2(x + 5)(x - 6)$ **45.** $(x + 3a)(x + a)$
47. $(y + 5b)(y - 6b)$ **49.** $(x - 5y)(x + 6y)$ **51.** $(r - s)(r - s)$ **53.** $(p - 5q)(p + 2q)$
55. $a^3(a + 4b)(a - b)$ **57.** $yz(y + 3z)(y - 2z)$ **59.** $z^8(z - 7y)(z + 3y)$

Section 4.3 (page 144)

1. $x - 1$ **3.** $b - 3$ **5.** $4y - 3$ **7.** $5x + 4$ **9.** $m + 10$ **11.** $3a - 4b$ **13.** $k + 3m$
15. $2x^2 - 5x - 3; x - 3$ **17.** $6m^2 + 7m - 20; 2m + 5$ **19.** $(2x + 1)(x + 3)$ **21.** $(3a + 7)(a + 1)$
23. $(4r - 3)(r + 1)$ **25.** $(3m - 1)(5m + 2)$ **27.** $(2m - 3)(4m + 1)$ **29.** $(5a + 3)(a - 2)$
31. $(3r - 5)(r + 2)$ **33.** $(y + 17)(4y + 1)$ **35.** $(19x + 2)(2x + 1)$ **37.** $(2x + 3)(5x - 2)$
39. $(2w + 5)(3w + 2)$ **41.** $(2q + 3)(3q + 7)$ **43.** $(5m - 4)(2m - 3)$ **45.** $(4k - 5)(2k + 3)$
47. $(5m - 8)(2m + 3)$ **49.** $(4x - 1)(2x - 3)$ **51.** $(8m - 3)(5m + 2)$ **53.** $2m(m + 5)(m - 4)$
55. $2a^2(4a - 1)(3a + 2)$ **57.** $4w^4(z - 1)(8z + 3)$ **59.** $(4p - 3q)(3p + 4q)$ **61.** $(5a + 2b)(5a + 3b)$
63. $(3a - 5b)(2a + b)$ **65.** $2k^2(2k - 3w)(k + w)$ **67.** $m^4n(3m + 2n)(2m + n)$
69. $3zy(3z + 7y)(2z - 5y)$

Section 4.4 (page 148)

1. $(x + 4)(x - 4)$ **3.** $(p + 2)(p - 2)$ **5.** $(m + n)(m - n)$ **7.** $(a + b)(a - b)$ **9.** $(3m + 1)$
$(3m - 1)$ **11.** $(5m + 4)(5m - 4)$ **13.** $4(3t + 2)(3t - 2)$ **15.** $(5a + 4r)(5a - 4r)$ **17.** Cannot be
factored   **19.** $(p^2 + 6)(p^2 - 6)$ **21.** $(a^2 + 1)(a + 1)(a - 1)$ **23.** $(m^2 + 9)(m + 3)(m - 3)$
25. $(a + 2)^2$ **27.** $(x - 5)^2$ **29.** $(a + 7)^2$ **31.** $(k + 11)^2$ **33.** Not a perfect square   **35.** Not

a perfect square   **37.** $(4a - 5b)^2$ **39.** $25(2m + 1)^2$ **41.** $(7x + 2y)^2$ **43.** $(2c + 3d)^2$
45. $(5h - 2y)^2$ **47.** $a^2(3a - 2b)^2$ **49.** $xy(x + 3y)^2$

Miscellaneous Factoring Exercises (page 150)
1. $4(4x + 5)$ **3.** $8m(1 - 2m)$ **5.** $6(a + 2b + 3c)$ **7.** $8m^3(4m^6 + 2m^2 + 3)$ **9.** $15a^3b^2(3b^3 - 4a + 5a^3b^2)$ **11.** $(a - 6)(a + 2)$ **13.** $(y - 8)(y + 7)$ **15.** $(z - 6)(z - 6)$ or $(z - 6)^2$ **17.** $(p - 11)(p - 6)$ **19.** $6(y - 2)(y + 1)$ **21.** $3k(k - 5)(k + 1)$ **23.** $8a^3(a - 3)(a + 2)$ **25.** $(z - 5a)(z + 2a)$ **27.** $(y - 6k)(y + 2k)$ **29.** $(2m - 1)(m + 3)$ **31.** $(5z - 1)(z + 5)$ **33.** $(3y - 4)(2y + 1)$ **35.** $(6z + 1)(z + 5)$ **37.** $(3n - 2)(2n - 5)$ **39.** $(5z - 6)(2z + 1)$ **41.** $2(3a - 1)(a + 2)$ **43.** $7k(2k + 5)(k - 2)$ **45.** $6y^4(3y + 4)(2y - 5)$ **47.** $(2m - 3n)(m + 5n)$ **49.** $(4p + 3q)(3p - 2q)$ **51.** $(8a - b)(a + 3b)$ **53.** $(k + 4)(k - 4)$ **55.** $(2y + 5)(2y - 5)$ **57.** $(7z + 4y)(7z - 4y)$ **59.** $6(3m + 2z)(3m - 2z)$ **61.** $(y^2 + 4)(y + 2)(y - 2)$ **63.** Cannot be factored   **65.** $(a + 4)^2$ **67.** $(2k - 3)^2$ **69.** $(4r + 3m)^2$ **71.** Cannot be factored   **73.** $4(2k - 3)^2$ **75.** $5m^2(5m - 3n)(5m - 13n)$

Section 4.5 (page 154)
1. $2, -4$ **3.** $-5/3, 1/2$ **5.** $-1/5, 1/2$ **7.** $-9/2, 1/3$ **9.** $1, -5/3$ **11.** $7/3, -4$ **13.** $-2, -3$ **15.** $-1, 6$ **17.** $-7, 4$ **19.** $-8, 3$ **21.** $-1, 3$ **23.** $-1, -2$ **25.** -4 **27.** $1/3, -2$ **29.** $5/2, -2$ **31.** $-4/3, 1/2$ **33.** $1/3, -5/2$ **35.** $-4, 5/2$ **37.** $5/3, -4$ **39.** $2/5, -1/3$ **41.** $3/2, -3$ **43.** $5/4, -5/4$ **45.** $2, -2$ **47.** $5, 2$ **49.** $-12, 11/2$ **51.** $3, -1$ **53.** $1/4, 4$ **55.** $5/2, 1/3, 5$ **57.** $-7/2, 3, -1$ **59.** $0, -5, 5$ **61.** $0, 7/3, -7/3$ **63.** $0, 4, -2$ **65.** $0, -5, 4$

Section 4.6 (page 158)
1. width $= 6$, length $= 11$ **3.** 7 by 10   **5.** 4 by 8   **7.** 2 by 5   **9.** base $= 10$, height $= 5$ **11.** $B = 16$, $h = 6$ **13.** 19, 18   **15.** 4 by 6 by 5   **17.** 4, 5 or $-1, 0$ **19.** 12, 14, 16, or $-2, 0, 2$ **21.** 5, 6, or $-6, -5$ **23.** -2 **25.** 256 feet   **27.** 10 seconds   **29.** 48 seconds   **31.** 48 seconds

Section 4.7 (page 162)
1. $-2 < m < 5$;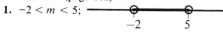

3.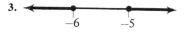

5.

7.

9.

11.

13.

15.

17.

19.

21.

23.

25.

27. $-2 \le a \le \dfrac{1}{3}$ or $a \ge 4$;

29. $r < -1$ or $2 < r < 4$;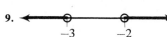

Chapter 4 Test (page 162)
1. $8m(2m - 3)$ **2.** $6y(x + 2y)$ **3.** $14p(2q + 1 + 4p)$ **4.** $3mn(m + 3 + 2n)$ **5.** Cannot be fac-

tored   **6.** $(x + 5)(x + 6)$ **7.** $(p + 7)(p - 1)$ **8.** $(2y + 3)(y - 5)$ **9.** $(2m - 1)(2m + 3)$
10. $(3x - 2)(x + 5)$ **11.** $(2z + 1)(5z + 1)$ **12.** $(5a + 1)(2a - 5)$ **13.** $(4r + 5)(3r + 1)$
14. Cannot be factored   **15.** $(a + 5b)(a - 2b)$ **16.** $(3r - 2s)(2r + s)$ **17.** $(x + 5)(x - 5)$
18. $(5m + 7)(5m - 7)$ **19.** $(2p + 3)^2$ **20.** $(5z - 1)^2$ **21.** $4p(p + 2)^2$ **22.** $5m^2(2m + 1)(m + 5)$
23. $-1, -2$ **24.** $1/3, -2$ **25.** $5/2, -4$ **26.** $2, -2$ **27.** $0, 4, -4$ **28.** 3 inches by 5 inches
29. $10, 3$ **30.** 8 and 17 or -7 and 2   **31.** $\xleftarrow{\qquad\qquad}\underset{-6}{\circ}\text{------}\underset{4}{\circ}\longrightarrow$

32. $\longleftarrow\text{------}\underset{-3}{\bullet}\text{------}\underset{1/2}{\bullet}\longrightarrow$ **33.** $\xleftarrow{\qquad}\underset{-2/3}{\bullet}\text{------}\underset{1/2}{\bullet}\longrightarrow$

CHAPTER 5
Section 5.1   (page 167)
1. 0   **3.** 4   **5.** -5 **7.** 5, 3   **9.** $3/2, -1$ **11.** none   **13.** (a) 1 (b) $-\dfrac{3}{2}$ **15.** (a) 2
(b) $-\dfrac{14}{3}$ **17.** (a) $\dfrac{256}{15}$ (b) not a real number   **19.** (a) -5 (b) $\dfrac{5}{23}$ **21.** (a) -5 (b) $\dfrac{15}{2}$ **23.** $\dfrac{2}{3}$
25. $2k$ **27.** $\dfrac{-4y^3}{3}$ **29.** $\dfrac{4m}{3p}$ **31.** $\dfrac{3}{4}$ **33.** $(x - 1)/(x + 1)$ **35.** $m - n$ **37.** $\dfrac{m}{2}$
39. $4r + 2s$ or $2(2r + s)$ **41.** $(m - 2)/(m + 3)$ **43.** $(x + 4)/(x + 1)$ **45.** 1   **47.** $-(x + 1)$ or
$-x - 1$ **49.** -1

Section 5.2   (page 171)
1. $\dfrac{3m}{4}$ **3.** $\dfrac{3}{32}$ **5.** $2a^4$ **7.** $\dfrac{1}{4}$ **9.** $\dfrac{1}{6}$ **11.** $\dfrac{6}{a + b}$ **13.** 2   **15.** $\dfrac{2}{9}$ **17.** $\dfrac{3}{10}$
19. $\dfrac{2r}{3}$ **21.** $(y + 4)(y - 3)$ **23.** $18/[(m - 1)(m + 2)]$ **25.** $-\dfrac{7}{8}$ **27.** -1 **29.** $(k + 2)/(k + 3)$
31. $(n + 4)/(n - 4)$ **33.** 1   **35.** $(m - 3)/(2m - 3)$ **37.** $(p - q)/(p + q)$ **39.** $(x + 2)(x + 1)$
41. $10/(x + 10)$

Section 5.3   (page 175)
1. 60   **3.** 120   **5.** 1800   **7.** $30p$ **9.** $150m$ **11.** $180y^4$ **13.** $300r^5$ **15.** $12p(p - 2)$
17. $32r^2(r - 2)$ **19.** $18(r - 2)$ **21.** $12p(p + 5)$ **23.** $8(y + 2)(y + 1)$ **25.** $a(a + 6)(a - 3)$
27. $(k + 7)(k - 5)(k + 8)$ **29.** $(2y - 1)(y + 4)(y - 3)$ **31.** $(3r - 5)(2r + 3)(r - 1)$
33. $\dfrac{42}{66}$ **35.** $\dfrac{54}{6r}$ **37.** $\dfrac{-88}{8m}$ **39.** $\dfrac{24y^2}{70y^3}$ **41.** $\dfrac{60m^2k^3}{32k^4}$ **43.** $\dfrac{57z}{6z - 18}$ **45.** $\dfrac{-4a}{18a - 36}$
47. $\dfrac{6(k + 1)}{k(k - 4)(k + 1)}$ **49.** $\dfrac{36r(r + 1)}{(r - 3)(r + 2)(r + 1)}$

Section 5.4   (page 180)
1. $\dfrac{7}{p}$ **3.** $\dfrac{-3}{k}$ **5.** 1   **7.** $m + n$ **9.** m **11.** 1   **13.** $\dfrac{6 + m}{2m}$ **15.** $(18 + 3m)/(2m)$
17. $(3y - 5)/(5y)$ **19.** $\dfrac{m}{3}$ **21.** $\dfrac{2 + k}{2}$ **23.** $(6 - 2y)/y^2$ **25.** $(9p + 8)/(2p^2)$ **27.** $\dfrac{4m + n}{2}$
29. $(-y - 3x)/(x^2y)$ **31.** $(2m^2 + 4m + 4)/[m(m + 2)]$ **33.** $\dfrac{4x + 24}{(x - 2)(x + 2)}$ **35.** $\dfrac{4m}{(m + n)(m - n)}$
37. $3/[(m + 1)(m - 1)(m + 2)]$ **39.** $2(m + 3)/[(m + 3)(m - 3)]$ **41.** $3/(m - 2)$ or $-3/(2 - m)$
43. $\dfrac{-1}{y - 3}$ or $\dfrac{1}{3 - y}$ **45.** $8m/(m + 2n)$ **47.** $(2x^2 + 6xy + 8y^2)/[(x + y)(x + y)(x + 3y)]$

Section 5.5   (page 183)
1. $1/(pq)$ **3.** $1/x$ **5.** x/y **7.** $b/[a(b + 1)]$ **9.** $2(2x + 3)/(x - 1)$ **11.** $2/y$
13. $(x + y)^2/(xy)$ **15.** x/y **17.** q **19.** $(m - n)/4$ **21.** $-(m - 1)/(m + 1)$ **23.** $(y + 1)^2/$
$(y - 1)$ **25.** $1/3$ **27.** $124/15$ **29.** $2/3$

Section 5.6 (page 189)
1. 1/2   **3.** 12   **5.** 1/4   **7.** 2/5   **9.** 24   **11.** 2   **13.** −7   **15.** 1   **17.** 2
19. 5   **21.** −6   **23.** −8   **25.** 8   **27.** 5   **29.** 4   **31.** 0   **33.** 3   **35.** 2
37. 4, 6   **39.** 3   **41.** no solution   **43.** 1, −24   **45.** no solution   **47.** 1/2, −6
49. 1, −4/3   **51.** −3/5, 3

Section 5.7 (page 193)
1. 9   **3.** $\frac{12}{17}$ **5.** 6, 9   **7.** 2/3, −3   **9.** 2/3 or 1   **11.** father = $60; son = $24

13. $13,125   **15.** 2 mph   **17.** 150 miles   **19.** 37/2 mph   **21.** $1\frac{1}{5}$ hours   **23.** 84/19 hours

25. $5\frac{3}{5}$ days   **27.** 100/11 minutes   **29.** 3 hours

Section 5.8 (page 199)
1. 3/2   **3.** 36/55   **5.** 2/5   **7.** 5/8   **9.** 1/10   **11.** 8/5   **13.** 1/6   **15.** 4/15
17. yes   **19.** yes   **21.** no   **23.** yes   **25.** no   **27.** 21   **29.** 40   **31.** 5
33. 16   **35.** 7/2   **37.** 24/9   **39.** 27/8   **41.** 15/2   **43.** 7/15   **45.** −31   **47.** 20 ounces
49. 5/2 or $2\frac{1}{2}$ bars   **51.** 9 pounds   **53.** 9 inches   **55.** 7 pounds   **57.** $75   **59.** $225

61. 96/5 or $19\frac{1}{5}$ yards

Chapter 5 Test (page 201)
1. $2/(mn^3)$ **2.** $5s(s − 1)/2$ **3.** x **4.** 40/27   **5.** $(3m − 2)/(3m + 2)$ **6.** $(77r)/(49r^2)$
7. $15/(24m − 48)$ **8.** $−1/x$ **9.** $11/[6(a + 1)]$ **10.** $(5k + 6)/[2k(k + 2)]$ **11.** $3(1 + x)/x$
12. $(1 − 2k)/(1 + 3k)$ **13.** 3/2   **14.** −2/3, 4   **15.** 1/4 or 1/2   **16.** 9/5   **17.** 20/9 hours
18. 1   **19.** −22/3   **20.** $17.60

CHAPTER 6

Section 6.1 (page 207)
1. 11   **3.** 29   **5.** −4   **7.** 3   **9.** 8   **11.** −2   **13.** 3   **15.** 7; 1; −1   **17.** 2; 8; 17

19. 9; 3; −15   **21.** 2; 3; −3   **23.** −3; 5; −5   **25.** $2; \frac{5}{2}; −\frac{5}{4}$ **27.** $−\frac{5}{4}; \frac{5}{6}; \frac{7}{4}$ **29.** −4; −4; −4

31. 3; 3; 3   **33.** −9; −9; −9   **35.** yes   **37.** yes   **39.** no   **41.** yes   **43.** yes
45. no

Section 6.2 (page 212)
1. (2, 5)   **3.** (−5, 5)   **5.** (7, 3)

13. (−3, 5)
9. (3, 5)
11. (−2, 4)   **19.** (0, 3)
18. (−5, 0)
22. (0, 0)   **7.** (6, 1)
17. (−2, 0)   **15.** (4, 0)
21. (0, −5)
10. (−4, −5)   **14.** (3, −5)

23. I   **25.** II   **27.** III   **29.** II   **31.** IV   **33.** none

35. 6; 10
    −3; −2

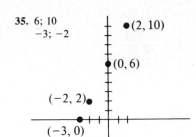

(2, 10)
(0, 6)
(−2, 2)
(−3, 0)

37. 3; −3
    5; −5

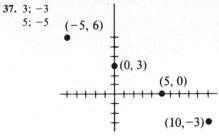

(−5, 6)
(0, 3)
(5, 0)
(10, −3)

39. 0; −6
    12; −1

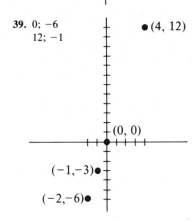

(4, 12)
(0, 0)
(−1, −3)
(−2, −6)

41. 3; 3
    3; 3

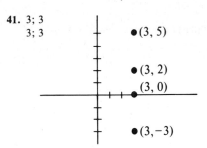

(3, 5)
(3, 2)
(3, 0)
(3, −3)

43. −2; −2
    −2; −2

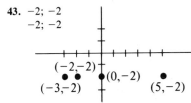

(−2, −2)
(0, −2)
(−3, −2)
(5, −2)

Section 6.3   (page 218)

1. 5; 5; 3

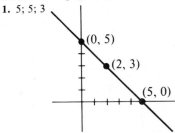

(0, 5)
(2, 3)
(5, 0)

3. 4; −4; 2

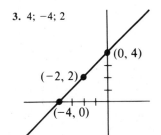

(0, 4)
(−2, 2)
(−4, 0)

5. −6; 2; 3

(3, 3)
(2, 0)
(0, −6)

7. 4; 10; 2

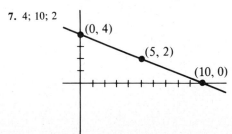

(0, 4)
(5, 2)
(10, 0)

9. −5; −5; −5

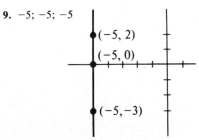

(−5, 2)
(−5, 0)
(−5, −3)

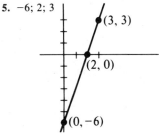

11.

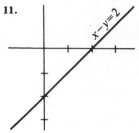

13.

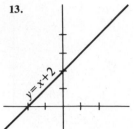

15.

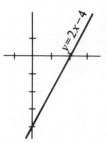

17.

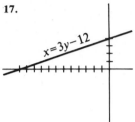

19.

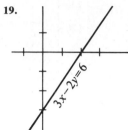

21.

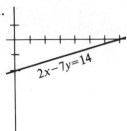

23.

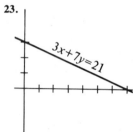

25.

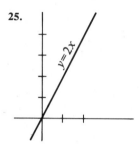

27.

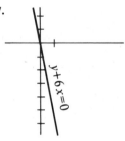

29.

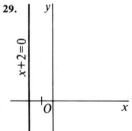

31.

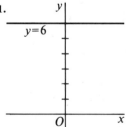

33.

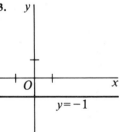

35.

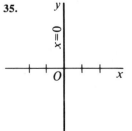

37. $x = y + 2$

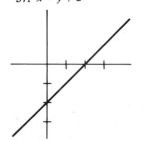

39. $y = 2x - 3$

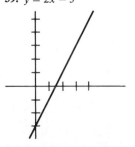

41. $3 + y = 2x - 4$
   $y = 2x - 7$

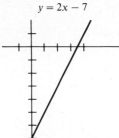

43. (a) 121 (b) 132 (c) 154 (d) 165 (e) 176

(f)
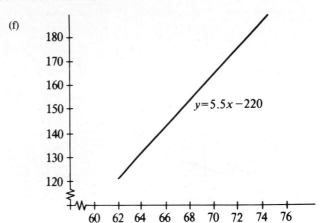

$y = 5.5x - 220$

Section 6.4   (page 226)
1. $-1/2$ **3.** $2/7$ **5.** 0 **7.** $7/8$ **9.** $9/2$ **11.** $-5/8$ **13.** 0 **15.** no slope
17. 2 **19.** -1 **21.** -5 **23.** -2 **25.** $3/2$ **27.** $-2/5$ **33.**
29.

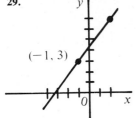
$(-1, 3)$

31.
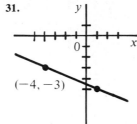
$(-4, -3)$

33.
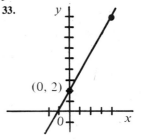
$(0, 2)$

35.
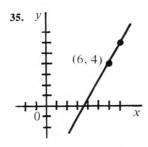
$(6, 4)$

37.
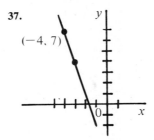
$(-4, 7)$

39.
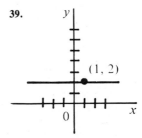
$(1, 2)$

41.
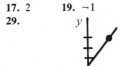
$(3, 5)$

43. $y = 2x - 7$ **45.** $y = -2x - 4$ **47.** $3y = 2x + 9$ **49.** $4y = -3x - 17$ **51.** $11y = -8x + 48$

53. $y = x - 2$ **55.** $5y = 3x + 11$ **57.** $-5y = 3x + 11$ **59.** $3y = -2x + 6$ **61.** parallel
63. perpendicular   **65.** parallel   **67.** perpendicular   **69.** neither

Section 6.5 (page 228)

1
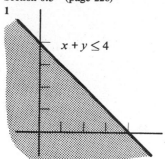
$x + y \leq 4$

3.
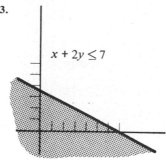
$x + 2y \leq 7$

5.
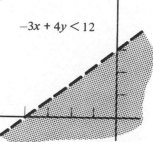
$-3x + 4y < 12$

7.
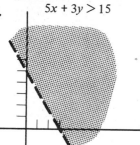
$5x + 3y > 15$

9.
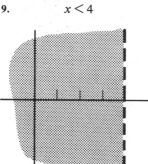
$x < 4$

11.
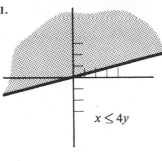
$x \leq 4y$

13.
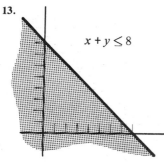
$x + y \leq 8$

15.
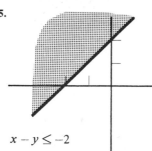
$x - y \leq -2$

17.
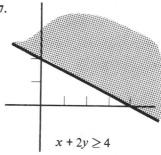
$x + 2y \geq 4$

19.
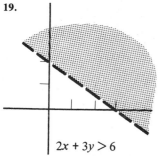
$2x + 3y > 6$

21
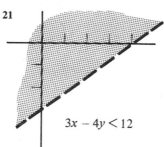
$3x - 4y < 12$

23.
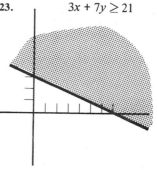
$3x + 7y \geq 21$

25. $4x - 5y \geq 20$

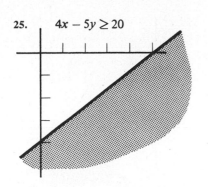

27. $4x + 7y \leq 14$

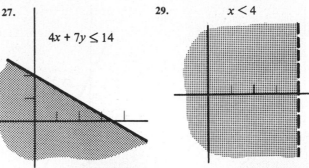

29. $x < 4$

31. $y \leq 2$

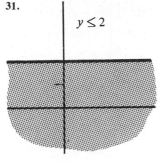

33. $x \geq -2$

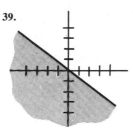

35. $x \leq 5y$

37.

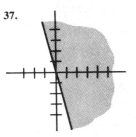

39.

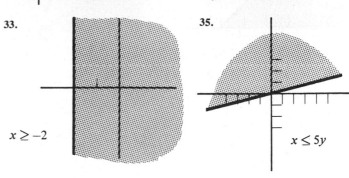

Section 6.6   (page 234)
1. yes   **3.** yes   **5.** yes   **7.** no   **9.** no   **11.** yes   **13.** no   **15.** yes   **17.** Both
domain and range are set of all real numbers   **19.** Both domain and range are set of all real numbers
21. Domain is set of all real numbers, range is set of all $y \geq -3$ **23.** Domain is set of all real numbers;
range is set of all $y \geq 0$ **25.** Domain is set of all real numbers, range is all $y \leq 6$ **27.** Domain is set of all
real numbers, range is all $y \leq 0$ **29.** Domain is set of all real numbers, range is all $y \geq 2$
31. Domain is set of all real numbers, range is all $y \geq 0$ **33.** 8; 2; −7   **35.** 2; 4; 7   **37.** −12; −4; 8
39. 6; 2; 11   **41.** 1; 9; 36   **43.** −16; −4; −1   **45.** −4; −2; −1   **47.** 0; 3; 8   **49.** 9; 24; −11
51. 1; −62; −7   **53.** Function   **55.** Not a function   **57.** Function   **59.** Not a function

Chapter 6   Test   (page 239)
1. −6; −16; 4   **2.** 3; 21/2; 15/7; 7/2   **3.** 0; 6; 8/3; −4   **4.** −4; −4; −4   **5.** 2; 2; 2; 2

6.

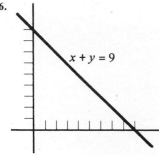

$x + y = 9$

7.

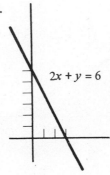

$2x + y = 6$

8.

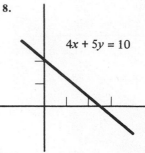

$4x + 5y = 10$

9.

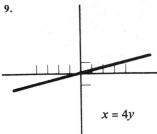

$x = 4y$

10.

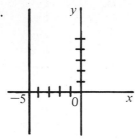

11.

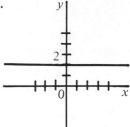

12. 1/4   **13.** −2/5

14.

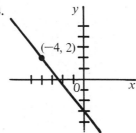

(−4, 2)

15. $y = 2x + 5$ **16.** $2y = -5x - 7$

17.

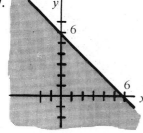

18.

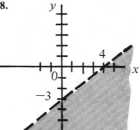

19.

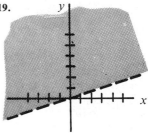

20.

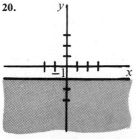

21. function   **22.** function   **23.** not a function   **24.** −20   **25.** 28

CHAPTER 7

Section 7.1   (page 245)
1. Yes   **3.** No   **5.** No   **7.** Yes   **9.** No   **11.** Yes   **13.** (5, 3)   **15.** (4, 8)
17. (4, −2)   **19.** (1, −3)   **21.** (3, −2)   **23.** (2, −1)   **25.** (−8, 6)   **27.** (−4, −1)
29. (5, 0)   **31.** (0, −2)   **33.** (5, 2)   **35.** (−1, 3)   **37.** (2, −3)   **39.** (6, −2)   **41.** (2, 7)
43. no solution   **45.** no solution   **47.** same line

Section 7.2   (page 250)
1. (1, −2)   **3.** (2, 0)   **5.** (6, 2)   **7.** (−2, 6)   **9.** (1/2, 2)   **11.** (3/2, −2)   **13.** (3, 0)
15. (2, −3)   **17.** (4, 4)   **19.** (2, −5)   **21.** (4, 9)   **23.** (−4, 0)   **25.** (4, −3)
27. (−9, −11)   **29.** (6, 3)   **31.** (6, −5)   **33.** (−6, 0)   **35.** (1/2, 2/3)   **37.** (3/8, 5/6)
39. (11, 15)   **41.** (22/9, 8/9)

Section 7.3   (page 255)
1. (2, 4)   **3.** (6, 4)   **5.** (8, −1)   **7.** (1, 5)   **9.** (2, −4)   **11.** (5, 1)   **13.** (−1, 2)
15. (−22/3, −6)   **17.** (5, −3)   **19.** (4, 1)   **21.** (2, −3)   **23.** (2, 8)   **25.** (4, −6)
27. (3, 2)   **29.** (7, 0)   **31.** (2, 0)   **33.** (−3, 6)   **35.** (6, 5)   **37.** (0, 3)
39. (18, −12)   **41.** (3, 2)   **43.** (3, −1)

Section 7.4   (page 258)
1. No solution   **3.** No solution   **5.** Same line   **7.** No solution   **9.** No solution   **11.** Same
line   **13.** (0, 0)   **15.** (3, 2)   **17.** No solution   **19.** Same line   **21.** Same line   **23.** No
solution   **25.** Same line   **27.** (0, 0)   **29.** No solution

Section 7.5   (page 263)
1. 43 and 9   **3.** 72 and 24   **5.** 10 inches by 20 inches   **7.** 22 tens, 63 twenties   **9.** 74 at 8¢, 96 at
10¢   **11.** 80 fives, 44 tens   **13.** 21 at $7 and 18 at $4   **15.** $7500 at 5% and $2500 at 7%   **17.** 4
liters of 90% and 16 liters of 75%   **19.** 4 of 25%, 8 of 55%   **21.** 30 of $6, 60 of $3   **23.** 30 barrels of
$40 olives and 20 barrels of $60 olives   **25.** 2 mph, 10 mph   **27.** plane, 470 mph; wind, 70 mph
29. John, 3 1/4 mph; Harriet, 2 3/4 mph   **31.** 4 girls, 3 boys

Section 7.6   (page 269)
1. 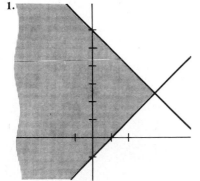   **3.**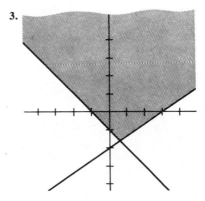

5.

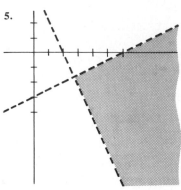

7.

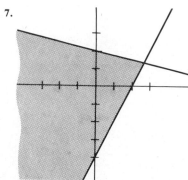

9.

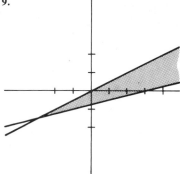

11.

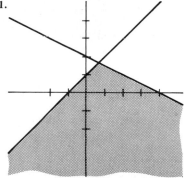

13.

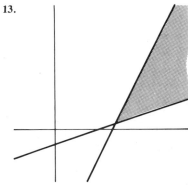

15.

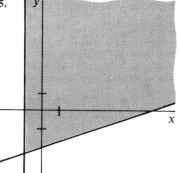

17.

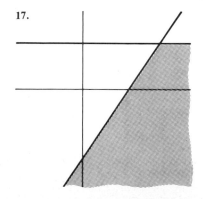

19.

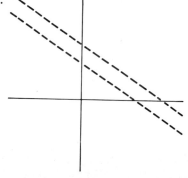

21.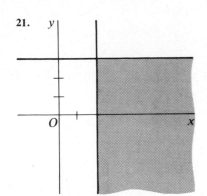

23.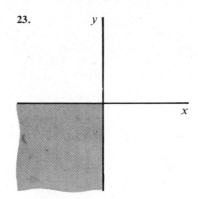

Chapter 7   Test   (page 270)
1. (4, −3)   **2.** (6, −5)   **3.** (4, 1)   **4.** (6, 5)   **5.** (8, −2)   **6.** (2, −5)   **7.** (0, −2)
8. (2, 2)   **9.** (3/2, −2)   **10.** (3, −5)   **11.** (−6, 8)   **12.** no solution   **13.** same line
14. (−6, 4)   **15.** 12 and 27   **16.** 2 at $5, 4 at $7.50   **17.** 45 miles per hour, 60 miles per hour
18. 75 liters of 40%, 25 liters of 60%
19. 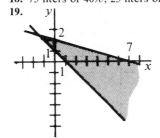   **20.**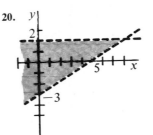

CHAPTER 8

Section 8.1   (page 275)
1. 3, −3   **3.** 11, −11   **5.** 20, −20   **7.** 25, −25   **9.** 39, −39   **11.** 63, −63   **13.** 2
15. 5   **17.** −8   **19.** 13   **21.** 30   **23.** −41   **25.** 51   **27.** −70   **29.** Does not exist
31. Does not exist   **33.** Rational; 4   **35.** Irrational; 3.873   **37.** Irrational; 6.856
39. Irrational; 8.246   **41.** Rational; −11   **43.** Irrational; 10.488   **45.** Irrational; −14.142
47. Rational; 20   **49.** Irrational; 23.875   **51.** 10   **53.** −2   **55.** 4   **57.** 3   **59.** Does not
exist   **61.** −2   **63.** −1   **65.** −2   **67.** 2   **69.** Does not exist

Section 8.2   (page 280)
1. 4   **3.** 6   **5.** 21   **7.** $\sqrt{21}$ **9.** $3\sqrt{3}$ **11.** $2\sqrt{7}$ **13.** $3\sqrt{2}$ **15.** $4\sqrt{3}$
17. $5\sqrt{5}$ **19.** $10\sqrt{7}$ **21.** $30\sqrt{3}$ **23.** 40   **25.** 36   **27.** 60   **29.** $7\sqrt{3}$
31. $15\sqrt{3}$ **33.** $20\sqrt{3}$ **35.** $10\sqrt{10}$ **37.** 10/3   **39.** 6/7   **41.** $\sqrt{5}/4$ **43.** $\sqrt{30}/7$
45. 2/5   **47.** 4/25   **49.** 5   **51.** 4   **53.** $3\sqrt{5}$ **55.** $5\sqrt{10}$ **57.** .1   **59.** .7
61. 1.1   **63.** .02   **65.** .04   **67.** y **69.** $\sqrt{xz}$ **71.** x **73.** x^2 **75.** xy^2
77. $x\sqrt{x}$ **79.** 4/x **81.** $\sqrt{11}/r^2$ **83.** $2\sqrt[3]{5}$ **85.** $3\sqrt[3]{2}$ **87.** $4\sqrt[3]{2}$ **89.** $5\sqrt[3]{3}$
91. $\dfrac{2}{3}$ **93.** $\dfrac{10}{3}$

Section 8.3   (page 283)
1. $7\sqrt{3}$ **3.** $-5\sqrt{7}$ **5.** $2\sqrt{6}$ **7.** $3\sqrt{17}$ **9.** $4\sqrt{7}$ **11.** $12\sqrt{2}$ **13.** $7\sqrt{5}$
15. $11\sqrt{2}$ **17.** $3\sqrt{3}$ **19.** $20\sqrt{2}$ **21.** $-13\sqrt{2}$ **23.** $19\sqrt{7}$ **25.** $-12\sqrt{5}$
27. $6\sqrt{2} + 7\sqrt{3}$ **29.** $-16\sqrt{2} + 8\sqrt{3}$ **31.** $20\sqrt{2} + 6\sqrt{3} + 15\sqrt{5}$ **33.** $2\sqrt{2}$ **35.** $3\sqrt{3} - 2\sqrt{5}$
37. $5\sqrt{3}$ **39.** $3\sqrt{21} - \sqrt{7}$ **41.** $6\sqrt{x}$ **43.** $13\sqrt{a}$ **45.** $15x\sqrt{3}$ **47.** $2x\sqrt{2}$ **49.** 0

Section 8.4 (page 287)
1. $6\sqrt{5}/5$ 3. $\sqrt{5}$ 5. $3\sqrt{7}/7$ 7. $8\sqrt{15}/5$ 9. $\sqrt{30}/2$ 11. $8\sqrt{3}/9$ 13. $3\sqrt{2}/10$
15. $\sqrt{2}$ 17. $9\sqrt{2}/8$ 19. 2   21. $\sqrt{2}$ 23. $2\sqrt{30}/3$ 25. $\sqrt{2}/2$ 27. $\sqrt{70}/7$
29. $3\sqrt{5}/5$ 31. $\sqrt{14}$ 33. $\sqrt{15}/10$ 35. $3\sqrt{14}/4$ 37. $\sqrt{3}/5$ 39. $4\sqrt{3}/27$ 41. $\sqrt{6}\,p/p$
43. $p\sqrt{2}\,pm/m$ 45. $x\sqrt{y}/(2y)$ 47. $3a\sqrt{5r}/5$ 49. $\sqrt[3]{4}/2$ 51. $\sqrt[3]{2}/4$ 53. $\sqrt[3]{121}/11$
55. $\sqrt[3]{50}/5$ 57. $\sqrt[3]{6}/2$ 59. $\sqrt[3]{42}/6$

Section 8.5 (page 291)
1. $27\sqrt{5}$ 3. $21\sqrt{2}$ 5. -4 7. $\sqrt{15} + \sqrt{35}$ 9. $2\sqrt{10} + 10$ 11. $-4\sqrt{7}$
13. $21 - \sqrt{6}$ 15. $87 + 9\sqrt{21}$ 17. $34 + 24\sqrt{2}$ 19. $37 - 12\sqrt{7}$ 21. 7   23. -4 25. 1
27. 16   29. 20   31. 2   33. $(3 - \sqrt{2})/7$ 35. $-10 + 5\sqrt{5}$ 37. $-2 - \sqrt{11}$
39. $-\sqrt{2} + 2$ 41. $-(\sqrt{5} + 5)/4$ 43. $3 - \sqrt{3}$ 45. $(-3 + 5\sqrt{3})/11$ 47. $3\sqrt{2} - 3 + \sqrt{10} - \sqrt{5}$
49. $-(31 - 11\sqrt{3})/13$ 51. $-(4\sqrt{3} + \sqrt{2} - 10\sqrt{6} - 5)/23$ 53. $\sqrt{21} + \sqrt{14} + \sqrt{6} + 2$

Section 8.6 (page 296)
1. 4   3. 1   5. 7   7. -7 9. -5 11. No solution   13. 49   15. No solution
17. 9   19. 16   21. 6   23. 7   25. -4 27. 5   29. 12   31. 5   33. $0, -1$
35. 5   37. 3   39. 9   41. 12   43. 9   45. 21   47. 8   49. (a) 90 mph (b) 120 mph
(c) 60 mph (d) 60 mph

Chapter 8   Test   (page 297)
1. 10   2. 8.775   3. 13.784   4. 39   5. -3 6. 5   7. 8/13   8. $2\sqrt{2}$ 9. $5\sqrt{2}$
10. $3\sqrt{3}$ 11. $2\sqrt[3]{4}$ 12. .05   13. $-\sqrt{5}$ 14. $8\sqrt{2}$ 15. cannot be simplified
16. $9\sqrt{7}$ 17. $-7\sqrt{3x}$ 18. $4xy\sqrt{2y}$ 19. $4\sqrt{3}/3$ 20. $3\sqrt{6}$ 21. $\sqrt{3}$ 22. $\sqrt[3]{15}/3$
23. 31   24. $4 - 2\sqrt{3}$ 25. $11 + 2\sqrt{30}$ 26. $6\sqrt{2} - 3\sqrt{14} + 2 - \sqrt{7}$ 27. $-(1 + \sqrt{5})/2$
28. $(2\sqrt{3} + \sqrt{6} + 2 + \sqrt{2})/2$ 29. 16   30. 23   31. 4   32. -5 33. $-1, -2$

CHAPTER 9

Section 9.1 (page 301)
1. $5, -5$ 3. $8, -8$ 5. $\sqrt{13}, -\sqrt{13}$ 7. $\sqrt{2}, -\sqrt{2}$ 9. $2\sqrt{6}, -2\sqrt{6}$ 11. $6, -2$
13. $-4 + \sqrt{10}, -4 - \sqrt{10}$ 15. $1 + 4\sqrt{2}, 1 - 4\sqrt{2}$ 17. $2, -1$ 19. $-2/3, -8/3$ 21. $13/6, -3/2$
23. $(5 + \sqrt{30})/2, (5 - \sqrt{30})/2$ 25. $(1 + 3\sqrt{2})/3, (1 - 3\sqrt{2})/3$ 27. $(5 + 7\sqrt{2})/2, (5 - 7\sqrt{2})/2$
29. $(-4 + 2\sqrt{2})/3, (-4 - 2\sqrt{2})/3$ 31. About 1/2 second

Section 9.2 (page 305)
1. 1   3. 81   5. 81/4   7. 49   9. 25/4   11. $-1, -3$ 13. $-1 + \sqrt{6}, -1 - \sqrt{6}$
15. $-2, -4$ 17. $3 + 2\sqrt{2}, 3 - 2\sqrt{2}$ 19. $(-3 + \sqrt{17})/2, (-3 - \sqrt{17})/2$ 21. No real number
solutions   23. No real number solutions   25. $3 + \sqrt{5}, 3 - \sqrt{5}$ 27. $(2 + \sqrt{14})/2, (2 - \sqrt{14})/2$
29. $1, -1/3$ 31. $5 + \sqrt{17}, 5 - \sqrt{17}$ 33. $(3 + 2\sqrt{6})/3, (3 - 2\sqrt{6})/3$ 35. $-2 + \sqrt{3}, -2 - \sqrt{3}$

Section 9.3 (page 311)
1. $3, 4, -8$ 3. $-8, -2, -3$ 5. $2, -3, 2$ 7. $1, 0, -2$ 9. $3, -8, 0$ 11. $1, 1, -12$
13. $9, 9, -26$ 15. $-1 + \sqrt{3}, -1 - \sqrt{3}$ 17. -2 19. $1, -13$ 21. $(-6 + \sqrt{26})/2,$
$(-6 - \sqrt{26})/2$ 23. $1/5, -1$ 25. $5/2, -1$ 27. -3 29. $3/2$ 31. $0, -1$ 33. $0, 5/3$
35. $2\sqrt{5}, -2\sqrt{5}$ 37. $4/3, -4/3$ 39. $0, -2$ 41. No real number solutions   43. No real number
solutions   45. $(-1 + \sqrt{73})/6, (-1 - \sqrt{73})/6$ 47. $(2 + \sqrt{22})/6, (2 - \sqrt{22})/6$ 49. $1 + \sqrt{2},$
$1 - \sqrt{2}$ 51. $(1 + \sqrt{3})/3, (1 - \sqrt{3})/3$ 53. No real number solutions

Section 9.4   (page 316)

1. (0, 0)

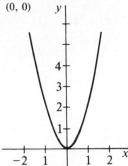

3. (−1, 0)

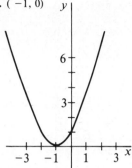

5. (−1, 0)

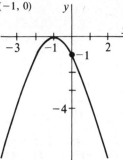

7. (0, 1)

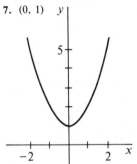

9. (0, −2)

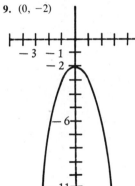

11. (0, 8)

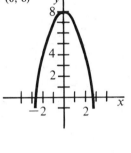

13. (2, 3)

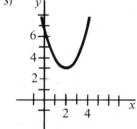

15. (−2, 1)

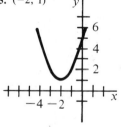

17. (4, −2)

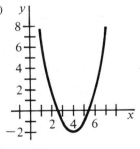

19. (−2, −3)

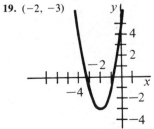

21. (3, −2)

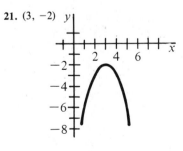

23. (5, 4)

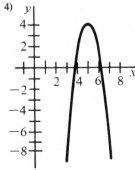

Chapter 9   Test   (page 317)
1. $\sqrt{5}, -\sqrt{5}$ **2.** 10, −4   **3.** $(2 + \sqrt{35})/3, (2 - \sqrt{35})/3$ **4.** 0, 5/2   **5.** 1/5, −2   **6.** 4
7. 2, 1/3   **8.** $(5 + \sqrt{13})/6, (5 - \sqrt{13})/6$ **9.** $(3 + 3\sqrt{2})/2, (3 - 3\sqrt{2})/2$ **10.** 3/2, −1/4   **11.** −1/3
12. no real number solution   **13.** $(5 + \sqrt{13})/6, (5 - \sqrt{13})/6$

14.

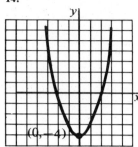

((0, −4))

15. (−1, −5)

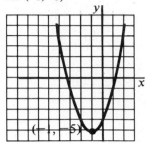

(−1, −5)

APPENDIX A   (page 328)

1. $\dfrac{1}{2}$ **3.** $\dfrac{5}{6}$ **5.** $\dfrac{8}{9}$ **7.** $\dfrac{2}{3}$ **9.** $\dfrac{2}{3}$ **11.** $\dfrac{27}{20}$ or $1\dfrac{7}{20}$ **13.** $\dfrac{3}{25}$ **15.** $\dfrac{6}{5}$ or $1\dfrac{1}{5}$ **17.** $\dfrac{3}{10}$

19. $\dfrac{1}{9}$ **21.** $\dfrac{3}{20}$ **23.** $\dfrac{5}{12}$ **25.** $\dfrac{13}{3}$ or $4\dfrac{1}{3}$ **27.** 28   **29.** $\dfrac{1}{3}$ **31.** $\dfrac{7}{10}$ **33.** $\dfrac{10}{9}$ or $1\dfrac{1}{9}$

35. $\dfrac{19}{22}$ **37.** $\dfrac{1}{15}$ **39.** $\dfrac{8}{15}$ **41.** $9\dfrac{3}{8}$ **43.** $5\dfrac{1}{6}$ **45.** $1\dfrac{5}{12}$ **47.** $\dfrac{49}{30}$ or $1\dfrac{19}{30}$ **49.** $\dfrac{13}{28}$

51. $\dfrac{17}{24}$ **53.** $14\dfrac{7}{16}$ **55.** $8\dfrac{23}{24}$ **57.** 36

APPENDIX B   (page 334)

1. 20,000 mm   **3.** 70 mm   **5.** 8 cm   **7.** .32 m   **9.** 5.2 km   **11.** 7800 m   **13.** 6000 g
15. 1920 g   **17.** 8.2 kg   **19.** 6.94 cg   **21.** 810 cg   **23.** 9000 ml   **25.** 57 L   **27.** 2.96 cl
29. 11.0 m   **31.** 2.0 m   **33.** .6 m   **35.** 196.3 km   **37.** 3813.6 g   **39.** 49.9 kg
41. 7.6 L   **43.** 287.7 L   **45.** 39.4 yards   **47.** 131.2 feet   **49.** 372.8 miles   **51.** 1.5 pounds
53. 10.8 pounds   **55.** 8.5 quarts   **57.** 20.3 gallons

APPENDIX C   (page 336)

1. $(y + 1)(y^2 - y + 1)$ **3.** $(r - t)(r^2 + rt + t^2)$ **5.** $(2a + 1)(4a^2 - 2a + 1)$ **7.** $(3x - 5)(9x^2 + 15x + 25)$
9. $(2p + q)(4p^2 - 2pq + q^2)$ **11.** $(3a - 4b)(9a^2 + 12ab + 16b^2)$ **13.** $(4x + 5y)(16x^2 - 20xy + 25y^2)$
15. $(5m - 2p)(25m^2 + 10mp + 4p^2)$ **17.** $(10z + 3x)(100z^2 - 30zx + 9x^2)$ **19.** $(4y^2 + 1)(16y^4 - 4y^2 + 1)$
21. $(2k^2 - 3q)(4k^4 + 6k^2q + 9q^2)$ **23.** $(10a - 7b^3)(100a^2 + 70ab^3 + 49b^6)$ **25.** $(a + 2b)(x + y)$
27. $(b + c)(2 + a)$ **29.** $(a^2 + b^2)(3a + 2b)$ **31.** $(1 - a)(1 - b)$ or $(a - 1)(b - 1)$ **33.** $(4 - 3y^3)(2 - 3y)$

Index

We would appreciate it if you would take a few minutes to answer these questions. Then cut the page out, fold it, seal it, and mail it. No postage is required.

Which chapters did you cover?
(circle)   1   2   3   4   5   6   7   8   9   All _____

Which helped most?
Explanations _____ Examples _____ Exercises _____ All three _____

Does the book have enough worked-out examples? Yes _____ No _____

enough exercises?   Yes _____ No _____

Were the answers in the back of the book helpful?   Yes _____ No _____

Did you use the *Study Guide?*
Yes _____ No _____ Did not know of it _____

If YES, was the *Study Guide* helpful?
Yes _____ For some topics _____ No _____

How was your course taught?   Regular class _____ Self paced _____

For you, was the course elective _____ required by _____

Do you plan to take more mathematics courses?   Yes _____ No _____

If YES, which ones?

Intermediate algebra _____ Geometry _____ Math for elementary teachers _____

Business math _____ Nursing (or allied health) math _____
Technical math _____

Introduction to math (survey) _____ College algebra _____
Data processing _____

Other _____

How much algebra did you have before this course?   None _____

Terms in high school   (circle)   1   2   3   4
Courses in college   1   2   3

If you had algebra before, how long ago?
Last 2 years _____ 3-5 years _____ 5 years or more _____

What is your major or your career goal? _____ Your age? _____

We would appreciate knowing of any errors you found in this book.

What did you like most about the book?

What did you like least about the book?

Fold here

College _____ State _____

Fold here

BUSINESS REPLY MAIL

FIRST CLASS   PERMIT NO. 31   GLENVIEW, IL

Postage will be paid by
SCOTT, FORESMAN AND COMPANY
College Division   Attn: Lial/Miller
1900 East Lake Avenue
Glenview, Illinois   60025

NO POSTAGE
NECESSARY
IF MAILED
IN THE
UNITED STATE

Formulas

Rectangle   The length is l, the width is w.

  Perimeter $P = 2l + 2w$

  Area $A = lw$

Square   Side is s.

  Perimeter $P = 4s$

  Area $A = s^2$

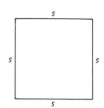

Trapezoid   The two parallel sides are b and B.
Altitude (height) is h.

  Area $A = \frac{1}{2}(b + B)h$

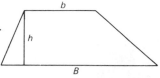

Rectangular solid   The height is h.

  Volume $V = lwh$

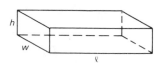

Triangle   Sides are a, b, c, where b is the base.
Altitude is h.

  Perimeter $P = a + b + c$

  Area $A = \frac{1}{2}bh$

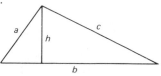